Handbook of Statistical Distributions

STATISTICS

Textbooks and Monographs

A SERIES EDITED BY

Volume 1: The Generalized Jackknife Statistic, *H. L. Gray and W. R. Schucany*

Volume 2: Multivariate Analysis, *Anant M. Kshirsagar*

Volume 3: Statistics and Society, *Walter T. Federer*

Volume 4: Multivariate Analysis: A Selected and Abstracted Bibliography, 1957-1972, *Kocherlakota Subrahmaniam and Kathleen Subrahmaniam*

Volume 5: Design of Experiments: A Realistic Approach, *Virgil L. Anderson and Robert A. McLean*

Volume 6: Statistical and Mathematical Aspects of Pollution Problems, *John W. Pratt*

Volume 7: Introduction to Probability and Statistics (in two parts)
Part I: Probability; Part II: Statistics, *Narayan C. Giri*

Volume 8: Statistical Theory of the Analysis of Experimental Designs, *J. Ogawa*

Volume 9: Statistical Techniques in Simulation (in two parts), *Jack P. C. Kleijnen*

Volume 10: Data Quality Control and Editing, *Joseph I. Naus*

Volume 11: Cost of Living Index Numbers: Practice, Precision, and Theory, *Kali S. Banerjee*

Volume 12: Weighing Designs: For Chemistry, Medicine, Economics, Operations Research, Statistics, *Kali S. Banerjee*

Volume 13: The Search for Oil: Some Statistical Methods and Techniques, *edited by D. B. Owen*

Volume 14: Sample Size Choice: Charts for Experiments with Linear Models, *Robert E. Odeh and Martin Fox*

Volume 15: Statistical Methods for Engineers and Scientists, *Robert M. Bethea, Benjamin S. Duran, and Thomas L. Boullion*

Volume 16: Statistical Quality Control Methods, *Irving W. Burr*

Volume 17: On the History of Statistics and Probability, *edited by D. B. Owen*

Volume 18: Econometrics, *Peter Schmidt*

Volume 19: Sufficient Statistics: Selected Contributions, *Vasant S. Huzurbazar (edited by Anant M. Kshirsagar)*

Volume 20: Handbook of Statistical Distributions, *Jagdish K. Patel, C. H. Kapadia, and D. B. Owen*

OTHER VOLUMES IN PREPARATION

Handbook of Statistical Distributions

JAGDISH K. PATEL
Department of Mathematics
University of Missouri
Rolla, Missouri

C. H. KAPADIA and D. B. OWEN
Department of Statistics
Southern Methodist University
Dallas, Texas

MARCEL DEKKER, INC. New York and Basel

MARCEL DEKKER, INC.

270 Madison Avenue, New York, New York 10016

LIBRARY OF CONGRESS CATALOG CARD NUMBER: 76-48474

ISBN: 0-8247-6362-9

Current printing (last digit)
10 9 8 7 6 5 4 3 2 1

PRINTED IN THE UNITED STATES OF AMERICA

CONTENTS

Preface

This handbook is the outcome of an attempt to collect, in as concise a form as is possible, many results which statisticians find useful. In so doing the authors have not always quoted original sources of the discoveries given, but rather the most readily available sources.

This text is not intended as a book of statistical theory but instead as a source book where concise statements and references may be found.

Throughout the text, all expressions given are regarded as being implicitly restricted to the case where all quantities contained therein exist and are finite. In cases where questions might arise, the authors have noted these restrictions.

It is hoped that students in graduate statistics courses will find this summary particularly useful. Research workers should also find the book to be helpful in tracing references to material they desire.

In the preparation of the manuscript the authors have checked and rechecked the information given. However, considering the diversity of the material, one hundred percent accuracy cannot be achieved. Readers are cordially invited to contact the authors regarding any errors or suggestions for improvements in presentation.

The authors are particularly grateful to Mr. William Parr who read the manuscript and gave valuable comments and suggestions. They also wish to acknowledge the initial typing of the manuscript by Jeannie Alley and Mary Surovik, the final production typing by Beverly Mullins and Christy Brawand and the copy editing by Molly Petri.

August, 1976

J. K. Patel
C. H. Kapadia
D. B. Owen

To My Mother and the Memory of My Father - J.K.P.

To My Mother and the Memory of My Father - C.H.K.

To My Wife and Our Children - D.B.O.

Chapter 1

MOMENTS, CUMULANTS, AND GENERATING FUNCTIONS

1.1 MOMENTS AND CUMULANTS

The moments and cumulants are a set of constants of a distribution which are useful for measuring its properties and, under certain circumstances, for specifying it.

1.1.1 DEFINITIONS

(1) Expectation (One-Dimensional Case). Let X be a random variable and h(•) be a function with both domain and range the real line. The expectation or expected value of the function h(•) of the random variable X, denoted by E[h(X)], is defined by

$$E[h(X)] = \int_{-\infty}^{\infty} h(x)f(x)\, dx$$

if X is continuous with probability density function (pdf) f(x) provided the integral converges absolutely (i.e., $\int_{-\infty}^{\infty} |h(x)|f(x)\, dx < \infty$); and by

$$E[h(X)] = \sum_x h(x)f(x)$$

if X is discrete with probability function (pf) f(x) provided the sum converges absolutely (i.e., $\sum_x |h(x)|f(x) < \infty$). The summation is over all possible values of x.

If the integral or the sum in the above definition does not converge absolutely, we say E[h(X)] does not exist.

(2) Expectation (Two-Dimensional Case). Let (X,Y) be a bivariate random variable. The expected value of a function h(•,•) of the bivariate random variable, denoted by E[h(X,Y)], is defined to be

$$E[h(X,Y)] = \int_{-\infty}^{\infty}\int_{-\infty}^{\infty} h(x,y)f_{X,Y}(x,y)\ dx\ dy$$

if the random variable is continuous with pdf, $f_{X,Y}(x,y)$; and is defined to be

$$E[h(X,Y)] = \sum_x \sum_y h(x,y)f_{X,Y}(x,y)$$

if the random variable is discrete with pf $f_{X,Y}(x,y)$. The summation is over all possible values of (x,y).

If the integral or the sum in the above definition does not converge absolutely, we say E[h(X,Y)] does not exist.

(3) Conditional Expectation. Let (X,Y) be a bivariate random variable and g(•,•) a function of two variables. The conditional expectation of g(X,Y) given X = x, denoted by $E_{Y|X}[g(X,Y)|X = x]$, is defined to be

$$E_{Y|X}[g(X,Y)|X = x] = \int_{-\infty}^{\infty} g(x,y)f_{Y|X}(y|x)\ dy$$

if the random variable is continuous with $f_{Y|X}(y|x)$ as the conditional probability density function of Y given X = x and

$$E_{Y|X}[g(X,Y)|X = x] = \sum_y g(x,y)f_{Y|X}(y|x)$$

if the random variable is discrete with $f_{Y|X}(y|x)$ as the conditional probability function of Y given X = x. The summation is over all possible values of y.

(4) The Moment of Order r (r = 1, 2, 3, ...). $\mu_r'(b) = E[(X - b)^r]$ is called the rth moment of a random variable X about a constant b. When b = 0, it is called the rth moment of the random variable X about the origin and is denoted by μ_r'. When b = E(X), it is called the rth central moment of the random variable X and is denoted by μ_r.

(5) The Absolute Moment of Order r (r = 1, 2, 3, ...). $\nu_r'(b) = E[|X - b|^r]$ is called the rth absolute moment of a random variable X about a constant b. When b = 0, it is called the rth absolute moment of the random variable X and is denoted by ν_r'. When b = E(X), it is called the rth absolute central moment of the random variable X and is denoted by ν_r.

(6) The Factorial Moment of Order r (r = 1, 2, 3, ...). $\mu_{(r)}'(b) = E[(X - b)^{(r)}]$ is called the rth factorial moment of a random variable X about a constant b. Here $Y^{(r)} = Y(Y - 1)(Y - 2) \cdots (Y - \{r - 1\})$. When b = 0, it is called the rth factorial moment of the random variable X and is denoted by $\mu_{(r)}'$. When b = E(X), it is called the rth factorial central moment of the random variable X and is denoted by $\mu_{(r)}$.

(7) The Cumulants of Order r (r = 1, 2, 3, ...). The cumulants $\kappa_1, \kappa_2, \cdots, \kappa_r$ are defined by the identity in t in the following expression:

$$\exp\left(\kappa_1 t + \kappa_2 \frac{t^2}{2} + \cdots + \kappa_r \frac{t^2}{r!} + \cdots\right)$$
$$= \left(1 + \mu_1' t + \mu_2' \frac{t^2}{2} + \cdots + \mu_r' \frac{t^r}{r!} + \cdots\right) .$$

[Kendall and Stuart (1958), p. 67]

(8) The Mode. The mode (or modal value) m_0 is that value of a random variable which is observed with the greatest frequency. If the distribution function is continuous and differentiable the mode m_0 is the solution of $df(x)/dx = 0$, $d^2f(x)/dx^2 < 0$. The mode is a measure of location.

(9) The Quantile (or Fractile). The pth quantile ξ_p of a distribution function (or a random variable X) is defined by $P(X < \xi_p) \leq p \leq P(X \leq \xi_p)$. If the distribution function is continuous and strictly increasing $P(X \leq \xi_p) = p$ and ξ_p is unique. If p is such that $100p = k$, then ξ_p is called the kth percentile of the distribution. The quantile (or percentile) is a measure of location.

(10) The Range. The range R of a distribution function is the difference between the largest and the smallest values of the random variable. It is a measure of dispersion. It is invariant under a transformation on location.

1.1.2a COMMENTS

(1) $\mu = \mu_1'$ is called the mean of the random variable X. It is a measure of central tendency.

(2) $\mu_2 = \sigma^2 = \text{var}(X)$ is called the variance of the random variable X. $\sigma = +\sqrt{\sigma^2}$ is called the standard deviation of the random variable X. Both are measures of dispersion. They are invariant under location transformation.

(3) ν_1 is called the mean deviation of the random variable X. It is a measure of dispersion. It is also invariant under a transformation on the location. $\nu_1'(a)$ is a minimum when a is the median.

(4) $\gamma_1 = \mu_3/\mu_2^{3/2} = \kappa_3/\kappa_2^{3/2}$ is called the coefficient of skewness. It is a measure of departure from symmetry of a frequency curve. It is invariant under a linear transformation. If $\gamma_1 = 0$, the curve is not skewed, if $\gamma_1 > 0$, the curve is positively skewed, and if $\gamma_1 < 0$, the curve is negatively skewed [Rahman (1968), pp. 104-106].

(5) $\gamma_2 = \mu_4/\mu_2^2 - 3 = \kappa_4/\kappa_2^2$ is called the coefficient of excess or kurtosis. It is a measure of the degree of flattening of a frequency curve. It is invariant under linear transformation. If $\gamma_2 = 0$, the curve is called mesokurtic. If $\gamma_2 > 0$, the curve is called leptokurtic and if $\gamma_2 < 0$, it is called platykurtic [Rahman (1968), p. 106].

(6) σ/μ is called the coefficient of variation. It is a measure of dispersion. It is independent of the scale of measurement.

(7) When $p = 0.50$, ξ_p is called a median of the frequency distribution. When $p = 0.25k$ ($k = 1, 2$, or 3), ξ_p is called a kth quartile of the frequency distribution. When $p = 0.10k$ ($k = 1, 2, \ldots$, or 9) ξ_p is called a kth decile of the frequency distribution. The difference $\xi_{0.75} - \xi_{0.25}$ is called the interquartile range and the difference $\xi_{0.90} - \xi_{0.10}$ is called the interdecile range of the frequency distribution.

(8) $\mu'_{2r}(b) = \nu'_{2r}(b)$, $r = 1, 2, \ldots$; $\mu'_2(a) \geq \mu_2$; $\nu_1 \leq \sigma$

$$\kappa_1 = \mu'_1, \quad \kappa_2 = \mu_2, \quad \kappa_3 = \mu_3, \quad \kappa_4 = \mu_4 - 3\mu_2^2, \quad \kappa_5 = \mu_5 - 10\mu_3\mu_2,$$

etc.

(9)
$$\frac{\partial \mu'_r}{\partial \kappa_i} = \binom{r}{i}\mu'_{r-i}, \quad \begin{pmatrix} i = 1, 2, \ldots, r \\ r = 1, 2, \ldots \end{pmatrix}$$

[Kendall and Stuart (1958), p. 69]

(10) All cumulants (except κ_1) are translation invariant.

(11) $\mathrm{Cov}(X,Y) = E[XY] - [E(X)][E(Y)]$ is called the covariance of the random variables X and Y. $\rho(X,Y) = \mathrm{cov}(X,Y)/\sqrt{\mathrm{var}(X)\,\mathrm{var}(Y)}$ is called the correlation coefficient of the random variables X and Y. Both are measures of association. $\rho(X,Y)$ is independent of the scale of measurement.

1.1.2b COMMENTS

(1) Moments and cumulants do not always exist.

Examples:

(a) Cauchy distribution: $f(x) = \dfrac{1}{\pi(1 + x^2)}, \quad -\infty < x < \infty$

No moments exist.

(b) $f(x) = \dfrac{6}{\pi^2 x^2}, \quad x = 1, 2, 3, \ldots$

No moments exist.

(c) $f(x) = \dfrac{r\alpha^r}{(x + \alpha)^{r+1}}, \quad x \geq 0, \; \alpha > 0$

Only moments up to order $(r - 1)$ exist.

[Lachenbruch and Brogan (1971), p. 46]

(2) $\mu_r'(b)$ exists if and only if $\nu_r'(b)$ exists.

(3) If $\mu_r'(b)$ exists then $\mu_s'(b)$ and $\nu_s'(b)$ exist provided $s \leq r$.

(4) κ_r exists if the moments of orders r and lower exist.

(5) In a symmetrical continuous distribution, all odd central moments and all odd cumulants (except κ_1) vanish when they exist; and also the mean, median and mode coincide.

A continuous distribution need not be symmetric even though all its central odd moments vanish.

Example:

$$f(x) = \frac{1}{48} \exp(-|x|^{1/4}) [1 - k \sin |x|^{1/4}]; \quad -\infty < x < \infty,$$

$$k = \begin{cases} -1 & \text{if } x < 0 \\ +1 & \text{if } x \geq 0 \end{cases}$$

f(x) is asymmetric, but all odd moments are zero.

[Churchill (1946), p. 245]

1.1.3 RECURRENCE RELATIONS BETWEEN MOMENTS

Let b - a = c and r = 1, 2, 3, ...

(1) $\mu'_r(a) = \sum_{i=0}^{r} \binom{r}{i} \mu'_{r-i}(b)c^i$ [Kendall and Stuart (1958), p. 56]

Two special cases are

(a) $\mu'_r = \sum_{i=0}^{r} \binom{r}{i} \mu_{r-i}\mu_1'^{\,i}$

(b) $\mu_r = \sum_{i=0}^{r} (-1)^i \binom{r}{i} \mu'_{r-i}\, \mu_1'^{\,i}$

(2) $\mu'_{(r)}(a) = \sum_{i=0}^{r} \binom{r}{i} \mu'_{(r-i)}(b)c^{(i)}$

[Kendall and Stuart (1958), p. 64]

Two special cases are

(a) $\mu'_{(r)} = \sum_{i=0}^{r} \binom{r}{i} \mu_{(r-i)}\mu_1'^{\,(i)}$

(b) $\mu_{(r)} = \sum_{i=0}^{r} (-1)^i \binom{r}{i} \mu'_{(r-1)}\, \mu_1'^{\,(i)}$

(3) $\mu'_{(r)} = \sum_{i=1}^{r} u_{i,r}\mu'_i$

$\mu'_r = \sum_{i=1}^{r} v_{i,r}\mu'_{(i)}$ [Harris (1966), p. 101]

where $u_{i,r}$ and $v_{i,r}$ are Stirling numbers of the first and second kind (see Ch. 10, §7) respectively.

1.1.4 USEFUL FORMULAS

(1) If X is a continuous random variable with cumulative distribution function (cdf) F(x),

$$E(X^r) = \int_0^\infty ry^{r-1}[1 - F(y) + (-1)^r F(-y)]\, dy$$

[Parzen (1960), p. 212]

(2) If X is a continuous random variable with pdf f(x) and $a < X < b$, (a finite, b finite or infinite),

$$E(X^r) = a^r + r\int_a^b x^{r-1}[1 - F(x)]\, dx, \quad r = 1, 2, 3, \ldots$$

where F(x) is the cdf of the random variable X.

(3) If X is a discrete random variable taking nonnegative integer values, a, a + 1, ..., b (a finite, b finite or infinite),

$$E(X^r) = a^r + \sum_{x=a}^{b-1} \{(x + 1)^r - x^r\}\{1 - F(x)\}, \quad r = 1, 2, 3, \ldots$$

(4) $$E|X - a| = \int_{-\infty}^{a} F(y)\, dy + \int_a^\infty [1 - F(y)]\, dy$$

[Mardia and Thompson (1972), p. 131]

(5) (a) $E(X) = E_Y[E_{X|Y}(X|Y)]$

(b) $E(XY) = E_X[XE_{Y|X}(Y|X)]$

(c) $\mathrm{var}(X) = E_Y[\mathrm{var}_{X|Y}(X|Y)] + \mathrm{var}_Y[E_{X|Y}(X|Y)]$

(d) $\mathrm{var}(XY) = [E(Y)]^2\, \mathrm{var}(X) + [E(X)]^2\, \mathrm{var}(Y) + \mathrm{var}(x)\, \mathrm{var}(Y)$ provided X and Y are independent.

(e) Let X_1, X_2 be two random variables and a_1, a_2 be two constants. Then

$$\mathrm{var}\left(\sum_{i=1}^{2} a_i X_i\right) = \sum_{i=1}^{2} \sum_{j=1}^{2} a_i a_j\, \mathrm{cov}(X_i, X_j)$$

where $\mathrm{cov}(X_i, X_i) = \mathrm{var}(X_i)$.

(f) Let U and V be two linear functions of the sets of random variables (X_1,X_2), (Y_1,Y_2), namely,

$$U = \sum_{i=1}^{2} a_i X_i, \quad V = \sum_{j=1}^{2} b_j Y_j$$

Then

$$\text{cov}(U,V) = \sum_{i=1}^{2} \sum_{j=1}^{2} a_i b_j \text{ cov}(X_i,Y_j)$$

(g) $\text{cov}(X,Y) = \text{cov}[X,E_{Y|X}(Y|X)]$ [Wallenius (1971), p. 33]
[Raj (1968), pp. 9-13]

1.1.5 THE PROBLEM OF MOMENTS

A distribution function determines a set of moments when they exist. On the other hand, it is of some interest to consider how far a set of moments (assuming that they all exist) determine a distribution function uniquely.

(1) Let F(x) be a cdf of a random variable X with finite moments μ'_r (r = 1, 2, ...). If the series $\sum_{r=1}^{\infty} \mu'_r c^r/r!$ is absolutely convergent for some c > 0 then F(x) is the only cdf having these moments [Rao (1973), p. 106].

(2) If X is a bounded random variable; i.e., there is a positive real number m such that $P[|X| < m] = 1$, then its cdf F(x) is uniquely determined by its moments μ'_r (r = 1, 2, ...) [Harris (1966), p. 103].

(3) Carleman's criterion. Let X be a random variable with range $(-\infty,\infty)$ and finite μ'_r (r = 1, 2, ...). If $\sum_{r=1}^{\infty} (\mu'_{2r})^{-(1/2r)} = \infty$, then the sequence (μ'_r) uniquely determines F(x) [Harris (1966), p. 103].

(4) Any one of the following two conditions is also a sufficient condition for the moments μ'_r (r = 1, 2, ...) to determine its distribution function F(x).

(a) $\sum_{r=0}^{\infty} \left(\frac{1}{\mu'_r}\right)^{1/2r} = \infty$, when the range of the random variable is $(0,\infty)$.

(b) $\limsup_{n \to \infty} \left[\frac{(\mu'_{2n})^{1/2n}}{2n} \right]$ is finite [Rao (1973), p. 106].

(5) A set of moments satisfying

$$\begin{vmatrix} 1 & \mu'_1 & \cdots & \mu'_r \\ \mu'_1 & \mu'_2 & \cdots & \mu'_{r+1} \\ \mu'_r & \mu'_{r+1} & \cdots & \mu'_{2r} \end{vmatrix} \geq 0$$

determines at least one distribution but that there may be no unique distribution [Godwin (1964), p. 14].

(6) If $\mu_4 = (\mu_2)^2$ then frequency is piled up at exactly two points that are one standard deviation away from the mean.

[Guttman (1948), p. 277]

(7) Let $\{m_{2r-1}, r = 1, 2, 3, \ldots\}$ be a sequence of real numbers. Then there exists a distribution having as central odd moments the given numbers [Churchill (1946), p. 245].

(8) The following are two of several examples of distributions which are not determined uniquely by their moments.

(a) Lognormal distribution

$$f_1(x) = \begin{cases} [\sigma(x - a)(2\pi)^{1/2}]^{-1} \exp\left[- \frac{[\log (x - a) - m]^2}{2\sigma^2} \right], & a < x < \infty,\ \sigma > 0 \\ 0, & x \leq a \end{cases}$$

and the distribution

$$f_2(x) = \begin{cases} f_1(x)\left(1 + \varepsilon \sin\left\{\frac{2\pi k}{\sigma^2}[\log(x - a)] - m\right\}\right), & a < x < \infty \\ 0, & x \le a \end{cases}$$

($0 < \varepsilon < 1$, k any positive integer) have exactly the same moments

$$\mu'_r = \sum_{i=0}^{r} \binom{r}{i} a^{r-i} \exp\left(mi + \frac{1}{2} i^2\sigma^2\right), \quad r = 0, 1, 2, \ldots$$

[Heyde (1963), p. 392]

(b) The distributions

$$f_1(x) = \begin{cases} c \exp(-x^{\mu} \cos \mu\pi), & x > 0 \\ 0, & x < 0 \end{cases}$$

and

$$f_2(x) = \begin{cases} f_1(x)[1 + \sin(x^{\mu} \sin \mu\pi], & x > 0 \\ 0, & x < 0 \end{cases}$$

($c = [\mu(\cos \mu\pi)^{1/\mu}]/\Gamma(\frac{1}{\mu})$, $0 < \mu < \frac{1}{2}$) have exactly the same moments

$$\mu'_r = \frac{\frac{\Gamma(r + 1)}{\mu}}{\Gamma\left(\frac{1}{\mu}\right)} (\cos \mu\pi)^{-r/\mu}, \quad r = 0, 1, 2, \ldots$$

[Lukacs (1970), p. 20]

1.1.6 SOME USEFUL RESULTS

(1) Let X be a discrete random variable defined on the set of integers (0, 1, 2, ..., n). Then

$$f(x) = \sum_{r=x}^{n} (-1)^{r+x} \binom{r}{x} \frac{\mu'_{(r)}}{r!}$$

$$1 - F(x - 1) = \sum_{r=x}^{n} (-1)^{r+x} \binom{r-1}{x-1} \frac{\mu'_{(r)}}{r!} \quad \text{[Laurent (1965), p. 437]}$$

(2) Let X and Y be continuous random variables with pdf's f and g, respectively. If

$$E(X^k) = E(Y^k),\ k = 1, 2, \ldots, n$$

then the graphs of $Z = f(x)$ and $Z = g(x)$ cross each other at least $(n + 1)$ times [Isii (1957), p. 5].

(3) Let X and Y be independent random variables with ith $(i = 1, 2, 3, \ldots)$ moments $\mu_{i,X}$, and $\mu_{i,Y}$, respectively, and ith $(i = 1, 2, 3, \ldots)$ cumulants $\kappa_{i,X}$ and $\kappa_{i,Y}$, respectively. Then the rth moment of $(X + Y)$ is

$$E(X + Y)^r = \sum_{s=0}^{r} \binom{r}{s} \mu_{s,X}\mu_{(r-s),Y}$$

and the rth cumulant of $(X + Y)$ is $\kappa_{r,X} + \kappa_{r,Y}$ $(r = 1, 2, 3, \ldots)$.

[Moran (1968), p. 267]

(4) Let $f(x)$ be a pdf symmetrical about $x = 0$ and with $-a < x < a$. If $f(x)$ has a single maximum at $x = 0$, then $\mu_{2r} < a^{2r}/(2r + 1)$, $(r = 1, 2, \ldots)$ [Kendall and Stuart (1958), p. 89].

(5) For the normal, Poisson, binomial, and negative binomial distributions, $\nu_1 = 2$(variance)(frequency at C), where C = greatest integer $\leq \mu$ [Kamat (1965a), p. 52].

(6) cov(X,Y) is positive (negative) according as $E_{Y|X}(Y|X)$ is increasing (decreasing) if all expectations mentioned exist.

[Serfling (1967), p. 33]

1.2. GENERATING FUNCTIONS

The generating functions reflect certain properties of distribution functions. They are often thought of as "transforms" of the density function (or probability function) defining the distribution. They could be used to generate moments and cumulants. They also have a particular usefulness in connection with sums of independent random variables.

1.2.1 DEFINITIONS

(1) *The Moment Generating Function* of a random variable X, denoted by M(t), is defined by

$$M(t) = E(e^{tX})$$

for all real values of t.

(2) *The Characteristic Function* of a random variable, denoted by $\phi(t)$, is defined by

$$\phi(t) = E(e^{itX})$$

for all real values of t.

(3) *The Factorial (Probability) Generating Function* of a continuous (discrete) random variable X, denoted by $\psi(t)$, is defined by

$$\psi(t) = E(t^X)$$

for all real values of t.

(4) *The Cumulant Generating Function* of a random variable X, denoted by $\eta(t)$, is defined by

$$\eta(t) = \log M(t)$$

for all real values of t.

(5) *The Joint Moment Generating Function* of a bivariate random variable (X_1, X_2) is defined by

$$M_{X_1,X_2}(t_1,t_2) = E\left(\exp\sum_1^2 t_iX_i\right)$$

for all real values of t_i (i = 1, 2).

1.2.2 COMMENTS

(1) $M(t)$, $\psi(t)$ and $\eta(t)$ do not exist for every distribution and for all values of t.

Examples:

(a) Cauchy: $f(x) = \dfrac{1}{\pi(1+x^2)}$, $-\infty < x < \infty$

$\phi(t) = e^{-|t|}$. $\phi'(0)$ does not exist. $M(t)$ exists only for $t = 0$.

(b) $f(x) = \dfrac{6}{\pi^2 x^2}$, $x = 1, 2, 3, \ldots$

$M(t)$ does not exist for $t > 0$ [Hogg and Craig (1970), p. 51].

(2) $\phi(t)$ exists for every distribution and for all values of t.

(3) $M(it) = \phi(t)$, $\phi(t/i) = M(t)$; if $M(t)$ exists.

(4) $\psi(t) = M(\log t)$, $M(t) = \psi(e^t)$; if they exist.

1.2.3 RELATIONS BETWEEN GENERATING FUNCTIONS AND MOMENTS

(1) If $M(t)$ can be expanded in powers of t; i.e., if

$$M(t) = \sum_{r=0}^{\infty} a_r \frac{(t)^r}{r!}$$

then $\mu'_r = a_r$, the coefficient of $t^r/r!$ in the expansion of $M(t)$ as a power series in t.

(2) If $\phi(t)$ can be expanded in powers of t; i.e., if

$$\phi(t) = \sum_{r=0}^{\infty} a_r \frac{(it)^r}{r!}$$

then $\mu'_r = a_r$, the coefficient of $(it)^r/r!$ in the expansion of $\phi(t)$ as a power series in t.

(3) If $\psi(t)$ can be expanded in powers of t; i.e., if

$$\psi(t) = \sum_{r=0}^{\infty} b_r \frac{(t)^r}{r!}$$

then $\mu'_{(r)} = b_r$, the coefficient of $t^r/r!$ in the expansion of $\psi(t)$ as a power series in t.

(4) If $\eta(t)$ can be expanded in powers of t; i.e., if

$$\eta(t) = \sum_{r=0}^{\infty} c_r \frac{(t)^r}{r!}$$

then $\kappa_r = c_r$, the coefficient of $t^r/r!$ in the expansion of $\eta(t)$ as a power series in t.

1.2.4 USEFUL FORMULAS

If the appropriate quantities exist,

(1) $$\mu'_r = \frac{\partial^r}{\partial t^r} M(t) \bigg|_{t = 0}$$

(2) $$\mu'_r = \frac{1}{(i)^r} \frac{\partial^r}{\partial t^r} \phi(t) \bigg|_{t = 0}$$

(3) $$\mu'_{(r)} = \frac{\partial^r}{\partial t^r} \psi(t) \bigg|_{t = 1}$$

(4) $$\mu = \frac{\partial}{\partial t} \log M(t) \bigg|_{t = 0}$$

$$\mu_2 = \frac{\partial^2}{\partial t^2} \log M(t) \bigg|_{t = 0}$$

$$\operatorname{cov}(X,Y) = \frac{\partial^2}{\partial t_1 \partial t_2} \log M(t_1, t_2) \bigg|_{t_1 = 0,\ t_2 = 0}$$

[Parzen (1962), p. 18]

1.3 MORE ON CHARACTERISTIC FUNCTIONS

1.3.1 *CONDITIONS FOR A FUNCTION TO BE A CHARACTERISTIC FUNCTION*

(1) Cramér's Criterion. A bounded and continuous function $\phi(t)$ is a characteristic function if and only if (iff)

(a) $\phi(0) = 1$

(b) $\psi(x,A) = \int_0^A \int_0^A \phi(t - u) \exp\{ix(t - u)\}dt\, du$ is real and nonnegative for all real x and for all $A > 0$ [Lukacs (1970), p. 73].

(2) (Bochner's Theorem). A complex-valued function of a real variable t is a characteristic function iff

(a) $\phi(t)$ is nonnegative definite

(b) $\phi(0) = 1$ [Lukacs (1970), p. 71].

(3) Pólya's (Sufficient) Condition. Let $\phi(t)$ be a real-valued and continuous function which is defined for all real t and which satisfies the following conditions.

(a) $\phi(0) = 1$

(b) $\phi(-t) = \phi(t)$

(c) $\phi(t)$ is convex for $t > 0$

(d) $\lim_{t\to\infty} \phi(t) = 0$

Then $\phi(t)$ is the characteristic function of an absolutely continuous distribution $F(x)$ [Lukacs (1970), p. 70].

(4) Necessary conditions for $\phi(t)$ to be a characteristic function are that

(a) $\phi(t)$ must be continuous in t

(b) $\phi(t)$ is defined in every finite t-interval

(c) $\phi(0) = 1$

(d) $\phi(t)$ and $\phi(-t)$ shall be conjugate quantities

(e) $|\phi(t)| \leq 1$ [Kendall and Stuart (1958), p. 102].

1.3.2 *COMMENTS*

In the following, let

$$\phi^{(k)}(0) = \left.\frac{d^k\phi(t)}{dt^k}\right|_{t = 0}$$

(1) If ν'_r exists, then its characteristic function $\phi(t)$ has an rth derivative and for $k \leq r$, $\phi^{(k)}(0) = i^k\mu'_k$ [Gnendenko (1962), p. 252].

(2) Existence of $\phi^{(1)}(0)$ does not imply the existence of absolute moments [Zygmund (1947), p. 272].

(3) If $\phi^{(k)}(0)$ exists, then μ'_k (k even) or μ'_{k-1} (k odd) exist.

[Lukacs (1970), p. 22]

(4) The product of two characteristic functions is also a characteristic function [Lukacs (1970), p. 38].

(5) Any finite polynomial in characteristic functions with nonnegative coefficients adding to unity is also a characteristic function [Moran (1968), p. 275].

(6) The characteristic function of the sum of an arbitrary finite number of independent random variables equals the product of their characteristic functions [Fisz (1963), p. 113].

(7) The only characteristic functions for which reciprocals are also characteristic functions belong to degenerate distributions.

[Lukacs (1970), p. 19]

(8) If $\phi(t)$ is a characteristic function then $\exp[\phi(t) - 1]$. $\overline{\phi(t)}$, $|\phi(t)|^2$, $\text{Re}\phi(t)$, etc. are also characteristic functions.

[Moran (1968), p. 275]

(9) If $\eta(t)$ is a probability generating function, then $\eta(\phi(t))$ is also a characteristic function [Moran (1968), p. 275].

(10) Let $\phi(t)$ be the characteristic function of a nonnegative random variable X whose kth moment μ'_k is finite. Let $\phi_k(t) = [(i)^k \mu'_k]^{-1} \phi^{(k)}(t)$, where $\phi^{(k)}(t)$ is the kth derivative of $\phi(t)$ at t. Then $\phi_k(t)$ is also a characteristic function.

[Neuts (1973), p. 293]

(11) Let $Y = ax + b$, then

$$\phi_Y(t) = \phi(at)\, e^{itb}$$

1.3.3 SOME USEFUL RESULTS

(1) *Inversion Theorem.* Let $\phi(t)$ be the characteristic function of the distribution function F(x). Then

$$F(a + h) - F(a) = \lim_{T\to\infty} \frac{1}{2\pi} \int_{-T}^{T} \frac{1 - e^{-ith}}{it}\, e^{-ita}\, \phi(t)\, dt$$

provided that a and a + h (h > 0) are continuity points of F(x).

[Lukacs (1970), p. 31]

(2) If a characteristic function $\phi(t)$ is absolutely integrable over $(-\infty,\infty)$ then the corresponding distribution function F(x) is absolutely continuous and the formula

$$f(x) = F'(x) = \frac{1}{2\pi} \int_{-\infty}^{\infty} e^{-itx} \phi(t)\, dt$$

expresses its pdf f(x) in terms of the characteristic function. The pdf f(x) is continuous [Lukacs (1970), p. 33].

(3) Let $\phi(t)$ be an arbitrary characteristic function. For every real x, the limit

$$f(x) = \lim_{T\to\infty} \frac{1}{2T} \int_{-T}^{T} e^{-itx} \phi(t)\, dt$$

exists and is equal to the saltus of the distribution function of $\phi(t)$ at the point x [Lukacs (1970), p. 35].

(4) Uniqueness Theorem. Two distribution functions $F_1(x)$ and $F_2(x)$ are identical iff their characteristic functions $\phi_1(t)$ and $\phi_2(t)$ are identical [Lukacs (1970), p. 28].

(5) Convolution Theorem. A distribution function F is the convolution of two distributions F_1 and F_2 iff the corresponding characteristic function satisfies the relation $\phi(t) = \phi_1(t)\phi_2(t)$.

[Lukacs (1970), p. 37]

(6) Continuity Theorem. Let $\{F_n(x)\}$ be a sequence of distribution functions and let $\{\phi_n(t)\}$ be the sequence of the corresponding characteristic functions. The sequence $\{F_n(x)\}$ converges weakly to a distribution function F(x) iff the sequence $\{\phi_n(t)\}$ converges for every t to a function $\phi(t)$ which is continuous at $t = 0$. The function $\phi(t)$ is then the characteristic function of F(x).

[Lukacs (1970), p. 48]

The following example illustrates that the continuity of the limiting characteristic functions at $t = 0$ is an essential requirement of this theorem.

Let

$$F_n(x) = \begin{cases} 0 & \text{if } x < -n \\ \dfrac{n + x}{2n} & \text{if } -n \le x \le n \\ 1 & \text{if } x \ge n \end{cases} \qquad (n = 1, 2, \ldots)$$

Then $\lim_{n\to\infty} F_n(x) = \frac{1}{2}$ is not a distribution function. The characteristic function of $F_n(x)$ is $\phi_n(t) = (\sin tn)/tn$ and

$$\lim_{n\to\infty} \phi_n(t) = \phi(t) = \begin{cases} 1 \text{ if } t = 0 \\ 0 \text{ if } t \neq 0 \end{cases}$$

Then $\phi(t)$ is not continuous for $t = 0$ [Lukacs (1970), p. 51].

(7) Let k be an odd positive integer. Necessary and sufficient conditions for the existence of $\phi^{(k)}(0)$ are

(a) $\lim_{x\to\infty} x^k\{F(-x) + 1 - F(x)\} = 0$

(b) $\lim_{T\to\infty} \int_{-T}^{T} x^k dF(x)$ exists.

Then

$$\phi^{(k)}(0) = i^k \lim_{T\to\infty} \int_{-T}^{T} x^k dF(x) \quad \text{[Pitman (1956), p. 1156].}$$

1.4 MOMENTS, CUMULANTS, AND GENERATING FUNCTIONS FOR SOME USEFUL DISCRETE DISTRIBUTIONS

1.4.1 BINOMIAL

$$f(x) = \binom{n}{x} p^x (1 - p)^{n-x}; \quad x = 0, 1, 2, \ldots, n, \ 0 \le p \le 1$$

(1) (a) Mean: np

(b) Variance: $np(1 - p)$

(c) Mean deviation: $2m\binom{n}{m}p^m(1 - p)^{n-m+1}$, where $m = [\mu] + 1$ is the smallest integer greater than the mean μ [Kamat (1965a), p. 52].

(d) Mode m_0: $p(n + 1) - 1 \le m_0 \le p(n + 1)$

(e) Coefficient of variation: $\left(\frac{1 - p}{np}\right)^{1/2}$

(f) Coefficient of skewness: $\frac{(1 - 2p)}{[np(1 - p)]^{1/2}}$

(g) Coefficient of excess: $\frac{1 - 6p(1 - p)}{np(1 - p)}$

(2) (a) $\mu_r = np(1 - p) \sum_{i=0}^{r-2} \binom{r - 1}{i} \mu_i - p \sum_{i=0}^{r-2} \binom{r - 1}{i} \mu_{i+1}, \quad r \ge 2$

[Kendall and Stuart (1958), p. 122]

(b) $\mu_{r+1} = p(1 - p)\left[nr\mu_{r-1} + \frac{d\mu_r}{d_p}\right], \quad r \geq 1$

[Kendall and Stuart (1958), p. 122]

(c) $\mu'_{r+1} = p(1 - p)\left[\frac{n}{1 - p}\mu'_r + \frac{d\mu'_r}{dp}\right], \quad r \geq 1$

[Johnson and Kotz (1969), p. 52]

(d) $\mu'_{(r)} = n^{(r)}p^r$ [Kendall and Stuart (1958), p. 122]

(e) $\kappa_{r+1} = p(1 - p)\frac{d\kappa_r}{dp}, \quad r > 1$

[Kendall and Stuart (1958), p. 143]

(3) (a) Moment generating function: $(q + pe^t)^n$

(b) Characteristic function: $(q + pe^{it})^n$

(c) Probability function: $(q + pt)^n$

1.4.2 POISSON

$$f(x) = \frac{e^{-\theta}\theta^x}{x!}; \quad x = 0, 1, 2, \ldots, \theta > 0$$

(1) (a) Mean: θ

(b) Variance: θ

(c) Mean deviation: $\frac{2m\, e^{-\theta}\theta^m}{m!}$ where $m = [\theta] + 1$ is the smallest integer greater than θ [Kamat (1965), p. 52].

(d) Mode m_0: $\theta - 1 \leq m_0 \leq \theta$

(e) Median $\xi_{1/2}$: $[\theta] - 1 \leq \xi_{1/2} \leq [\theta]$, $[\theta] \leq \xi_{1/2} \leq [\theta] + 1$ according as the fractional part of θ is > or < $(1 - R)$, where R is the Ramanujan's number [Haight (1967), p. 12].

(f) Coefficient of variation: $\frac{1}{\sqrt{\theta}}$

(g) Coefficient of skewness: $\frac{1}{\sqrt{\theta}}$

(h) Coefficient of excess: $\frac{1}{\theta}$

(2) (a) $\mu_r = \theta \sum_{i=0}^{r-2} \binom{r-1}{i} \mu_i, \quad r = 2, 3, \ldots$

[Kendall and Stuart (1958), p. 126]

(b) $\mu_{r+1} = r\theta\mu_{r-1} + \theta \frac{\partial \mu_r}{\partial \theta}, \quad r = 1, 2, \ldots$

[Kendall and Stuart (1958), p. 126]

(c) $\mu'_{r+1} = \theta\mu'_r + \theta \frac{\partial \mu'_r}{\partial \theta}, \quad r = 1, 2, \ldots$ [Haight (1967), p. 6]

(d) $\mu'_r = \sum_{j=1}^{r} (\mu'_1)^j \sum_{i=1}^{j} \frac{(-1)^{j-i}(i)^r}{(j-i)!i!}$ [Philipson (1963), p. 243]

(e) $\mu'_{(r)} = \theta^r$ [Johnson and Kotz (1969), p. 90]

(f) $\kappa_r = \theta, \quad r = 2, 3, \ldots$ [Johnson and Kotz (1969), p. 91]

(3) (a) Moment generating function: $\exp\{\theta(e^t - 1)\}$

(b) Characteristic function: $\exp\{\theta(e^{it} - 1)\}$

(c) Probability generating function: $\exp\{\theta(t - 1)\}$

1.4.3 NEGATIVE BINOMIAL

$$f(x) = \binom{s+x-1}{x} q^x p^s; \; x = 0, 1, 2, \ldots, \; q = 1 - p, \; 0 < p \leq 1$$

(1) (a) Mean: $\frac{sq}{p}$

(b) Variance: $\frac{sq}{p^2}$

(c) Mean Deviation: $2m\binom{n+m-1}{m} q^m p^{n-1}$, where $m = [\mu] + 1$ is the smallest integer greater than mean μ [Kamat (1965a), p. 52].

(d) Coefficient of variation: $\frac{1}{(sq)^{1/2}}$

(e) Coefficient of skewness: $\frac{1 + q}{(sq)^{1/2}}$

(f) Coefficient of excess: $\frac{6q + p^2}{sq}$

(2) (a) $\mu_{r+1} = q\left(\frac{\partial \mu_r}{\partial q} + \frac{rs}{p^2}\mu_{r-1}\right)$

(b) $\mu'_{(r)} = (s + r - 1)^{(r)}\left(\frac{q}{p}\right)^r$ [Johnson and Kotz (1969), p. 126]

(c) $\kappa_{r+1} = PQ\frac{d\kappa_r}{dQ}$; $r \geq 1$, $P = \frac{q}{p}$, $Q = \frac{1}{p}$

[Johnson and Kotz (1969), p. 126]

(d) $\kappa_{r+1} = q\frac{d\kappa_r}{dp}$; $s = 1$, $r \geq 1$

(3) (a) Moment generating function: $p^s(1 - qe^t)^{-s}$

(b) Characteristic function: $p^s(1 - qe^{it})^{-s}$

(c) Probability generating function: $p^s(1 - qt)^{-s}$

1.4.4 HYPERGEOMETRIC

$$f(x) = \frac{\binom{M}{x}\binom{N - M}{n - x}}{\binom{N}{n}}, \quad \max(0, n - N + M) \leq x \leq \min(M, n)$$

(1) (a) Mean: $\frac{nM}{N}$

(b) Variance: $\left(\frac{N - n}{N - 1}\right)\frac{nM}{N}\left(1 - \frac{M}{N}\right)$

[Lieberman and Owen (1961), p. 21]

(c) Mean deviation: $\dfrac{2m(N - M - n + m)\binom{M}{m}\binom{N - M}{n - m}}{N\binom{N}{n}}$ where

$m = [\mu] + 1$ is the smallest integer greater than mean μ.

[Kamat (1965a), p. 52]

(d) Mode: $\left[\dfrac{(n + 1)(M + 1)}{N + 2}\right]$, where $[x]$ is the greatest integer $\leq x$.

(e) Coefficient of variation: $\left[\dfrac{(N - M)(N - n)}{nM(N - 1)}\right]^{1/2}$

(f) Coefficient of skewness: $\dfrac{(N - 2M)(N - 1)^{1/2}(N - 2n)}{[NM(N - M)(N - n)]^{1/2}(N - 2)}$

(2) $\mu'_{(r)} = \dfrac{n^{(r)}M^{(r)}}{N^{(r)}} = r!\dfrac{\binom{M}{r}\binom{n}{r}}{\binom{N}{r}}$ [Johnson and Kotz (1969) p. 144]

[Mood et al. (1974), p. 539]

(3) (a) Moment generating function:

$\dfrac{(N - M)!(N - n)!}{N!} F(-n, -M; N - M - n + 1; e^{t})$

[Johnson and Kotz (1969), p. 144]

(b) Moment generating function:

$\dfrac{(N - n)}{N!} \dfrac{\partial^{(n)}}{\partial y^{(n)}} [(1 + ye^{t})^{M}(1 + y)^{N-M}]\Big|_{y = 0}$ [Lessing (1973), p. 115]

(c) Characteristic function:

$\dfrac{(N - M)!(N - n)!}{n!} F(-n, -M; N - M - n + 1; e^{it})$

(d) Probability generating function:

$\dfrac{(N - M)^{(n)}}{N^{(n)}} F(-n, -M; N - M - n + 1; t)$ where $F(\alpha, \beta; \gamma; x)$ is a hypergeometric function (see Ch. 10, §9).

[Kendall and Stuart (1958), p. 134]

1.4.5 LOGARITHMIC SERIES

$$f(x) = \alpha \frac{\theta^x}{x}, \quad x = 1, 2, \ldots, \quad 0 < \theta < 1, \quad \alpha = -[\log(1 - \theta)]^{-1}$$

(1) (a) Mean: $\dfrac{\alpha\theta}{(1 - \theta)}$

(b) Variance: $\dfrac{\alpha\theta(1 - \alpha\theta)}{(1 - \theta)^2}$

(c) Mean deviation: $2\alpha \dfrac{\theta}{1 - \theta} (\theta^{m-1} - \alpha_0)$

where

$$\alpha_0 = \sum_{x=m}^{\infty} \alpha \frac{\theta^x}{x}$$

and where $m = [\mu] + 1$ is the smallest integer greater than mean μ.

[Kamat (1965a), p. 52]

(d) Mode: 1

(e) Coefficient of variation: $\left(\dfrac{1 - \alpha\theta}{\alpha\theta}\right)^{1/2}$

(f) Coefficient of skewness: $\dfrac{(1 + \theta) - 3\alpha\theta + 2\alpha^2\theta^2}{(\alpha\theta)^{1/2}(1 - \alpha\theta)^{3/2}}$

(g) Coefficient of excess:

$$\frac{1 + 4\theta + \theta^2 - 4\alpha\theta(1 + \theta) + 6\alpha^2\theta^2 - 3\alpha^3\theta^3}{\alpha\theta(1 - \alpha\theta)^2} - 3$$

(2) (a) $\mu'_{r+1} = \theta \dfrac{\partial \mu'_r}{\partial \theta} + \dfrac{\alpha\theta}{(1 - \theta)} \mu'_r$

and

$$\mu_{r+1} = \theta \frac{\partial \mu_r}{\partial \theta} + r\mu_2\mu_{r-1}$$ [Johnson and Kotz (1969), p. 167]

(b) $\mu'_{(r)} = \dfrac{\alpha\theta^r (r - 1)!}{(1 - \theta)^r}$ [Johnson and Kotz (1969), p. 166]

(c) $\kappa_r = \theta \dfrac{\partial \kappa_{r-1}}{\partial \theta}$ [Johnson and Kotz (1969), p. 168]

(3) (a) Moment generating function: $\dfrac{\log(1 - \theta e^t)}{\log(1 - \theta)}$

[Johnson and Kotz (1969), p. 166]

(b) Characteristic function: $\dfrac{\log(1 - \theta e^{it})}{\log(1 - \theta)}$

(c) Probability generating function: $\dfrac{\log(1 - \theta t)}{\log(1 - \theta)}$

1.4.6 UNIFORM

$$f(x) = \frac{1}{N + 1}, \quad x = 0, 1, 2, \ldots, N, \quad N \text{ a nonnegative integer.}$$

(1) (a) Mean: $\dfrac{N}{2}$

(b) Variance: $\dfrac{N(N + 2)}{12}$

(c) Mode m_0: no mode

(d) Median $\xi_{1/2}$: $\begin{cases} \dfrac{N}{2} & \text{for N even} \\ \dfrac{N - 1}{2} \le \xi_{1/2} < \dfrac{N + 1}{2} & \text{for N odd} \end{cases}$

(e) Coefficient of variation: $\left(\dfrac{N + 2}{3N}\right)^{1/2}$

(f) Coefficient of skewness: 0

(g) Coefficient of excess: $-\dfrac{6}{5}\left[1 + \dfrac{2}{N(N + 2)}\right]$

(2) (a) $\mu_{2r-1} = 0, \quad r = 1, 2, \ldots$

and

$$\mu_{2r} = \frac{1}{N + 1} \sum_{j=0}^{N} \left(j - \frac{1}{2}N\right)^{2r}, \quad r = 1, 2, \ldots$$

[Johnson and Kotz (1969), p. 239]

(b) $\kappa_{2r+1} = 0, \quad r = 1, 2, \ldots$

and

$$\kappa_{2r} = \frac{[(N + 1)^{2r} - 1]B_{2r}}{2r}, \quad r = 1, 2, \ldots$$

where B_{2r} is a Bernoulli number [Rahman (1968), p. 191].

(3) (a) Moment generating function: $$\frac{e^{Nt/2}\,\dfrac{\sin h[(N + 1)t/2]}{(N + 1)t/2}}{\dfrac{\sin h(t/2)}{t/2}}$$

[Rahman (1968), p. 190]

(b) Characteristic function: $$\frac{[1 - e^{it(N+1)}]}{(1 - e^{it})(N + 1)}$$

(c) Probability generating function: $$\frac{(1 - t^{N+1})}{(N + 1)(1 - t)}$$

[Johnson and Kotz (1969), p. 239]

1.5 MOMENTS, CUMULANTS, AND GENERATING FUNCTIONS FOR SOME USEFUL CONTINUOUS DISTRIBUTIONS

1.5.1 NORMAL

$$f(x) = \frac{1}{\sigma\sqrt{2\pi}} \exp\left\{-\frac{(x - \mu)^2}{2\sigma^2}\right\}; \quad -\infty < x < \infty,\ -\infty < \mu < \infty,\ \sigma > 0$$

(1) (a) Mean: μ

(b) Variance: σ^2

(c) Mean deviation: $\left(\frac{2\sigma^2}{\pi}\right)^{1/2}$

(d) Mode: μ

(e) Median: μ

(f) Coefficient of variation: $\frac{\sigma}{\mu}$

(g) Coefficient of skewness: 0

(h) Coefficient of excess: 0

(2) (a) $\mu_{2r+1} = 0, \quad r = 1, 2, \ldots$

and

$$\mu_{2r} = \nu_{2r} = \frac{(2r)!}{(2^r)(r!)} (\sigma)^{2r}, \quad r = 1, 2, \ldots$$

[Kendall and Stuart (1958), p. 135]

(b) $$\mu'_{2r-1} = (\sigma)^{2r-1} \sum_{i=1}^{r} \frac{(2r-1)!\mu^{2i-1}}{(2i-1)!(r-i)!\, 2^{r-i}}, \quad r = 1, 2, \ldots$$

and

$$\mu'_{2r} = (\sigma)^{2r} \sum_{i=0}^{r} \frac{(2r)!\mu^{2i}}{(2i)!(r-i)!2^{r-i}}, \quad r = 1, 2, \ldots$$

[Bain (1969), p. 34]

(c) $$\nu_{2r-1} = \frac{1}{\sqrt{2\pi}} (r-1)!(2^r)(\sigma)^{2r-1}, \quad r = 1, 2, \ldots$$

[Lukacs (1970), p. 13]

(d) $\kappa_2 = \sigma^2, \quad \kappa_r = 0, \quad r = 3, 4, \ldots$

[Kendall and Stuart (1958), p. 136]

(3) (a) Moment generating function: $\exp\left\{t\mu + \frac{t^2\sigma^2}{2}\right\}$

[Kendall and Stuart (1958), p. 135]

(b) Characteristic function: $\exp\left\{it\mu - \frac{1}{2} t^2\sigma^2\right\}$

1.5.2 LOGNORMAL

$$f(x) = \frac{1}{\sigma x\sqrt{2\pi}} \exp\left\{-\frac{1}{2\sigma^2} (\log x - \theta)^2\right\}; \quad x > 0, -\infty < \theta < \infty, \sigma > 0$$

(1) (a) Mean: $\exp\left\{\theta + \frac{1}{2} \sigma^2\right\}$

(b) Variance: $\omega(\omega - 1)e^{2\theta}$ where $\omega = \exp\{\sigma^2\}$

(c) Mode: $\exp\{\mu - \sigma^2\}$

(d) Median: e^{μ}

(e) Coefficient of variation: $(\omega - 1)^{1/2}$

(f) Coefficient of skewness: $(\omega + 2)(\omega - 1)^{1/2}$

(g) Coefficient of excess: $\omega^4 + 2\omega^3 + 3\omega^2 - 6$

(2) (a) $\mu'_r = \exp\left\{r\theta + \frac{1}{2} r^2\sigma^2\right\}$

(b) $$\mu_r = \frac{(\mu_2)^{n/2}}{(\omega - 1)^{n/2}} \sum_{j=0}^{r} (-1)^j \binom{r}{j} \omega^{(1/2)(r-j)(r-j-1)}$$

[Johnson and Kotz (1970a), p. 115]

1.5.3 INVERSE GAUSSIAN

$$f(x) = \sqrt{\frac{\lambda}{2\pi x^3}} \exp\left\{-\frac{\lambda(x - \mu)^2}{2\mu^2 x}\right\}; \quad x > 0,\ \lambda > 0,\ \mu > 0$$

(1) (a) Mean: μ

(b) Variance: $\frac{\mu^3}{\lambda}$

(c) Mode: $\mu\left\{\left(1 + \frac{9}{4\phi^2}\right)^{1/2} - \frac{3}{2\phi}\right\}, \quad \lambda = \mu\phi$

(d) Coefficient of variation: $\left(\frac{\mu}{\lambda}\right)^{1/2}$

(e) Coefficient of skewness: $3\left(\frac{\mu}{\lambda}\right)^{1/2}$

(f) Coefficient of excess: $15\left(\frac{\mu}{\lambda}\right)$

(2) (a) $$\mu'_r = (\mu)^r \sum_{s=0}^{r-1} \frac{(r - 1 + s)!}{s!(r - 1 - s)!\left(2\frac{\lambda}{\mu}\right)^s}$$ [Tweedie (1957), p. 366]

(b) $\kappa_r = 1 \cdot 3 \cdot 5 \cdots (2r - 3)\mu^{2r-1}\lambda^{1-r}$

[Johnson and Kotz (1970a), p. 139]

(3) (a) Moment generating function: $\exp\left[\frac{\lambda}{\mu}\left\{1 - \left(\frac{1 + \mu^2 t}{\lambda}\right)^{1/2}\right\}\right]$

(b) Characteristic function: $\exp\left[\frac{\lambda}{\mu}\left\{1 - \left(\frac{1 + \mu^2 it}{\lambda}\right)^{1/2}\right\}\right]$

1.5.4 CAUCHY

$$f(x) = \frac{1}{\pi\lambda\left[1 + \left(\frac{x - \theta}{\lambda}\right)^2\right]}; \quad -\infty < x < \infty, \ -\infty < \theta < \infty, \ \lambda > 0$$

(1) Moments & cumulants do not exist. Mode: θ. Median: θ.

(2) $M(t)$, $\psi(t)$ and $\eta(t)$ do not exist.

(3) $\phi(t) = \exp\{it\theta - |t|\lambda\}$ [Johnson and Kotz (1970a), p. 156].

1.5.5 GAMMA

$$f(x) = \frac{e^{-x\theta}x^{\alpha-1}\theta^{\alpha}}{\Gamma(\alpha)}; \quad x \geq 0, \ \theta > 0, \ \alpha > 0$$

(1) (a) Mean: $\frac{\alpha}{\theta}$

(b) Variance: $\frac{\alpha}{\theta^2}$

(c) Mode: $\frac{\alpha - 1}{\theta}$, $\alpha \geq 1$

(d) Median $\xi_{1/2}$: $\frac{1}{2} = P(\alpha, \xi_{1/2}\theta)$, where $P(a, x)$ is the incomplete gamma function ratio.

(e) Coefficient of variation: $\alpha^{-1/2}$

(f) Coefficient of skewness: $2\alpha^{-1/2}$

(g) Coefficient of excess: $\frac{6}{\alpha}$

(2) (a) $\mu'_r = \nu'_r = \dfrac{\Gamma(r + \alpha)}{\Gamma(\alpha)} \dfrac{1}{\theta^r} = \sum_{i=0}^{r-1} (\alpha + i) \dfrac{1}{\theta^r}, \quad r = 1, 2, 3, \ldots$

(b) $\kappa_r = \dfrac{(r - 1)!\alpha}{\theta^r}, \quad r = 1, 2, \ldots$ [Rahman (1968), p. 123]

(3) (a) Moment generating function: $\left(\dfrac{\theta}{\theta - t}\right)^{\alpha}$

(b) Characteristic function: $\left(\dfrac{\theta}{\theta - it}\right)^{\alpha}$

1.5.6 WEIBULL

$F(x) = 1 - \exp\{-\theta x^c\}; \quad x \geq 0, \theta > 0, c > 0$

(1) (a) Mean: $\dfrac{\Gamma\left(1 + \frac{1}{c}\right)}{\theta^{1/c}}$

(b) Variance: $\dfrac{\Gamma\left(1 + \frac{2}{c}\right)}{\theta^{2/c}} - \dfrac{\left\{\Gamma\left(1 + \frac{1}{c}\right)\right\}^2}{\theta^{2/c}}$

(c) Mode: $\left\{\dfrac{1}{\theta}\left(1 - \dfrac{1}{c}\right)\right\}^{1/c} \quad c \geq 1$

(d) Median: $\left\{\dfrac{\log 2}{\theta}\right\}^{1/c}$

(e) Coefficient of variation: $\left\{\dfrac{\Gamma\left(\frac{2}{c} + 1\right)}{\left[\Gamma\left(\frac{1}{c} + 1\right)\right]^2} - 1\right\}^{1/2}$

(2) $\mu'_r = \dfrac{\Gamma\left(1 + \frac{r}{c}\right)}{\theta^{r/c}}$

(3) Factorial moment generating function: $\dfrac{\Gamma\left(1 + \frac{t}{c}\right)}{\theta^{t/c}}$

[Mood et al. (1974), p. 543]

1.5.7 BETA

$$f(x) = \frac{x^{a-1}(1 - x)^{b-1}}{B(a, b)} ; \quad 0 \le x \le 1, a > 0, b > 0$$

where B(a, b) is the beta function.

(1) (a) Mean: $\frac{a}{a + b}$

(b) Variance: $\frac{ab}{(a + b + 1)(a + b)^2}$

(c) Mean deviation: $\frac{2a^a b^b}{(a + b)^{a+b}} \frac{\Gamma(a + b)}{\Gamma(a)\Gamma(b)}$

[Johnson and Kotz (1970b), p. 40]

(d) Mode: $\frac{a - 1}{a + b - 2}$; $a > 1, b > 1$

(e) Median $\xi_{1/2}$: $\frac{1}{2} = I_{\xi_{1/2}}(a, b)$ where $I_x(a, b)$ is the incomplete beta function ratio.

(f) Coefficient of variation: $\left[\frac{b}{a(a + b + 1}\right]^{1/2}$

(g) Coefficient of skewness: $\frac{2(b - a)(a + b + 1)^{1/2}}{(a + b + 2)(ab)^{1/2}}$

(h) Coefficient of excess: $\frac{3(a + b)(a + b + 1)(a + 1)(2b - a)}{ab(a + b + 2)(a + b + 3)} + \frac{a(a - b)}{a + b} - 3$

(2) $$\mu'_r = \frac{B(a + r, b)}{B(a, b)} = \prod_{i=0}^{r-1} \left(\frac{a + i}{a + b + i}\right)$$

[Johnson and Kotz (1970b), p. 40]

(3) Characteristic function:

$$M(a, a + b, it) = \frac{\Gamma(a + b)}{\Gamma(a)} \sum_{j=0}^{\infty} \frac{\Gamma(a + j)}{\Gamma(a + b + j)} \frac{(it)^2}{\Gamma(j + 1)}$$

where $M(\alpha; \beta; x)$ is a confluent hypergeometric function.
[Abramowitz and Stegun (1970), p. 930]

1.5.8 POWER FUNCTION

$$F(x) = \left(\frac{x}{\theta}\right)^c; \quad 0 < x < \theta,\ \theta > 0,\ c > 0$$

(1) (a) Mean: $\frac{c\theta}{(c + 1)}$

(b) Variance: $\theta^2 \frac{c}{(c + 2)(c + 1)^2}$

(c) Mode: θ if $c > 1$

(d) Median: $\frac{\theta}{2^{1/c}}$

(e) Coefficient of variation: $\left\{\frac{1}{c(c + 2)}\right\}^{1/2}$

(f) Coefficient of skewness: $\frac{2(1 - c)(2 + c)^{1/2}}{(3 + c)c^{1/2}}$

(g) Coefficient of excess: $\frac{3(c + 1)^2(4 - c^2)}{c(3 + c)(4 + c)} + \frac{c(c - 1)}{(c + 1)} - 3$

(2) $\mu'_r = \theta^r\left(\frac{c}{c + r}\right)$

1.5.9 UNIFORM

$$f(x) = \frac{1}{b - a}; \quad a < x < b,\ -\infty < a < b < \infty$$

(1) (a) Mean: $\frac{a + b}{2}$

(b) Variance: $\frac{(b - a)^2}{12}$

(c) Mean deviation: $\frac{b - a}{4}$

(d) Mode: no mode

(e) Median: $\frac{a + b}{2}$

(f) Coefficient of variation: $\frac{(b - a)}{(a + b)\sqrt{3}}$

(g) Coefficient of skewness: 0

(h) Coefficient of excess: $-\frac{6}{5}$

(2) (a) $\mu'_r = \frac{b^{r+1} - a^{r+1}}{(b - a)(r + 1)}, \quad r = 1, 2, \ldots$

(b) $\mu_{2r-1} = 0, \quad r = 1, 2, \ldots$

and

$$\mu_{2r} = \frac{(b - a)^{2r}}{2^{2r}(2r + 1)}, \quad r = 1, 2, \ldots$$ [Lukacs (1970), p. 13]

(c) $\nu_r = \frac{(b - a)^r}{2^r(r + 1)}, \quad r = 1, 2, \ldots$ [Lukacs (1970), p. 13]

(d) $\kappa_{2r} = \frac{(b - a)^{2r}}{2r} B_{2r}, \quad r = 1, 2, \ldots; \quad \kappa_{2r+1} = 0, \; r = 1, 2, \ldots$

where B_j $(j = 1, 2, \ldots)$ are the Bernoulli numbers.

[Rahman (1968), p. 119]

(3) (a) Moment generating function: $\frac{e^{tb} - e^{ta}}{(b - a)t}$

(b) Characteristic function: $\frac{e^{itb} - e^{ita}}{(b - a)it}$

1.5.10 PARETO

$$F(x) = 1 - \left(\frac{a}{x}\right)^{\theta}, \quad x \geq a, \; \theta > 0$$

(1) (a) Mean: $\frac{\theta a}{\theta - 1}, \; \theta > 1$

(b) Variance: $\dfrac{\theta a^2}{(\theta - 1)^2(\theta - 2)}$, $\theta > 2$

(c) Mean deviation: $2a \dfrac{(\theta - 1)^{\theta-2}}{\theta^{\theta-1}}$

(d) Mode: a

(e) Median: $a2^{1/\theta}$

(f) Coefficient of variation: $\left[\dfrac{1}{\theta(\theta - 2)}\right]^{1/2}$, $\theta > 2$

(2) $\mu'_r = \dfrac{\theta a^r}{\theta - r}$, $\theta > r$ [Mood et al. (1974), p. 543]

(3) M(t) does not exist [Mood et al. (1974), p. 543]

1.5.11 EXTREME-VALUE

$$F(x) = \exp\left\{-e^{-(x-\alpha)/\beta}\right\}; \quad -\infty < x < \infty, \ -\infty < \alpha < \infty, \ \beta > 0$$

(1) (a) Mean: $\alpha + \gamma\beta$ ($\gamma \doteq 0.5772 \ldots$ is Euler's constant)

(b) Variance: $\dfrac{\pi^2\beta^2}{6}$

(c) Mode: α

(d) Median: $\alpha - \beta \log(\log 2)$

(e) Coefficient of variation: $\dfrac{\pi\beta}{(\alpha + \gamma\beta)6^{1/2}}$

(f) Coefficient of skewness: 1.29857

(g) Coefficient of excess: 2.4

(2) $\kappa_2 = \frac{\pi^2\beta^2}{6}$, $\kappa_r = (-\beta)^r\,\psi^{(r-1)}(1)$ for $r \geq 2$, $\psi(\cdot)$ is a digamma function [Mood et al. (1974), p. 543].

(3) (a) Moment generating function: $e^{\alpha t}\Gamma(1 - \beta t)$, $t < \frac{1}{\beta}$

(b) Characteristic function: $e^{i\alpha t}\Gamma(1 - i\beta t)$

1.5.12 LAPLACE

$$f(x) = \frac{1}{2\beta}\exp\left\{-\frac{|x - \alpha|}{\beta}\right\}; \quad -\infty < x < \infty,\ -\infty < \alpha < \infty,\ \beta > 0$$

(1) (a) Mean: α

(b) Variance: $2\beta^2$

(c) Mean deviation: β

(d) Mode: α

(e) Median: α

(f) Coefficient of variation: $\left(\frac{\beta}{\alpha}\right)\sqrt{2}$

(g) Coefficient of skewness: 0

(h) Coefficient of excess: 3

(2) (a) $\mu_{2r-1} = 0$, $r = 1, 2, \ldots$

and

$$\mu_{2r} = (2r)!\beta^r, \quad r = 1, 2, \ldots$$

(b) $\nu_r = \beta^r(r!)$ [Lukacs (1970), p. 13]

(c) $\kappa_2 = 2\beta^2$, $\kappa_{2r-1} = 0$ $(r = 2, 3, \ldots)$

and

$$\kappa_{2r} = \frac{(2r)!}{r}(\beta)^{2r}, \quad r = 1, 2, \ldots$$

[Johnson and Kotz (1970b), p. 23]

(3) (a) Moment generating function: $\dfrac{e^{\alpha t}}{1 - \beta^2 t^2}$

(b) Characteristic function: $\dfrac{e^{i\alpha t}}{(1 + \beta^2 t^2)}$

[Mood et al. (1974), p. 54]

1.5.13 LOGISTIC

$$F(x) = \left[1 + e^{-(x-\alpha)/\beta}\right]^{-1} = \frac{1}{2}\left[1 + \tan h\left(\frac{x - \alpha}{2\beta}\right)\right];$$

$$-\infty < x < \infty, \ -\infty < \alpha < \infty, \ \beta > 0$$

(1) (a) Mean: α

(b) Variance: $\beta^2 \dfrac{\pi^2}{3}$

(c) Mean deviation: $2\beta \displaystyle\sum_{j=1}^{\infty} (-1)^{j-1} \frac{1}{j}$

(d) Mode: α

(e) Median: α

(f) Coefficient of variation: $\dfrac{\beta\pi}{\alpha\sqrt{3}}$.

(g) Coefficient of skewness: 0

(h) Coefficient of excess: 1.2

(2) (a) $\nu_r = \beta^r \Gamma(r + 1) \displaystyle\sum_{j=1}^{\infty} (-1)^{j-1} j^{-r}, \quad r > 0$

[Johnson and Kotz (1970b), p. 14]

(b) $\kappa_{2r-1} = 0$, $r = 1, 2, \ldots$; $\kappa_{2r} = 6(2^{2r} - 1)\beta^{2r}B_{2r}$, $r = 1, 2, \ldots$ where B_{2r} is a Bernoulli number.

(3) (a) Moment generating function: $\exp(\alpha t)\pi\beta t \csc(\pi\beta t)$

(b) Characteristic function: $\exp(\alpha it)\pi\beta it \csc(\pi\beta it)$

1.5.14 CHI

$$f(x) = \frac{x^{n-1}e^{-x^2/2}}{2^{(n/2)-1}\Gamma\left(\frac{n}{2}\right)}; \quad x \geq 0,\ n > 0$$

where n is the degrees of freedom.

(1) (a) Mean: $\dfrac{\Gamma\left(\frac{n+1}{2}\right)}{\Gamma\left(\frac{n}{2}\right)}$

(b) Variance: $\dfrac{\Gamma\left(\frac{n+2}{2}\right)}{\Gamma\left(\frac{n}{2}\right)} - \left[\dfrac{\Gamma\left(\frac{n+1}{2}\right)}{\Gamma\left(\frac{n}{2}\right)}\right]^2$

(c) Mode: $\sqrt{(n-1)}$, $n \geq 1$

(d) Median $\xi_{1/2}$: $\frac{1}{2} = P\left(\frac{n}{2}, \frac{\xi_{1/2}^2}{2}\right)$, where $P(a, x)$ is the incomplete gamma function ratio.

(2) (a) $\mu'_r = \dfrac{\Gamma\left(\frac{n+r}{2}\right)}{\Gamma\left(\frac{n}{2}\right)}$ [Johnson and Kotz (1970a), p. 197]

(b) $$\mu_{2r} = \frac{n}{2^r}\sum_{i=0}^{r} a^{2i}\left[\binom{2r}{2i}\pi_{2r-2i} - \binom{2r}{2i-1}\pi_{2r-2i+1}\right]n^{i-1}$$

$r = 1, 2, \ldots$

and

$$\mu_{2r+1} = \frac{\sqrt{n}}{2^{r+(1/2)}} \sum_{i=0}^{r} a^{2i} \left[\binom{2r+1}{2i} \pi_{2r-2i+1} - \binom{2r+1}{2i+1} \pi_{2r-2i}\right] n^{i}$$

$$r = 0, 1, 2, \ldots$$

where

$$\binom{2r}{-1} = 0, \quad a = \frac{\mu}{\sqrt{n/2}}$$

and

$$\pi_q = (n + q - 2)(n + q - 4)(n + q - 6) \ldots$$

$q = 2, 3, 4, \ldots,$ the last factor is the smallest integer not smaller than n [Hodges and Lehmann (1967), p. 187].

1.5.15 CHI SQUARE

$$f(x) = \frac{e^{-x/2}(x)^{(\nu-2)/2}}{2^{\nu/2}\Gamma(\nu/2)}; \quad x > 0, \ \nu = 1, 2, \ldots$$

where ν is referred to as the degrees of freedom.

(1) (a) Mean: ν

(b) Variance: 2ν

(c) Mean deviation: $\dfrac{(\nu)^{\nu/2} e^{-\nu/2}}{2^{(\nu-2)/2}\Gamma\left(\frac{\nu}{2}\right)}$

(d) Mode: $(\nu - 2)$, $\nu > 2$

(e) Median $\xi_{1/2}$: $\frac{1}{2} = P\left(\frac{\nu}{2}, \frac{\xi_{1/2}}{2}\right)$ where $P(a, x)$ is the incomplete gamma function ratio.

(f) Coefficient of variation: $\left(\frac{2}{\nu}\right)^{1/2}$

(g) Coefficient of skewness: $\dfrac{2^{3/2}}{\nu^{1/2}}$

(h) Coefficient of excess: $\frac{12}{\nu}$

(2) (a) $\mu'_r = \frac{2^r \Gamma\left(\frac{\nu}{2} + r\right)}{\Gamma\left(\frac{\nu}{2}\right)} = 2^r \prod_{i=0}^{r-1} \left(i + \frac{\nu}{2}\right), \quad r = 1, 2, 3$

(b) $\kappa_r = 2^{r-1}\nu[(r - 1)!], \quad r = 1, 2, 3, \ldots$

(3) (a) Moment generating function: $(1 - 2t)^{-\nu/2}, \quad t < \frac{1}{2}$

(b) Characteristic function: $(1 - 2it)^{-\nu/2}$

1.5.16 STUDENT'S t

$$f(x) = \frac{\left(1 + \frac{x^2}{n}\right)^{-(n+1)/2}}{\sqrt{n}\, B\left(\frac{1}{2}, \frac{n}{2}\right)}; \quad -\infty < x < \infty, \ n = 1, 2, \ldots$$

where B(a, b) is the incomplete beta function and n is referred to as the degrees of freedom.

(1) (a) Mean: 0 for n = 2, 3, ... (undefined for n = 1)

(b) Variance: $\frac{n}{n - 2}, \quad n = 3, 4, \ldots$

(c) Mode: 0

(d) Mean deviation: $\frac{2n^{1/2}\Gamma\left(\frac{n+1}{2}\right)}{(n - 1)\Gamma\left(\frac{1}{2}\right)\Gamma\left(\frac{n}{2}\right)}$ [Kamat (1965b), p. 291]

(e) Coefficient of variation: undefined

(f) Coefficient of skewness: 0, n = 4, 5, ...

(g) Coefficient of excess: $\frac{6}{n - 4}, \quad n = 5, 6, \ldots$

(2) (a)

$$\mu_r = \begin{cases} 0 & \text{for } n > r \text{ and } r \text{ odd} \\ n^{r/2} \dfrac{B\left(\frac{r+1}{2}, \frac{n-r}{2}\right)}{B\left(\frac{1}{2}, \frac{n}{2}\right)} = n^{r/2} \dfrac{1 \cdot 3 \cdot 5 \cdots (r - 1)}{(n - 2)(n - 4)\ldots(n - r)} & \text{for } n > r \text{ and } r \text{ even} \end{cases}$$

(b) $$\nu_{2r-1} = \frac{2^r (n)^{r-(1/2)} (r-1)!\Gamma\left(\frac{n+1}{2}\right)}{(n-1)(n-3)\dots(n-2r+1)\Gamma\left(\frac{1}{2}\right)\Gamma\left(\frac{n}{2}\right)}, \quad 2r - 1 < n$$

[Lukacs (1970), p. 13]

(3) (a) Moment generating function: does not exist

[Mood et al. (1974), p. 543]

(b) Characteristic function: $$\frac{1}{B\left(\frac{1}{2}, \frac{n}{2}\right)} \int_{-\infty}^{\infty} \frac{\exp(itz\sqrt{n})}{(1+z^2)^{(n+1)/2}}\, dz$$

[Ifram (1970), p. 352]

1.5.17 F

$$f(x) = \frac{\left(\frac{n_1}{n_2}\right)^{n_1/2} x^{(n_1-2)/2}}{B\left(\frac{n_1}{2}, \frac{n_2}{2}\right)} \left(1 + \frac{n_1}{n_2} x\right)^{-(n_1+n_2)/2}$$

$x > 0,\ n_1, n_2 = 1, 2, \dots$

where n_1 is the degrees of freedom for the numerator and n_2 is the degrees of freedom for the denominator.

(1) (a) Mean: $\frac{n_2}{n_2 - 2}$, $n_2 > 2$

(b) Variance: $\frac{2n_2^2(n_1 + n_2 - 2)}{n_1(n_2 - 2)^2(n_2 - 4)}$ for $n_2 > 4$

(c) Mode: $\frac{n_2(n_1 - 2)}{n_1(n_2 + 2)}$, $n_1 > 2$

(d) Coefficient of variation: $\left\{\frac{2(n_1 + n_2 - 2)}{n_1(n_2 - 4)}\right\}^{1/2}$, $n_2 > 4$

(e) Coefficient of skewness: $\frac{(2n_1 + n_2 - 2)\{8(n_2 - 4)\}^{1/2}}{\sqrt{n_1}(n_2 - 6)(n_1 + n_2 - 2)^{1/2}}$,

$n_2 > 6$

(f) Coefficient of excess:

$$\frac{12\{(n_2 - 2)^2(n_2 - 4) + n_1(n_1 + n_2 - 2)(5n_2 - 22)\}}{n_1(n_2 - 6)(n_2 - 8)(n_1 + n_2 - 2)}, \quad n_2 > 8$$

(2) $$\mu_r' = \left(\frac{n_2}{n_1}\right)^r \frac{\Gamma\left(\frac{n_1}{2} + r\right)\Gamma\left(\frac{n_2}{2} - r\right)}{\Gamma\left(\frac{n_1}{2}\right)\Gamma\left(\frac{n_2}{2}\right)}$$

(3) (a) Moment generating function: does not exist

[Mood et al. (1974), p. 543]

(b) Characteristic function: $$\phi\left(\frac{n_1}{n_2}t\right) = \frac{G(n_1, n_2, t)}{B\left(\frac{n_1}{2}, \frac{n_2}{2}\right)}$$

where the G - function is defined by

$$(m + n - 2)G(m, n, t) = (m - 2)G(m - 2, n, t) + 2itG(m, n - 2, t), \quad m, n > 2$$

$$mG(m, n, t) = (n - 2)G(m + 2, n - 2, t) - 2itG(m + 2, n - 4, t), \quad n > 4$$

$$nG(2, n, t) = 2 + 2itG(2, n - 2, t), \quad n > 2$$

[Ifram (1970), p. 350]

1.5.18 NONCENTRAL CHI SQUARE

$$f(x) = \frac{\exp\left\{-\frac{1}{2}(x + \lambda)\right\}}{2^{\nu/2}} \sum_{j=0}^{\infty} \frac{(x)^{(\nu/2)+j-1}\lambda^j}{\Gamma\left(\frac{\nu}{2} + j\right)2^{2j}j!}; \quad x > 0, \lambda > 0$$

where ν is referred to as the degrees of freedom and λ is the noncentrality parameter.

(1) (a) Mean: $\nu + \lambda$

(b) Variance: $2(\nu + 2\lambda)$

(c) Coefficient of variation: $\dfrac{\sqrt{2(\nu + 2\lambda)}}{(\nu + \lambda)}$

(d) Coefficient of skewnes: $\dfrac{\sqrt{8}(\nu + 3\lambda)}{(\nu + 2\lambda)^{3/2}}$

(e) Coefficient of excess: $\dfrac{12(\nu + 4\lambda)}{(\nu + 2\lambda)^2}$

(2) (a) $\mu_r' = 2^r\Gamma\left(r + \frac{\nu}{2}\right)\sum_{j=0}^{\infty}\binom{r}{j}\dfrac{\left(\frac{\lambda}{2}\right)^j}{\Gamma\left(j + \frac{\nu}{2}\right)}$

[Johnson and Kotz (1970b), p. 135]

(b) $\kappa_r = 2^{r-1}(r - 1)!(\nu + r\lambda)$

[Johnson and Kotz (1970b), p. 134]

(3) (a) Moment generating function: $(1 - 2t)^{-\nu/2}\exp\left[\dfrac{\lambda t}{1 - 2t}\right]$

(b) Characteristic function: $(1 - 2it)^{-\nu/2}\exp\left[\dfrac{\lambda it}{1 - 2it}\right]$

[Johnson and Kotz (1970b), p. 134]

1.5.19 NONCENTRAL t

$$f(x) = \frac{(\nu)^{\nu/2}}{\Gamma\left(\frac{\nu}{2}\right)} \frac{e^{-\delta^2/2}}{\sqrt{\pi}\,(\nu + x^2)^{(\nu+1)/2}} \sum_{i=0}^{\infty}\Gamma\left(\frac{\nu + i + 1}{2}\right)\left(\frac{\delta^i}{i!}\right)\left(\frac{2x^2}{\nu + x^2}\right)^{i/2}$$

where ν is the degrees of freedom and δ is the noncentrality parameter.

$$\mu_r' = c_r \frac{\Gamma\left(\frac{\nu - r}{2}\right)(\nu)^{r/2}}{2^{r/2}\Gamma\left(\frac{\nu}{2}\right)}, \quad \nu > r$$

where

$$c_{2r-1} = \sum_{i=1}^{r}\frac{(2r - 1)!\delta^{2r-1}}{(2i - 1)!(r - i)!2^{r-i}}, \quad r = 1, 2, 3, \ldots$$

$$c_{2r} = \sum_{i=0}^{r} \frac{(2r)!\delta^{2i}}{(2i)!(r-i)!2^{r-i}}, \quad r = 1, 2, 3, \ldots$$

[Bain (1969), p. 34]

1.5.20 NONCENTRAL F

$$f(x) = \sum_{i=0}^{\infty} \frac{\Gamma\left(\dfrac{2i + r_1 + r_2}{2}\right)\left(\dfrac{r_1}{r_2}\right)^{(2i+r_1)/2} x^{(2i+r_1-2)/2}\, e^{-\lambda/2}\left(\dfrac{\lambda}{2}\right)}{\Gamma\left(\dfrac{r_2}{2}\right)\Gamma\left(\dfrac{2i + r_1}{2}\right) r_i! \left(1 + \dfrac{r_1}{r_2}x\right)^{(2i+r_1+r_2)/2}}$$

where (r_1, r_2) are the degrees of freedom and λ is the noncentrality parameter.

(1) (a) Mean: $\dfrac{(r_1 + \lambda)r_2}{(r_2 - 2)r_1}$, $r_2 > 2$

(b) Variance: $\dfrac{(r_1 + \lambda)^2 + 2(r_1 + \lambda)r_2^2}{(r_2 - 2)(r_2 - 4)r_1^2} - \dfrac{(r_1 + \lambda)^2 r_2^2}{(r_2 - 2)^2 r_1^2}$, $r_2 > 4$

(2) $\mu'_r = c_r \dfrac{\Gamma\left(\frac{1}{2} r_2 - r\right) r_2^r}{\Gamma\left(\frac{1}{2} r_2\right)(2r_1)^r}$, $r_2 > 2r$

where c_r is the rth moment of a noncentral chi square distribution with r_1 degrees of freedom and noncentrality parameter λ.

[Bain (1969), p. 34]

Chapter 2

INEQUALITIES

In this chapter, two types of inequalities are considered -- moment inequalities and Chebyshev type inequalities. Moment inequalities hold between moments of different orders and Chebyshev type inequalities involve moments and give bounds on the probability of certain events. These inequalities do not require complete knowledge of the distributions of the random variables involved. Appropriate quantities are assumed to exist in the following summary.

2.1 MOMENT INEQUALITIES

2.1.1 SOME WELL-KNOWN INEQUALITIES

(1) Hölder's Inequality

$$E|XY| \leq (E|X|^r)^{1/r}(E|Y|^s)^{1/s}; \quad r > 1, \ \frac{1}{r} + \frac{1}{s} = 1$$

$$E|XY|^2 \leq E|X|^2 \, E|Y|^2 \quad \text{(Schwartz' inequality)}$$

$$E(|X|^t)^{1/t} \leq (E|X|^r)^{1/r}, \quad 0 < t \leq r$$

$$(E|X|^t)^{2t} \le (E|X|^{t-1})^t (E|X|^{t+1})^t, \quad t \ge 1$$ [Rao (1973), p. 149]
[Fisz (1963), p. 77]

(2) Minkowski's Inequality

$$(E|X + Y|^r)^{1/r} \le (E|X|^r)^{1/r} + (E|Y|^r)^{1/r}, \quad r \ge 1$$

[Rao (1973), p. 149]

(3) Liapounov's Inequality

$$(E|X|^b)^{a-c} \le (E|X|^c)^{a-b} (E|X|^a)^{b-c}, \quad 0 \le c \le b \le a$$

[Kendall and Stuart (1958), p. 63]

(4) c_r *- Inequality*

$$E|X + Y|^r \le c_r E|X|^r + c_r E|Y|^r$$

where $c_r = 1$ if $0 < r \le 1$ and $c_r = 2^{r-1}$ if $r > 1$.

[Loève (1960), p. 155]

(5) Jensen's Inequality. Let g(x) be convex, then

$$g[E(X)] \le E[g(X)]$$

The inequality will reverse when g(x) is concave.

$$|E(X)|^r \le (E|X|)^r \le E|X|^r, \quad r \ge 1$$

$$(E|X|^s)^r \le E|X|^{rs}; \quad r \ge 1, \ s > 0$$ [Parzen (1960), p. 434]

(6) Gurland's Inequalities

(a) Let h_1 and h_2 be two monotonic functions defined on a subset of the real numbers. Suppose one of these functions, say h_1, is continuous. Then, if h_1 and h_2 are both nonincreasing or both nondecreasing,

$$E[h_1(X)h_2(X)] \le [Eh_1(X)][Eh_2(X)]$$

The inequality will reverse if h_1 is nondecreasing and h_2 nonincreasing, or vice versa. Let X be a nonnegative random variable.

$$E(X^{r-1}) \le E(X^r)E(X^{-1}), \quad r > 0$$ [Gurland (1967), p. 25]

(b) Let $h_1, h_2, \ldots, h_n$ be continuous monotonic functions of a random variable X which are all nondecreasing (nonincreasing) and for which $h_i(X) \geq 0$, $i = 1, 2, \ldots, n$. Then

$$E \prod_{i=1}^{n} h_i(X) \geq \prod_{i=1}^{n} Eh_i(X)$$

Let X be a nonnegative random variable

$$E(X^r) \geq [E(X)]^r \geq [E(X^{-1})]^{-r} \geq [E(X^{-r})]^{-1}, \quad r \geq 1 \text{ or } r \leq 0$$

[Gurland (1968), p. 27]

(7) Keilson's Inequalities

(a) Discrete distributions. Let $f(x)$ $(x = 0, 1, 2, \ldots, \infty)$ be log concave (i.e., $f^2(x) \geq f(x + 1)f(x - 1)$). Then

$$\left(\frac{\mu'_{(r+1)}}{(r + 1)!}\right)^{1/(r+1)} \leq \left(\frac{\mu'_{(r)}}{r!}\right)^{1/r}, \quad r = 1, 2, 3, \ldots$$

(b) Continuous distributions. Let $f(x)$ be log concave. Then

$$\left(\frac{\mu'_{r+1}}{(r + 1)!}\right)^{1/(r+1)} \leq \left(\frac{\mu'_r}{r!}\right)^{1/r}, \quad r = 1, 2, 3 \ldots$$

[Keilson (1972), pp. 1702-1703]

2.1.2 SOME OTHER INEQUALITIES

(1) Let X be a positive random variable

$$E(X^{-r}) \geq \frac{E[X^{-(r-1)}]}{E(X)} \geq \cdots \geq \frac{E(X^{-1})}{[E(X)]^{r-1}} \geq \frac{1}{[E(X)]^r}, \quad r \geq 0$$

$$E(X^{r-1+h})E(X^r) \leq E(X^{r+h})E(X^{r-1}); \quad r > 0,\ h \geq 0$$

[Sclove et al. (1967), p. 34]

(2) Let X be a nonnegative random variable

$$E(X^r) \geq [E(X^{r/s})]^s \geq [E(X)]^r + [E(X^{r/s}) - \{E(X)\}^{r/s}]^s, \quad r \geq s \geq 1$$

$E(X^r) \geq \mu^r + \sigma^r$ when $r \geq 2$ [Tong (1970), p. 1244]

(3) $$-1 \le \frac{\operatorname{cov}(X, Y)}{\sqrt{\operatorname{var}(X)\operatorname{var}(Y)}} \le 1$$

(4) $\operatorname{cov}(X, Y) \le \operatorname{var}\left(\frac{X + Y}{2}\right)$. If X and Y are positive random variables then

$$\operatorname{cov}(X, Y) \le \operatorname{var}\left[\frac{1}{2}(X^{\beta} + Y^{\beta})\right]^{1/\beta}, \quad 0 \le \beta \le 1$$

$$\operatorname{cov}\left(X, \frac{Y}{X}\right) \le \operatorname{var}(\sqrt{Y})$$ [Kimeldorf and Sampson (1973), pp. 228, 230]

(5) Let X and Y be independent random variables

$$E\left(\frac{X}{Y}\right)^r \ge \frac{E(X^r)}{E(Y^r)}, \quad r = 1, 2, \ldots$$

$$\operatorname{var}\left(\frac{X}{Y}\right) \ge \frac{\operatorname{var}(X)}{\operatorname{var}(Y)} \quad \text{if } E(X) = E(Y) = 0 \text{ and } E(Y^{-1}) \text{ exists}$$

[Mullen (1967), pp. 30-31]

(6) Let X and Y be real-valued random variables

$$\operatorname{var}(X) \ge \frac{[\operatorname{cov}(X, Y)]^2}{\operatorname{var}(Y)}$$ [Blyth and Roberts (1972), p. 19]

(7) Let X be a discrete random variable with $P(X = x_i) = p_i$ $(i = 1, 2, \ldots, n)$. Let $c = \max_i(x_i)$ and $b = \min_i(x_i)$. Let $\sum_1^n p_i x_{(r)} = a$.

$$\operatorname{var}(X) \le \frac{(c - b)^2}{4}$$

$$\operatorname{var}(X) \le (c - a)(a - b)$$ [Moors and Muilwijk (1971), p. 385]

(8) Let X_i's be nonnegative random variables, then

$$E\left(\sum_1^n X_i\right)^p \begin{cases} \le \sum_1^n E(X_i)^p & \text{if } p \le 1 \\ \ge \sum_1^n E(X_i)^p & \text{if } p \ge 1 \end{cases}$$

$$E\left\{\left|\frac{1}{n}\sum_1^n x_i\right|^p\right\} \leq \frac{1}{n}\sum_1^n E(|X_i|^p) \quad \text{if } p > 1$$

$$E\left\{\left|\frac{1}{n}\sum_1^n X_i\right|^p\right\} \leq \left\{\frac{1}{n}\sum_1^n E(|X_i|^p)^{1/p}\right\}^p \text{ if } p > 1$$

[Chung (1968), pp. 46-47]

(9) Let $X_1, X_2, \ldots, X_n$ be independent random variables such that the median of the distribution of each X_i is zero, then

$$E\left(\left|\sum_1^n X_i\right|\right) \geq \frac{1}{2^{n-1}}\binom{n-1}{\left[\frac{n}{2}\right]} E\left(\sum_1^n |X_i|\right)$$

where $[\frac{n}{2}]$ is the greatest integer $\leq \frac{n}{2}$ [Tukey (1946), p. 75].

(10)

$$E\left|\sum_1^n X_i\right|^r \leq \begin{cases} n^{r-1}\left(\sum_1^n E|X_i|^r\right), & r > 1 \\ \sum_1^n E|X_i|^r, & r \leq 1 \end{cases}$$

If $E_{Y|X}(Y|X) = 0$, then

$$E|X + Y|^r \geq E|X|^r, \quad r \geq 1$$

If X and Y are independent variables and have the same distribution such that $E(X) = 0$ then

$$\frac{1}{2} E|X - Y|^r \leq E|X|^r \leq E|X - Y|^r, \quad 1 \leq r \leq 2$$

[Bahr and Essen (1965), p. 301]

(11) If $E(X) = 0$, $\text{var}(X) = \sigma^2$ and $|X| \leq m$, then

$$\mu'_r \leq \nu'_r \leq m^{r-2}\sigma^2, \quad r \geq 2$$

$$\mu'_r \leq m^{r-2}\sigma^2\left[\frac{1 - \left(\frac{\sigma}{m}\right)^{2(r-1)}}{1 + \left(\frac{\sigma}{m}\right)^2}\right] \leq m^{r-2}\sigma^2, \quad r = 3, 5, 7, \ldots$$

[Bennett (1965), pp. 560-561]

(12) $\mu - \sigma\left(\frac{1-p}{p}\right)^{1/2} \le E(X|X \le \xi_p) \le \xi_p \le E(X|X \ge \xi_p) \le \mu + \sigma\left(\frac{p}{1-p}\right)^{1/2}$

where $0 < p < 1$ and ξ_p is the quantile of order p.

$$\xi_q - \xi_p \le E(X|X \ge \xi_q) - E(X|X \le \xi_p) \le \sigma\left[\frac{1}{p} + \frac{1}{1-q}\right]^{1/2}, \quad p < q$$

$$\mu - \frac{1}{2}\nu_1 p \le E(X|X \le \xi_p) \le \xi_p \le E(X|X \ge \xi_p) \le \mu + \frac{1}{2}\left(\frac{\nu_1}{1-p}\right)$$

$$|\mu - \xi_{1/2}| \le E\left(|X - \xi_{1/2}|\right) \le \nu_1 \le \sigma$$

[Mallows and Richter (1969), pp. 1926-1927]

2.2 CHEBYSHEV INEQUALITIES

A good discussion of some of these inequalities is in Savage (1961) and Karlin and Studden (1966). In the following let $\nu_s = E|X - \mu|^s$, $E(X) = \mu$, $E(X - \mu)^2 = \sigma^2$, and $\delta = \nu_1/\sigma$.

2.2.1 *INEQUALITIES USING A SINGLE RANDOM VARIABLE*

(1) *Chebyshev.* $P(|X - \mu| \ge k\sigma) \le \frac{1}{k^2}, \quad k > 0$ [Savage (1961), p. 213]

(2) *Pearson*

(a) $P(|X - \mu| \ge k\nu_r^{1/r}) \le \frac{1}{k^r}, \quad k > 0$

(b) $P(|X - \mu| \ge k\sigma) \le \frac{\nu_r}{\sigma^r k^r}, \quad k > 0$

For $r = 2$, Pearson's inequality becomes Chebyshev's inequality. For large values of k the last inequality (with additional knowledge of ν_r) may provide a smaller bound when compared with Chebyshev's inequalit

[Savage (1961), p. 214]

(3) Cantelli

(a) $$P(|X - \mu| \geq k) \leq \frac{\nu_r}{k^r} \quad \text{if } k^r \leq \frac{\nu_{2r}}{\nu_r}$$

$$\leq \frac{\nu_{2r} - \nu_r^2}{(k^r - \nu_r)^2 + \nu_{2r} - \nu_r^2} \quad \text{if } \frac{\nu_{2r}}{\nu_r} \leq k^r$$

The first part is equivalent to the Pearson inequality (2.2.1(2)) but (with additional knowledge of ν_r and ν_{2r}) provides smaller bounds for large values of k [Savage (1961), p. 217].

(b) $$P(X - \mu \leq k) \leq \frac{\sigma^2}{\sigma^2 + k^2}, \quad k < 0$$

$$\geq 1 - \frac{\sigma^2}{\sigma^2 + k^2}, \quad k \geq 0 \qquad \text{[Rao (1973), p. 145]}$$

(4) Peek. $$P(|X - \mu| \geq k\sigma) \leq \frac{1 - \delta^2}{k^2 - 2k\delta + 1}, \quad k \geq \delta$$

This is a special case of the Cantelli inequality (2.2.1(3a)). For a unimodal distribution with mode equal to mean μ

$$P(|X - \mu| \geq k\sigma) \leq \frac{4}{9}\,\frac{1 - \delta^2}{(k - \delta)^2}, \quad k \geq \delta$$

[Savage (1961), p. 217]

(5) Markov. $$P(|X| \geq k) \leq \frac{\nu'_r}{k^r}, \quad k > 0 \qquad \text{[Loève (1960), p. 158].}$$

(6) Gauss (Camp-Meidell). For a unimodal distribution with mode m_0 and $\tau^2 = \sigma^2 + (\mu - m_0)^2$,

$$P(|X - m_0| \geq k\tau) \leq \begin{cases} 1 - \dfrac{k}{\sqrt{3}} & \text{if } k \leq \dfrac{2}{\sqrt{3}} \\[2ex] \dfrac{4}{9k^2} & \text{if } k \geq \dfrac{2}{\sqrt{3}} \end{cases}$$

$$P(|X - \mu| \geq k\sigma) \leq \frac{4}{9}\,\frac{(1 + s^2)}{(k - s)^2}$$

with $s = |\mu - \mu_0|/\sigma$ and $k > s$ [Savage (1961), p. 216].

(7) Selberg. Let $-\alpha < 0 < \beta$, $\alpha_0 = \min(\alpha, \beta)$.

$$P(-\alpha < X - \mu < \beta) \geq \begin{cases} \dfrac{4(\alpha\beta - \sigma^2)}{(\alpha + \beta)^2} & \text{if } \alpha\beta - \alpha_0^2 \leq 2\sigma^2 \leq 2\alpha\beta \\[2ex] \dfrac{\alpha_0^2}{\sigma^2 + \alpha_0^2} & \text{if } 2\sigma^2 \leq \alpha\beta - \alpha_0^2 \\[2ex] 0 & \text{if } \alpha\beta \leq \sigma^2 \end{cases}$$

[Karlin and Studden (1966), p. 475]

(8) Guttman. Let $0 \leq \alpha < \beta$, $\nu_r \varepsilon (\alpha^r, \beta^r)$ and $\alpha_0^2 = \min\{(\beta^r - \nu_r)^2, (\nu_r - \alpha^r)^2\}$.

$$P(-\beta < X - \mu < -\alpha, \alpha < X - \mu < \beta)$$

$$\geq \begin{cases} \dfrac{4[(\beta^r - \nu_r)(\nu_r - \alpha^r)] - 4(\nu_{2r} - \nu_r^2)}{[(\beta^r - \nu_r) + (\nu_r - \alpha^r)]^2} \\[2ex] \qquad \text{if } \dfrac{(\beta^r - \nu_r)(\nu_r - \alpha^r) - \alpha_0^2}{2} \leq (\nu_{2r} - \nu_r^2) \\[2ex] \qquad\qquad \leq (\beta^r - \nu_r)(\nu_r - \alpha^r) \\[2ex] \dfrac{\alpha_0^2}{(\nu_{2r} - \nu_r^2) + \alpha_0^2} \quad \text{if } \nu_{2r} - \nu_r^2 \leq \dfrac{(\beta^r - \mu_r)(\nu_r - \alpha^r) - \alpha_0^2}{2} \\[2ex] 0 \quad \text{if } \nu_{2r} - \nu_r^2 \geq (\beta^r - \nu_r)(\nu_r - \alpha^r) \end{cases}$$

[Karlin and Studden (1966), p. 479-480]

(9) Royden. For a unimodal distribution with mode at zero and $\nu_1 > 0$ $(\mu = 0)$,

$$P(|X| < k) \geq \begin{cases} \dfrac{k}{2\nu_1} & \text{if } 0 \leq k \leq \nu_1 \\ 1 - \dfrac{\nu_1}{2k} & \text{if } \nu_1 \leq k \leq \dfrac{3\nu_2}{4\nu_1} \\ 1 - \dfrac{4\nu_1^2}{3\nu_2} + \dfrac{8\nu_1^3 k}{9\nu_2^2} & \text{if } \dfrac{3\nu_2}{4\nu_1} \leq k \leq \dfrac{\nu_2}{\nu_1} \\ 1 - \dfrac{3\nu_2 - 4\nu_1^2}{3\eta^2 - 8\nu_1\eta + 3\nu_2} & \text{if } \dfrac{\nu_2}{\nu_1} \leq k \end{cases}$$

where η is the largest root of $2\eta^3 - (3k + 4\nu_1)\eta^2 + 8\nu_1 k\eta - 3\nu_2 k = 0$.

[Karlin and Studden (1966), p. 492]

(10) Glasser

$$P(-k_1\nu_1 < X - \mu < k_2\nu_1) \geq \max\left\{0,\ 1 - \frac{1}{2}\left(\frac{1}{k_1} + \frac{1}{k_2}\right)\right\} \quad \text{if } \frac{1}{2}\left(\frac{1}{k_1} + \frac{1}{k_2}\right) \leq 1$$

[Karlin and Studden (1966), p. 481]

(11) For a unimodal distribution with mode m_o and $P(X \geq 0) = 1$ $(k > 0)$,

$$P(X \geq k) \leq \begin{cases} 1 - \dfrac{k - m_o}{2(\mu - m_o)} & \text{if } k \geq m_o \text{ and } 2 - m_o \geq k + \sqrt{k^2 - m_o k} \\ \dfrac{2\mu - m_o}{\sqrt{k} + \sqrt{k - m_o}} & \text{if } k \geq m_o \text{ and } 2\mu - m_o \leq k + \sqrt{k^2 - m_o k} \\ \dfrac{2\mu - k}{m_o} & \text{if } k \leq m_o \text{ and } 2\mu - m_o \leq k \\ 1 & \text{if } k \leq m_o \text{ and } 2\mu - m_o \geq k \end{cases}$$

$$P(X \geq k) \leq \begin{cases} 1 & \text{if } k \leq \mu \\ \frac{2\mu}{k} - 1 & \text{if } \mu \leq k \leq \frac{3}{2}\mu \\ \frac{\mu}{2k} & \text{if } k \geq \frac{3}{2}\mu \end{cases}$$

[Karlin and Studden (1966), pp. 488-489, 491]

(12) (a) If H(x) is a nonnegative function of a random variable X, then

$$P[h(X) \geq k] \leq \frac{E[h(X)]}{k}, \quad k > 0$$

The Chebyshev inequality (2.2.1(1)) is a special case of this inequality [Hogg and Craig (1970), p. 54].

(b) If, in addition to the condition in (a), h(x) satisfies the inequality $h(x) \geq c > 0$ for all $x \geq k$,

$$P(X \geq k) \leq \frac{E[h(X)]}{c} \quad \text{[Fisz (1963), p. 101]}$$

(c) If, in addition to the condition in (a), h(x) is even and nondecreasing for positive values of x,

$$P(|X| \geq k) \leq \frac{E[h(X)]}{h(k)}, \quad k > 0 \quad \text{[Fisz (1963), p. 102]}$$

(d) If h(x) satisfies all the assumptions of (c) and the relation $|h(x)| \leq k$ holds for all x,

$$P(|X| \geq k) \geq \frac{E[h(X)] - h(k)}{k}, \ k > 0 \quad \text{[Fisz (1963), p. 102]}$$

(e) If h(x) satisfies all the assumptions of (c) and also $P(|X| \leq m) = 1$, then

$$P(|X| \geq k) \geq \frac{E[h(X)] - h(k)}{h(m)}, \quad k > 0 \quad \text{[Fisz (1963), p. 102]}$$

(13) Let X be a random variable such that $E(e^{aX})$ exists for $a > 0$, then

$$P(X \geq k) \leq \frac{E(e^{aX})}{e^{ak}}, \quad a > 0 \quad \text{[Gnendenko (1962), p. 249]}$$

(14) Let $h(x)$ be a positive nondecreasing function. If $E[h(|X - \mu|)] = m$ exists,

$$P(|X - \mu| \geq k) \leq \frac{m}{h(k)}, \quad k > 0 \quad \text{[Gnedenko (1962), p. 249]}$$

(15) Let $M(t)$ be the moment generating function of X and $-h < t < h$.

$$P(X \leq a) \leq e^{-at}M(t), \quad -h < t < 0 \quad \text{[Hogg and Craig (1970), p. 56]}$$

2.2.2 *INEQUALITIES USING SUMS OF RANDOM VARIABLES*

(1) Kolmogorov

(a) Let $X_1, X_2, \ldots, X_n$ be n independent random variables such that $\mathrm{var}(X_i) = \sigma_i^2 < \infty$. Let $S_n = \sum_{i=1}^n X_i$ and $\sigma^2 = \sum_{i=1}^n \sigma_i^2$. Then for every $\varepsilon > 0$,

$$P\left\{\max_{1 \leq k \leq n} \left|S_k - E(S_k)\right| \geq \varepsilon\right\} \leq \frac{\sigma^2}{\varepsilon^2}$$

(b) Let $X_1, X_2, \ldots, X_n$ be n independent random variables such that $|X_i| \leq c$, $c > 0$ for all i. Let $\sigma^2 = \sum_1^n \mathrm{var}(X_i)$. Then for every $\varepsilon > 0$,

$$P\left\{\max_{1 \leq k \leq n} \left|S_k - E(S_k)\right| \geq \varepsilon\right\} \geq 1 - \frac{(\varepsilon + 2c)^2}{\sigma^2}$$

[Moran (1968), pp. 358-359]

(2) Hàjek-Renyi. Let $X_1, X_2, \ldots, X_n$ be n independent random variables such that $E(X_i) = 0$ and $\mathrm{var}(X_i) = \sigma_i^2 < \infty$. Let $S_n = \sum_{i=1}^n X_i$. If $c_1, c_2, \ldots$ is a nonincreasing sequence of positive constants, then for any positive integers m, n with $m < n$ and arbitrary $\varepsilon > 0$,

$$P\left\{\max_{m \leq k \leq n} c_k \left|S_k\right| \geq \varepsilon\right\} \leq \frac{1}{\varepsilon^2}\left(c_m^2 \sum_1^m \sigma_i^2 + \sum_{m+1}^n c_i^2 \sigma_i^2\right)$$

[Rao (1973), p. 143]

Kolmogorov inequality (2.2.2(1a)) is a special case of this inequality.

(3) Heyde. Let $X_1, X_2, \ldots, X_n$ be n random variables, and $S_n = \sum_{i=1}^n X_i$. Let $Y_1, Y_2, \ldots, Y_n$ be n independent random variables each with mean zero and finite variance and define $Z_k = X_k - Y_k$ for $k \geq 1$. Let

$c_1, c_2, \ldots$ be a nonincreasing sequence of positive numbers. Then for any $\varepsilon > 0$, $0 < \alpha < 1$ and any integers $n < m$,

$$P\left\{\max_{n \le k \le m} c_k |S_k| \ge \varepsilon\right\} \le \frac{c_n^2\left(\sum_1^n EY_k^2\right) + \sum_{n+1}^m c_k^2\, E(Y_k^2)}{(1-\alpha)^2\varepsilon^2} + \sum_{n+1}^m P(Z_k \ne 0) + P\left(c_n\left|\sum_1^n Z_k\right| \ge n\varepsilon\right)$$

[Tomkins (1971), p. 428]

(4) Kounias and Weng

(a) Let $X_1, X_2, \ldots, X_n$ be n random variables such that $E|X_i|^r < \infty$ for some $0 < r \le 1$ and all $i = 1, 2, \ldots$. Let $S_n = \sum_1^n X_i$. If c_1, c_2 is a nonincreasing sequence of positive constants, then for any positive integers m, n with $m < n$ and arbitrary $\varepsilon > 0$,

$$P\left\{\max_{m \le k \le n} c_k |S_k| \ge \varepsilon\right\} \le \left\{\frac{c_m^r\left(\sum_1^m E|X_i|^r\right) + \sum_{m+1}^n \left(c_i^r\, E|X_i|^r\right)}{\varepsilon^r}\right\}$$

(b) If $E|X_i|^r < \infty$ for some $r \ge 1$ and all $i = 1, 2, \ldots, n$ and the constants $c_1, \ldots, c_n$, m, are as in (a) then

$$P\left\{\max_{m \le k \le n} c_k |S_k| \ge \varepsilon\right\} \le \left\{\frac{c_m \sum_1^m (E|X_i|^r)^{1/r} + \sum_{m+1}^n c_i \left(E|X_i|^r\right)^{1/r}}{\varepsilon}\right\}^r$$

[Kounias and Weng (1969), pp. 1091-1092]

(5) Markov. Let $X_1, X_2, \ldots, X_n$ be n nonnegative random variables. Let $S_n = \sum_1^n X_i$ and $\mu_i = E(X_i)$. Then for $\varepsilon > 0$,

$$P\left\{S_n \ge \varepsilon\left(\sum_1^n \mu_i\right)\right\} \le \frac{1}{\varepsilon}$$ [Savage (1961), p. 213]

(6) Chebyshev. Let $X_1, X_2, \ldots, X_n$ be n random variables such that X_i and X_j are uncorrelated for $i \ne j$. Let $\bar{X} = (\sum_1^n X_i)/n$ and $\mu = E(X_i)$, $\text{var}(X_i) = \sigma^2 < \infty$. Then for $\varepsilon > 0$

$$P\{|\bar{X} - \mu| \geq \varepsilon\} \leq \frac{\sigma^2}{n\varepsilon^2} \quad \text{[Savage (1961), p. 213]}$$

(7) Birnbaum, Raymond and Zuckerman. Let $X_1, X_2, \ldots, X_n$ be n independent random variables such that $\mu_i = E(X_i)$ and $\sigma^2 = \text{var}(X_i)$ $(i = 1, 2, \ldots, n)$. If n is an even integer,

$$P\left\{\sum_1^n (X_i - \mu_i)^2 \geq \varepsilon^2\right\} \leq \begin{cases} 1 & \text{if } \varepsilon^2 \leq n\sigma^2 \\ \dfrac{n\sigma^2}{2\varepsilon^2 - n\sigma^2} & \text{if } n\sigma^2 \leq \varepsilon^2 \leq \dfrac{n\sigma^2}{4}(3 + \sqrt{5}) \\ \dfrac{n\sigma^2}{\varepsilon^2}\left(1 - \dfrac{n\sigma^2}{4\varepsilon^2}\right) & \text{if } \dfrac{n\sigma^2}{4}(3 + \sqrt{5}) \leq \varepsilon^2 \end{cases}$$

If n is an odd integer,

$$P\left\{\sum_1^n (X_i - \mu_i)^2 \geq \varepsilon^2\right\} \leq \begin{cases} 1 & \text{if } \varepsilon^2 \leq n\sigma^2 \\ \dfrac{(n + 1)\sigma^2}{2\varepsilon^2 - (n - 1)\sigma^2} & \text{if } n\sigma^2 \leq \varepsilon^2 \\ & \leq \dfrac{\sigma^2}{4}\left(3n + 1 + \sqrt{5n^2 + 6n + 5}\right) \\ \dfrac{n\sigma^2}{\varepsilon^2} - \dfrac{(n^2 - 1)}{4}\dfrac{\sigma^4}{\varepsilon^4} & \text{if} \\ & \dfrac{\sigma^2}{4}\left(3n + 1 + \sqrt{5n^2 + 6n + 5}\right) \leq \varepsilon^2 \end{cases}$$

[Savage (1961), p. 214]

(8) Guttman. Let $X_1, X_2, \ldots, X_n$ be n independent and identically distributed random variables. Let $S^2 = \sum_1^n (X_i - \bar{X})^2/n$, $\bar{X} = \sum_1^n X_i/n$, $\mu = E(X_i)$, $\sigma^2 = E(X_i - \mu)^2$. Then for $k \geq 1$,

$$P\left\{(\bar{X} - \mu)^2 \geq \frac{S^2}{(n - 1)} + \sigma^2\sqrt{\frac{2(\varepsilon^2 - 1)}{n(n - 1)}}\right\} \leq \frac{1}{k^2}$$

[Savage (1961), p. 215]

(9) Bernstein. Let $X_1, X_2, \ldots, X_n$ be n independent random variables such that $E(X_i) = \mu_i$, $\text{var}(X_i) = \sigma_i^2 < \infty$ and $P(|X_i - \mu_i| > m) = 0$. Let $\mu = \sum_1^n \mu_i$, $\sigma^2 = \sum_1^n \sigma_i^2$ and $S_n = \sum_1^n X_i$. Then

$$P\{|S_n - \mu| \geq \varepsilon\} \leq 2 \exp\left\{\frac{-\varepsilon^2}{2\sigma^2 + \frac{2}{3} m\varepsilon}\right\}$$ [Savage (1961), p. 218]

(10) Hoeffding

(a) Let $X_1, X_2, \ldots, X_n$ be n independent random variables such that $0 \leq X_i \leq 1$, $i = 1, 2, \ldots, n$ and $E(\bar{X}) = \mu$. Then for $0 \leq \varepsilon < 1 - \mu$

$$\begin{aligned} P\{\bar{X} - \mu \geq \varepsilon\} &\leq \left\{\left(\frac{\mu}{\mu + \varepsilon}\right)^{\mu+\varepsilon} \left(\frac{1 - \mu}{1 - \mu - \varepsilon}\right)^{1-\mu-\varepsilon}\right\}^n \\ &\leq \exp\{-n\varepsilon^2 g(\mu)\} \\ &\leq \exp\{-2n\varepsilon^2\} \end{aligned}$$

where

$$g(\mu) = \begin{cases} \dfrac{1}{1 - 2\mu} \log\left(\dfrac{1 - \mu}{\mu}\right), & 0 < \mu < \dfrac{1}{2} \\ \dfrac{1}{2\mu(1 - \mu)}, & \dfrac{1}{2} \leq \mu < 1 \end{cases}$$

(b) Let $X_1, X_2, \ldots, X_n$ be n independent random variables such that $a_i \leq X_i \leq b_i$, $i = 1, 2, \ldots, n$. Then for $\varepsilon > 0$,

$$P\{\bar{X} - \mu \geq \varepsilon\} \leq \exp\left\{\frac{-2n^2\varepsilon^2}{\sum_{i=1}^n (b_i - a_i)^2}\right\}$$

(c) Let $X_1, X_2, \ldots, X_n$ be n independent random variables such that $E(X_i) = 0$ and $X_i \leq b$, $i = 1, 2, \ldots, n$. Then for $0 < \varepsilon < b$,

$$P\{\bar{X} \geq \varepsilon\} \leq \left\{\left(1 + \frac{b\varepsilon}{\sigma^2}\right)^{-(1+[b\varepsilon/\sigma^2])\sigma^2(b^2+\sigma^2)^{-1}} \times \left(1 - \frac{\varepsilon}{b}\right)^{-(1-[\varepsilon/b])b^2(b^2+\sigma^2)^{-1}}\right\}^n$$

$$\leq \exp\left\{-\frac{n\varepsilon}{b}\left[\left(1 + \frac{\sigma^2}{b\varepsilon}\right)\log\left(1 + \frac{b\varepsilon}{\sigma^2}\right) - 1\right]\right\}$$

[Karlin and Studden (1966), pp. 535-536]

(11) Bennett. Let $X_1, X_2, \ldots, X_n$ be n independent random variables such that $E(X_i) = 0$, $\text{var}(X_i) = \sigma_i^2$ and $E|X_i|^2 \leq m^{r-2}\sigma_i^2$ ($r = 2, 3, \ldots$). Let $n\sigma^2 = \sum_1^n \sigma_i^2 = \sum_1^n E(X_i^2)$. Then

$$P\{\bar{X} \geq \varepsilon\} \leq \exp\left\{-\frac{n\varepsilon}{m}\left[\left(1 + \frac{\sigma^2}{m\varepsilon}\right)\log\left(1 + \frac{m\varepsilon}{\sigma^2}\right) - 1\right]\right\}$$

[Karlin and Studden (1966), p. 537]

Chapter 3

ORDER STATISTICS

3.1 ORDER STATISTICS

The subject of order statistics deals with the properties as well as applications of the ordered random variables and of functions involving them. Order statistics have in recent times come to play an important role in statistical inference. They are particularly useful in nonparametric statistics.

3.1.1 DEFINITION

Let $X_1, X_2, \ldots, X_n$ be n random variables. If they are rearranged in ascending order of magnitude and written as

$$X_{(1;n)} \le X_{(2;n)} \le \cdots \le X_{(n;n)}$$

then $X_{(r;n)}$ $(r = 1, 2, \ldots, n)$ is called the rth order statistic, from a sample of size n.

3.1.2 COMMENTS

(1) $X_{(1;n)}$, $(X_{n;n})$ are called extreme order statistics.

(2)

$$M = \begin{cases} X_{((n+1)/2;n)} & \text{if } n \text{ is odd} \\ \dfrac{X_{(n/2;n)} + X_{((n/2)+1;n)}}{2} & \text{if } n \text{ is even} \end{cases}$$

is called the median. It is a measure of central tendency.

(3) $R_m = X_{(n-m+1;n)} - X_{(m;n)}$ is called the quasi-range. For $m = 1$, $R = X_{(n,n)} - X_{(1;n)}$ is called the range. It is a measure of dispersion.

(4) $M_m = \frac{1}{2}\{X_{(n-m+1;n)} + X_{(m;n)}\}$ is called the mth mid-range. For $m = 1$, $M = \{X_{(n;n)} + X_{(1;n)}\}/2$ is called the mid-range. It is a measure of central tendency.

(5) If $X_{(r;n)}$ $(r = 1, 2, \ldots, n)$ are the order statistics from a continuous cumulative distribution function (cdf) $F(x)$, then $W_r = F(X_{r;n}) - F(X_{r-1;n})$ $(r = 1, 2, \ldots, n + 1)$ with $F(X_{(0;n)}) = 0$, and $F(X_{(n+1;n)}) = 1$ are called coverages.

3.2 DISTRIBUTION OF ORDER STATISTICS

Let $X_1, X_2, \ldots, X_n$ be n independently and identically distributed (iid) random variables (discrete or continuous), each with cdf $F(x)$. Let $F_{(r;n)}(x)$ $(r = 1, 2, \ldots, n)$ denote the cdf of the rth order statistic $X_{(r,n)}$. Then

$$F_{(r;n)}(x) = \sum_{i=r}^{n} \binom{n}{i} [F(x)]^i [1 - F(x)]^{n-i} = I_{F(x)}(r, n - r + 1)$$

where $I_p(a, b)$ is the incomplete beta function ratio.

[David (1970), pp. 7-8]

Two useful special cases are:

$$F_{(1;n)}(x) = 1 - [1 - F(x)]^n$$

and

$$F_{(n;n)}(x) = [F(x)]^n$$

3.2.1 CONTINUOUS DISTRIBUTION CASE

(1) Let the joint probability density function (pdf) of $X_{(r_1;n)}$, $X_{(r_2;n)}$, ..., $X_{(r_k;n)}$ $(1 \le r_1 < \cdots < r_k \le n,\ 1 \le k \le n)$ for $x_1 \le x_2 \le \cdots \le x_k$ be $f_{(r_1,r_2,\ldots,r_k;n)}(x_1, \ldots, x_k)$. Then

$$\begin{aligned} f_{(r_1,r_2,\ldots,r_k;n)}&(x_1, x_2, \ldots, x_k) \\ &= c[F(x_1)]^{r_1-1}[F(x_2) - F(x_1)]^{r_2-r_1-1}, \ldots, \\ &\quad [1 - F(x_k)]^{n-r_k}[f(x_1)f(x_2), \ldots, f(x_k)] \end{aligned}$$

where

$$c = \frac{n!}{(r_1 - 1)!(r_2 - r_1 - 1)! \cdots (n - r_k)!}$$

[David (1970), p. 9]

(a) The joint pdf of $X_{(r;n)}$ and $X_{(s;n)}$ for $r < s$ and $x \le y$ is

$$\begin{aligned} f_{(r,s;n)}(x, y) = \frac{n!}{(r - 1)!(s - r - 1)!(n - s)!} [F(x)]^{r-1}[F(y) \\ - F(x)]^{s-r-1}[1 - F(y)]^{n-s}f(x)f(y) \end{aligned}$$

(b) The pdf of $X_{(r;n)}$ is

$$f_{(r;n)}(x) = \frac{n!}{(r - 1)!(n - r)!} [F(x)]^{r-1}[1 - F(x)]^{n-r}f(x)$$

(2) Let the pdf and cdf of the range R be $f_R(x)$ and $F_R(x)$, respectively. Then

$$f_{(R)}(r) = n(n - 1) \int_{-\infty}^{\infty} [F(x + r) - F(x)]^{n-2}f(x)f(x + r)\, dx$$

and

$$F_{(R)}(r) = n\int_{-\infty}^{\infty} [F(x + r) - F(x)]^{n-1} f(x)\,dx$$

If the distribution of X is symmetric about zero,

$$F_{(R)}(r) = \left[F\left(\frac{r}{2}\right) - F\left(\frac{-r}{2}\right)\right]^n + 2n\int_{r/2}^{\infty} [F(x) - F(x - r)]^{n-1} f(x)\,dx$$

[David (1970), pp. 10-11, 21]

(3) The cdf of the mid-range M_1 is

$$F_{(M_1)}(m) = n\int_{-\infty}^{m/2} [F(m - x) - F(x)]^{n-1} f(x)\,dx$$

[Gumbel (1958), p. 108]

3.2.2 RECURRENCE RELATIONS BETWEEN CONTINUOUS DISTRIBUTION FUNCTIONS

Let $f_{(r;n)}(x)$ and $F_{(r;n)}(x)$ be the pdf and cdf of $X_{(r;n)}$, respectively, from a sample of size n. Also, let $F_{(r,s;n)}(x, y)$ be the joint cdf of $X_{(r;n)}$ and $X_{(s;n)}$ from a sample of size n.

(1) Let $X_1, X_2, \ldots, X_n$ be n independent or exchangeable random variables. (The X_i $(i = 1, 2, \ldots, n)$ are called exchangeable if $P[X_1 \le x_1, X_2 \le x_2, \ldots, X_n \le x_n]$ is symmetric in $x_1, x_2, \ldots, x_n$.)

[David (1970), p. 82]

(a) $$rf_{(r+1;n)}(x) = nf_{(r;n-1)}(x) - (n - r)f_{(r;n)}(x) \qquad r = 1, 2, \ldots, (n - 1)$$

$$rF_{(r+1;n)}(x) = nF_{(r;n-1)}(x) - (n - r)F_{(r;n)}(x) \qquad r = 1, 2, \ldots, (n - 1)$$

[Srikantan (1962), p. 169]

(b) $$nF_{(r,s;n-1)}(x, y) = rF_{(r+1,s+1;n)}(x, y) + (s - r)F_{(r,s+1;n)}(x, y) + (n - s)F_{(r,s;n)}(x, y)$$

[David (1970), p. 83]

(2) Let $X_1, X_2, \ldots, X_n$ be iid random variables

$$f_{(r;n)}(x) = \binom{n}{r}\sum_{j=0}^{n-r}(-1)^j\binom{n-r}{j}\left(\frac{r}{r+j}\right)f_{(r+j;r+j)}(x)$$

$$= \binom{n}{r}\sum_{j=0}^{r-1}(-1)^j\binom{r-1}{j}\left(\frac{r}{n-r+j+1}\right)f_{(1;n-r+j+1)}(x)$$

$$F_{(r;n)}(x) = \binom{n}{r}\sum_{j=0}^{n-r}(-1)^j\binom{n-r}{j}\left(\frac{r}{r+j}\right)\{F_{(1;1)}(x)\}^{r+j}$$

[Young (1967), p. 284]

3.2.3 *COMMENTS*

(1) The ranking of random variables $X_1, X_2, \ldots, X_n$ is preserved under any monotone increasing transformation of the random variables.

(2) Regarding the probability-integral transformation, if $X_{(r;n)}$ $(r = 1, 2, \ldots, n)$ are the order statistics from a continuous distribution $F(x)$, then the transformation $U_{(r)} = F(X_{(r)})$ produces a random variable which is the rth order statistic from a uniform distribution on $(0, 1)$.

(3) Even if $X_1, X_2, \ldots, X_n$ are independent random variables, order statistics are not independent random variables.

(4) Let $X_1, X_2, \ldots, X_n$ be iid random variables from a continuous distribution. Then the set of order statistics $(X_{(1;n)}, X_{(2;n)}, \ldots, X_{(n;n)})$ is both sufficient and complete (see Ch. 6).

[Lehman (1959), p. 133]

(5) Let X be a continuous or discrete random variable. Let $E[X_{(r;n)}] = \mu_{(r;n)}$.

(a) $\mu_{(r;n)}$ exists provided μ exists, but the converse is not necessarily true. Specifically, if μ does not exist, $\mu_{(r;n)}$ may exist for certain (but not all) values of r.

Example: Cauchy: $f(x) = \dfrac{1}{\pi[1 + x^2]}, \quad -\infty < x < \infty$

μ does not exist but $\mu_{(r;n)}$ exists (except for $r = 1, n$) [David (1970), p. 26].

(b) $\mu_{(1;n)}$ or $\mu_{(n;n)}$ for all n determine the distribution completely [Gupta (1974), pp. 287-289].

3.2.4 RECURRENCE RELATIONS BETWEEN EXPECTED VALUES (Continuous Distribution Case)

Let

$$E(X^k_{(r;n)}) = \mu^{(k)}_{(r;n)}, \quad E(X_{(r;n)}X_{(s;n)}) = \mu_{(r,s;n)}$$

$$E(X_{(r;n)} - \mu_{(r;n)})(X_{(s;n)} - \mu_{(s;n)}) = \sigma_{(r,s;n)}$$

$$W_{(r;n)} = X_{(n-r;n)} - X_{(r+1;n)}$$

$$E(W_{(r;n)}) = w_{(r;n)}, \quad E(W_{(r;n)}W_{(s;n)}) = a_{(r,s;n)}$$

$$b_{(r;n)} = E(X_{(r+1;n)} - X_{(r;n)}), \quad c_n = E(R)$$

(1) For an arbitrary distribution,

$$r\mu^{(k)}_{(r+1;n)} + (n - r)\,\mu^{(k)}_{(r;n)} = n\mu^{(k)}_{(r;n-1)}$$

$$r = 1, 2, \ldots, n - 1, \quad k = 1, 2, \ldots$$

[David (1970), p. 37]

(a) If n is even,

$$\mu^{(k)}_{((n/2)+1;n)} + \mu^{(k)}_{(n/2;n)} = 2\mu^{(k)}_{(n/2;n-1)}$$

(b) If the distribution is symmetric about the origin and n is even,

$$\mu^{(k)}_{(n/2;n)} = \begin{cases} \mu^{(k)}_{(n/2;n-1)} & \text{if } k \text{ even} \\ 0 \text{ if } k \text{ odd} \end{cases}$$

[David (1970), p. 37]

(2) For an arbitrary distribution,

$$\mu_{(r;n)}^{(k)} = \sum_{i=r}^{n} \binom{i-1}{r-1}\binom{n}{i}(-1)^{i-r}\mu_{(i;i)}^{(k)}$$

$$= \sum_{i=n-r+1}^{n} \binom{i-1}{n-r}\binom{n}{i}(-1)^{i-n+r-1}\mu_{(1;i)}^{(k)}$$

[David (1970), p. 38]

(3) For an arbitrary distribution ($1 \le r \le m \le n$),

(a) $$\binom{n}{m}\mu_{(r;m)} = \sum_{i=0}^{n-m} \binom{n-r-i}{m-r}\binom{r+i-1}{r-1}\mu_{(r+i;n)}$$

(b) $$\mu_{(r;m)} = r\binom{m}{r}\sum_{j=0}^{r-1}(-1)^j\binom{r-1}{j}\frac{1}{(m-r+j+1)}\mu_{(1;m-r+j+1)}$$

[Kadane (1971), p. 746]

(4) For an arbitrary distribution ($1 \le r \le s \le n$),

$$(r-1)\mu_{(r,s;n)} + (s-r)\mu_{(r-1,s;n)} + (n-s+1)\mu_{(r-1,s-1;n)}$$

$$= n\mu_{(r-1,s-1;n-1)}$$ [David (1970), p. 38]

(a) If the arbitrary distribution is symmetric about the origin ($1 \le r \le s \le n$),

$$\mu_{(r;n)} = -\mu_{(n-r+1;n)}$$

and

$$\sigma_{(r,s;n)} = \sigma_{(n-s+1,n-s+1;n)}$$ [David (1970), p. 28]

(b) For an arbitrary distribution and even n,

$$\mu_{(1,n;n)} = \sum_{r=1}^{(n-2)/2} (-1)^{r-1}\binom{n}{r}\mu_{(r,r)}\mu_{(n-r;n-r)}$$

$$+ \frac{1}{2}(-1)^{(n-2)/2}\binom{n}{n/2}\mu_{(n/2;n/2)}^2$$

[Govindarajulu (1963), p. 639]

(5) For an arbitrary distribution ($r = 0, 1, 2, \ldots, [(n-2)/2]$),

$$(n-r)\,w_{(r-1;n)} + rw_{(r;n)} = nw_{(r-1;n-1)}$$

and

$$a_{(r,s;n)} = 2(\mu_{(r+1,s+1;n)} - \mu_{(r+1,n-s;n)})$$

[Govindarajulu (1963), p. 648]

(6) For an arbitrary distribution,

$$nb_{(r-1;n-1)} - (n - r + 1)b_{(r-1;n)} = rb_{(r;n)}$$

[David (1970), p. 44]

(7) For an arbitrary distribution,

(a) $$c_{2n+1} = (2n + 1) \sum_{i=1}^{n-1} \frac{(-1)^{n+i+1}}{(n + i + 1)} c_{n+i+1}$$

[Carlson (1958), p. 55]

(b) $$c_n = \frac{1}{n} (b_{(1,n)} + b_{(n-1;n)}) + c_{n-1}$$

$$\mu_{(n-1;n)} - \mu_{(2;n)} = nc_{n-1} - (n - 1)c_n$$

[David (1970), pp. 43-44]

(8) For an arbitrary distribution, let h(x) be a function of x, and for $1 \le r \le m \le n$,

$$E[h(X_{r+1;n)})] = \binom{n}{r} E[h(X_{(r;n-1)})] - \left(\frac{n - r}{r}\right) E[h(X_{(r;n)})], \quad r < n$$

and

$$E[h(X_{r;m)})] = (-1)^{m-r+1}\left\{\sum_{j=m-r+1}^{m} (-1)^j \binom{m}{j}\binom{j - 1}{m - r} E[h(X_{(1;j)})]\right\}$$

$$= (-1)^r \sum_{j=r}^{m} (-1)^j \binom{m}{j}\binom{j - 1}{r - 1} E[h(X_{(j;j)})].$$

[Srikantan (1962), pp. 169-170]

(9) For an arbitrary distribution, $1 \le r \le m \le n$,

$$E[h(X_{(r;m)})] = \binom{m}{r} \sum_{j=0}^{k} (-1)^j \left(\frac{r}{r - k}\right) \frac{\binom{k}{j}}{\binom{m - k + j}{r - k}} E[h(X_{(r-k;m-k+j)})]$$

$$0 \le k \le r - 1$$

and

$$E[h(X_{(r;m)})] = \binom{m}{r} \sum_{j=0}^{\ell} (-1)^j \left(\frac{r}{r+j}\right) \frac{\binom{\ell}{j}}{\binom{m-\ell+j}{r+j}} E[h(X_{(r+j;m-\ell+j)})]$$

$$0 \leq \ell \leq m - r$$

[Krishnaiah and Rizvi (1966), p. 733]

(10) For an arbitrary distribution,

$$(r-1)E[h(X_{(r;n)})] = nE[h(X_{(r-1;n-1)})] - (n-r+1)E[h(X_{(r-1;n)})]$$

[Young (1967), p. 283]

(11) Let $E(r;n) = E[h(X_{(r;n)})]$; $M(s) = E(1, s) = E[h(X_{(1,s)})]$

(a) $$E(r;n) = \sum_{j=0}^{r-1} \frac{(-1)^j n!}{(r-1)!(n-r)!} \binom{r-1}{j} \frac{M(n-r+j+1)}{(n-r+j+1)}$$

$$= (-1)^{n-r+1} \sum_{j=n-r+1}^{n} (-1)^j \binom{n}{j}\binom{j-1}{n-r} M(j)$$

$$E(n;n) = -\sum_{j=1}^{n} (-1)^j \binom{n}{j} M(j)$$

(b) $$E(r+1;n) - E(r;n) = \sum_{j=0}^{r} \binom{n}{r} (-1)^j \binom{r}{j} M(n-r+j)$$

[White (1969), p. 374]

3.2.5 COMMENTS

For an arbitrary continuous distribution

(1) $$\sum_{i=1}^{n} \mu^{(k)}_{(i;n)} = n\mu'_k$$

(2) $$\sum_{i=1}^{n} \sum_{j=1}^{n} \sigma_{(i,j,n)} = n \operatorname{var}(X)$$

(3) $$\sum_{i=1}^{n-1} \sum_{j=i+1}^{n} E(X^r_{(i;n)} X^s_{(j;n)}) = \binom{n}{2} E(X^r_{(1;2)} X^s_{(2;2)}); \quad r \geq 0,\ s \geq 0$$

$$\sum_{i=1}^{n-1} \sum_{j=i+1}^{n} E(X_{(i;n)}^{r} X_{(j;n)}^{r}) = \binom{n}{2}(\mu_r')^2, \quad r \geq 0$$

[Govindarajulu (1963), pp. 636-637]

3.2.6 DISCRETE DISTRIBUTION CASE

Let $f(x)$ be the probability function of X defined over $x = 0, 1, 2, \ldots, M$, where M may be infinite.

(1) The probability function of $X_{(r;n)}$ is

(a) $$f_{(r;n)}(x) = F_{(r;n)}(x) - F_{(r;n)}(x - 1)$$
$$= I_{F(x)}(r, n - r + 1) - I_{F(x-1)}(r, n - r + 1)$$

(b) $$f_{(r;n)}(x) = \sum_{k=0}^{r-1} \sum_{m=0}^{n-r} \times \frac{n![F(x - 1)]^{r-1-k}[f(x)]^{k+m+1}[1 - F(x)]^{n-r-m}}{(r - 1 - k)!(k + m + 1)!(n - r - m)!}$$
$$= r\binom{n}{r} \sum_{k=0}^{r-1} \sum_{m=0}^{n-r} \binom{r - 1}{k}\binom{n - r}{m}[F(x - 1)]^{r-1-k} \times [1 - F(x)]^{n-r-m} f(x) \int_0^1 [yf(x)]^k[(1 - y)f(x)]^m \, dy$$
$$= r\binom{n}{r}\int_{F(x-1)}^{F(x)} y^{r-1} (1 - y)^{n-r} \, dy$$

where $F(x - 1) = 0$ when $x = 0$ [Khatri (1962b), pp. 167-168].

(2) The joint probability function of $X_{(r;n)}$ and $X_{(s;n)}$ is

$$f_{(r;s)}(x, y) = C\iint w^{r-1}(v - w)^{s-r-1}(1 - v)^{n-s} dv\, dw$$

The integration is over the region $w \leq v$, $F(x - 1) \leq w \leq F(x)$, and $F(x - 1) \leq v \leq F(x)$. Also, $C = n!/[(r - 1)!(s - r - 1)!(n - s)!]$.

$$F_{(r;s)}(x, y) = C\int_0^{F(x)}\int_w^{F(y)} w^{r-1}(v - w)^{s-r-1}(1 - v)^{n-s}\, dv\, dw$$

[Khatri (1962b), pp. 168-169]

(3) $$\mu_{(r;n)} = \sum_{x=0}^{M-1} [1 - F_{(r)}(x)], \quad r = 1, 2, \ldots, n$$

$$\mu_{(r;n)}^{(2)} = 2\sum_{x=0}^{M-1} x[1 - F_{(r)}(x)] + E(X_{(r)}), \quad r = 1, 2, \ldots, n$$

If $M = \infty$, then the upper limit in the summation may be replaced by ∞.

[Khatri (1962b), pp. 168-169]

(4) $$(n - r)\mu_{(r;n)}^{(k)} + r\mu_{(r+1;n)}^{(k)} = n\mu_{(r;n-1)}^{(k)}$$ [David (1970), p. 37]

3.2.7 SOME USEFUL FORMULAS

(1) $$E(R) = E\int_{-\infty}^{\infty} \{1 - [F(x)]^n - [1 - F(x)^n\}\, dx$$

if the distribution is continuous.

$$E(R) = \sum_{x=-\infty}^{\infty} \{1 - [F(x)]^n - [1 - F(x)]^n\}$$

if the distribution is discrete.

(2) $$E(R^2) = 2\int_{-\infty}^{\infty}\int_{-\infty}^{y} \{1 - [F(y]^n - [1 - F(x)]^n + [F(y) - F(x)]^n\}\, dx\, dy$$

if the distribution is continuous.

$$E(R^2) = 2\sum_{y=-\infty}^{\infty}\sum_{x=-\infty}^{y} \{1 - [F(y)]^n - [1 - F(x)]^n + [F(y) - F(x)]^n\}$$

if the distribution is discrete.

[David and Mishriky (1968), pp. 1392-1393]

(3) For any continuous distribution

$$\mu_{(r;n)} = \int_0^{\infty} [1 - F_{(r)}(x) - F_{(r)}(-x)]dx, \quad \text{and thus}$$

$$\mu_{(r;n)} = \int_0^{\infty} [F_{(n-r+1)}(x) - F_{(r)}(x)]dx$$

if the distribution is symmetric about $x = 0$ [David (1970), p. 29].

(4) For any continuous distribution symmetric about zero

$$\operatorname{cov}(w_{(r;n)}, w_{(s;n)}) = 2[\operatorname{cov}(X_{(r+1;n)}, X_{(s+1;n)}) - \operatorname{cov}(X_{(r+1;n)}, X_{(n-s;n)})]$$

$$\rho(w_{(r;n)}, w_{(s;n)}) = \frac{\rho_{(r+1,s+1;n)} - \rho_{(r+1,n-s;n)}}{(1 - \rho_{(r+1,n-r;n)})(1 - \rho_{(s+1,n-s;n)})}$$

$$0 \leq r \leq s \leq \left[\frac{n-2}{2}\right]$$

where $\rho(X, Y)$ is the correlation coefficient between X and Y, $\rho_{(a,b;n)}$ is the correlation coefficient between $X_{(a;n)}$ and $X_{(b;n)}$.

[Govindarajulu (1963), pp. 648-649]

(5) For any continuous distribution

$$E(X_{(r+1;n)} - X_{(r;n)}) = \binom{n}{r} \int_{-\infty}^{\infty} [F(x)]^r [1 - F(x)]^{n-r}\, dx, \qquad r = 1, 2, \ldots, n-1$$

[David (1970), p. 39]

(6) Let $R_n = X_{(n)} - X_{(1)}$ and let n be odd, then

$$E(R_{2n+1}) = (2n + 1) \sum_{i=1}^{n-1} \frac{(-1)^{n+i+1}}{(n + i + 1)} E(R_{n+i+1})$$

[Carlson (1958), p. 55]

3.2.8 FINITE POPULATION CASE

Let $x_1' < x_2' < \cdots < x_N'$ be the elements of a finite population Π of size N from which a sample $x_{(1)} < x_{(2)} < \cdots < x_{(n)}$, $n \leq N$ is taken without replacement. Then

(1) $$P(X_{(k)} = x_t') = \frac{\binom{t-1}{k-1}\binom{N-t}{n-k}}{\binom{N}{n}}, \qquad t = k, k+1, \ldots, N-n+k$$

This also can be viewed as the probability function of a random variable T. That is, the rank of the x value in Π to which the kth order statistic in the sample is equal.

(2) If S and T are the k_1th and k_2th order statistics ($k_1 < k_2$) in a sample of size n drawn from Π, then the joint probability function of (s, t) is

$$P\left(X_{(k_1)} = x'_s,\ X_{(k_2)} = x'_t\right) = \frac{\binom{s - 1}{k_1 - 1}\binom{t - s - 1}{k_2 - k_1 - 1}\binom{N - t}{n - k_2}}{\binom{N}{n}}$$

(3) $$E(T + r - 1)^{(r)} = \frac{(k + r - 1)^{(r)}\binom{N + r}{n + r}}{\binom{N}{n}}$$

$$E(T) = \frac{k(N + 1)}{(n + 1)}, \quad var(T) = \frac{k(N + 1)(N - n)(n - k + 1)}{(n + 1)^2(n + 2)}$$

where $(X)^{(r)} = X(X - 1), \ldots, (X - r + 1)$

$$cov(S, T) = \frac{k_1(n - k_2 + 1)(N - n)(n + 1)}{(n + 1)^2(n + 2)}$$

[For *(1)-(3)* see Wilks (1962), pp. 243-244, 252]

3.2.9 *BOUNDS FOR CERTAIN MOMENTS*

Let $X_1, X_2, \ldots, X_n$ ($n \geq 2$) be n independent random variables from a continuous distribution F with mean μ and variance σ^2.

(1) $$\mu_{(1;n)} \geq \mu - \frac{(n - 1)\sigma}{(2n - 1)^{1/2}}$$

$$\mu_{(n;n)} \leq \mu + \frac{(n - 1)\sigma}{(2n - 1)^{1/2}}$$ [David (1970), p. 47]

(2) If the distribution is continuous and symmetric about μ = 0 and $\sigma^2 = 1$, then

$$\mu_{(n;n)} \leq \left(\frac{n}{2}\right)\left\{\frac{2}{2n - 1}\left[1 - \frac{1}{\binom{2n - 2}{n - 1}}\right]\right\}^{1/2}$$

[David (1970), p. 49]

(3) If the distribution is standardized with $\mu = 0$ and $\sigma^2 = 1$, then

$$\mu_{(s;n)} - \mu_{(r;n)} \le \left\{\frac{2n}{\binom{2n}{n}}\left[\binom{2s-2}{s-1}\binom{2n-2s}{n-s} + \binom{2r-2}{r-1}\binom{2n-2r}{n-r} - 2\binom{r+s-2}{r-1}\binom{2n-r-s}{n-s}\right]\right\}^{1/2}, \quad s > r$$

$$|E(X_{(r;n)})| \le \left\{\frac{n\binom{2n-r}{n-r}\binom{2r-2}{r-1}}{\binom{2n-1}{n-1}} - 1\right\}^{1/2}$$

[David (1970), p. 51]

(4) If the distribution is defined on $[-A, A]$ and has $\mu = 0$ and $\sigma^2 = 1$ (A finite), then

$$E(R) \ge \min\left\{\begin{array}{l} 2\left[1 - \left(\frac{1}{2}\right)^{n-1}\right] \\ \dfrac{1 - p_0^n - (1 - p_0)^n}{\sqrt{p_0(1 - p_0)}} \end{array}\right.$$

where $p_0 = A^2/(1 + A^2)$ [Karlin and Studden (1966), p. 561].

(5) If the distribution is symmetric with $\mu = 0$ and $\sigma^2 = 1$, then

$$|E(X_{(r;n)})| \le \frac{1}{B(r, n - r + 1)\sqrt{2}}[B(2r - 1, 2n - 2r + 1) - B(n, n)]^{1/2}$$

where $B(a, b)$ is the beta function [David (1970), p. 68].

3.3 SOME USEFUL RESULTS

(1) For a random sample of size n from a continuous distribution, the conditional distribution of $X_{(s;n)}$, given $X_{(r;n)} = x_{(r)}$ $(s > r)$, is just the distribution of the $(s - r)$th order

statistic in a sample of (n - r) drawn from the parent distribution truncated on the left at $x = x_{(r)}$ [David (1970), p. 18].

(2) For a continuous symmetric distribution about μ

$$f_{(r;n)}(\mu + x) = f_{(n-r+1;n)}(\mu - x) \quad \text{[David (1970), p. 19]}$$

(3) If the parent distribution is unlimited, differentiable, symmetrical, and unimodal, then the distribution of the midrange is also unlimited, differentiable, symmetrical and unimodal.

[David (1970), p. 21]

(4) For any distribution symmetric about zero, the distributions of $X_{(i+1;n)}$ and $-X_{(n-i;n)}$ are identical, and the distributions of the product $X_{(i+1;n)}X_{(j+1;n)}$ and the product $X_{(n-i;n)}X_{(n-j;n)}$ are identical [Govindarajulu (1963), p. 648].

3.4 MOMENTS OF ORDER STATISTICS FROM SOME DISCRETE DISTRIBUTIONS

3.4.1 *GEOMETRIC*

$$f(x) = pq^{x-1}; \; x = 1, 2, \ldots, 0 \le p \le 1, q = 1 - p$$

(1)
$$\mu_{(r;n)} = n\binom{n-1}{r-1} \sum_{m=0}^{r-1} \frac{(-1)^m \binom{r-1}{m}}{(n-r+m+1)} \left(1 - q^{n-r+m+1}\right)^{-1}$$

$$\mu^{(2)}_{(r;n)} = n\binom{n-1}{r-1} \sum_{m=0}^{r-1} \frac{(-1)^m \binom{r-1}{m}}{(n-r+m+1)} \frac{(1 + q^{n-r+m+1})}{\left(1 - q^{n-r+m+1}\right)^2}$$

$$\mu^{(k)}_{(r;n)} = \left(\frac{n}{r-1}\right) \mu^{(k)}_{(r-1;n-1)} - \frac{(n-r+1)}{(r-1)} \mu^{(k)}_{(r-1;n)}$$

[Margolin and Winokur (1967), pp. 920-921]

(2) Tables: For $\mu_{(r;n)}$: $n = 1, 5(5)20$, $r = 1(1)5(5)20$, $1 \le r \le n$, $p = 0.25(0.25)0.75$.

For $\sigma_{(r,r;n)}$: $n = 1, 5(5)20$, $1 \le r \le n$, $p = 0.25(0.25)0.75$.

[Margolin and Winokur (1967), pp. 924-925]

3.4.2 NEGATIVE BINOMIAL

$$f(x) = \binom{x-1}{\lambda-1} p^{x-\lambda} q^{\lambda}; \; x = \lambda, \lambda+1, \ldots, 0 \le p \le 1, \; q = 1 - p$$

(1) $\mu^{(k)}_{(r;n)} = \sum_{t=0}^{r-1} \sum_{i=0}^{t} \binom{n}{t}\binom{t}{i}(-1)^i \mu^{(k)}_{(1;n-t+i)}$ [Young (1970), p. 182]

(2) Tables: For $\mu_{(r;n)}$: $n = 2(1)8$, $1 \le r \le n$, $\lambda = 1, 2$,
$p = 0.3(0.2)0.9, 0.99$.
[Young (1970), p. 184]

3.5 MOMENTS OF ORDER STATISTICS FROM SOME CONTINUOUS DISTRIBUTIONS

A good discussion of the use of order statistics from normal, uniform, exponential, gamma, Weibull, and other populations in testing and estimation, and the necessary tables are given by Harter (1969), Vols. I and II.

3.5.1 NORMAL

$$f(x) = \frac{1}{\sqrt{2\pi}} \exp\left(\frac{-x^2}{2}\right), \quad -\infty < x < \infty$$

(1) $\mu_{(r+1;n)} = \frac{1}{r}[n\mu_{(r;n-1)} - (n-r)\mu_{(r;n)}]$
[Harter (1961), p. 152]

$$\mu_{(r;n)} = -\mu_{(n-r+1;n)}$$

$$\mu_{((n+1)/2;n)} = 0 \text{ if } n \text{ is odd}$$

$$\sigma_{(r,s;n)} = \sigma_{(s,r;n)} = \sigma_{(n-r+1,n-s+1;n)} = \sigma_{(n-s+1,n-r+1;n)}$$

$\sum_{s=1}^{n} \sigma_{(r,s;n)} = 1$ [David (1970), p. 31]

(2) Tables: For $\mu_{(r;n)}$: $n = 2(1)100$, $1 \le r \le n$ and for values of n, none of whose prime factors exceeds 7, up through n = 40(
[Harter (1961), pp. 158-165]

For $\mu_{(r;n)}$: $n = 2(1)20$, $1 \le r \le n$.

For $\mu_{(r,s;n)}$: $n = 1(1)20$, $1 \le r \le s \le n$.

[Teichroew (1956), pp. 417-426]

[Also, see Harter (1969), Vols. I and II; Owen (1962).]

3.5.2 CAUCHY

$$F(x) = \frac{1}{2} + \frac{1}{\pi} \tan^{-1}(x), \quad -\infty < x < \infty$$

(1) $$\mu_{(r;n)} = \frac{n!}{\pi^n (r-1)!(n-r)!} \int_{-\pi/2}^{\pi/2} \tan x \left(\frac{\pi}{2} + x\right)^{r-1} \left(\frac{\pi}{2} - x\right)^{n-r} dx$$

$r \ne 1, n$

$$\mu^{(k)}_{(r;n)} = \frac{n}{(k-1)\pi} \left[\mu^{(k-1)}_{(r;n-1)} - \mu^{(k-1)}_{(r-1;n-1)} \right] - \mu^{(k-2)}_{(r;n)}$$

$k \le r < n - k$, $r \ne 1, n$

$$\mu_{(r;n)} = -\mu_{(n-r+1;n)}, \quad r \ne 1, n$$

$$\mu_{((n+1)/2;n)} = 0 \text{ if } n \text{ is odd}$$ [Barnett (1966), pp. 1208-1210]

[For $\mu_{(r,s;n)}$ see Barnett (1966), pp. 1208-1210.]

$$\mu_{(r,r;n)} = \frac{n}{\pi} [\mu_{(r;n-1)} - \mu_{(r-1;n-1)}] - 1.$$

$$\sigma_{(r,s;n)} = \sigma_{(s,r;n)} = \sigma_{(n-r+1,n-s+1;n)} = \sigma_{(n-s+1,n-r+1;n)}$$

[Barnett (1966), pp. 1208-1210]

(2) Tables: For $\mu_{(r;n)}$: $n = 3(1)20$.

[Barnett (1966), p. 1208]

For $\sigma_{(r,s;n)}$: $n = 5(1)16(2)20$, $3 \le r \le s \le n + 1 - r$.

[Barnett (1968), pp. 383-385]

3.5.3 EXPONENTIAL

$$F(x) = 1 - \exp(-x), \quad x \ge 0$$

(1) $$\mu_{(r;n)} = \sum_{i=n-r+1}^{n} (i)^{-1}$$

$$\sigma_{(r,s;n)} = \sigma_{(r,r;n)} = \sum_{i=n-r+1}^{n} (i)^{-2}, \quad r < s$$

[Sarhan and Greenberg (1962), p. 343]

(2) Tables: For $\mu_{(r;n)}$: $n = 2(1)10$, $r = 1(1)10$.

For $\sigma_{(r,s;n)}$: $n = 2(1)10$, $1 \le r \le s \le n$.

[Sarhan and Greenberg (1962), pp. 347-351]

3.5.4 *GAMMA*

$$f(x) = \frac{e^{-x}x^{m-1}}{\Gamma(m)}; \quad x > 0, \ m > 0$$

(1)

$$\mu_{(r;n)}^{(k)} = \frac{n!}{(r-1)!(n-r)!\Gamma(m)} \sum_{p=0}^{r-1} (-1)^p \binom{r-1}{p} \sum_{j=0}^{(m-1)(n-r+p)} a_j(m, n-r+p) \frac{\Gamma(m+k+j)}{(n-r+p+1)^{m+k+j}}$$

where $a_j(m,p)$ is the coefficient of t^j in the expansion of $[\sum_{i=0}^{m-1} (t^i/i!)]^p$.

$$\mu_{(r;n)}^{(k)} = \frac{n!}{(r-1)!(n-r)!} \sum_{p=0}^{r-1} (-1)^p \binom{r-1}{p} \frac{\mu_{(1;n-r+p+1)}^{(k)}}{(N-r+p+1)}$$

[Gupta (1960), p. 244]

$$\mu_{(r;n)}^{(k)} = \int_0^\infty \psi(r, n, k, m, \nu)\,d\nu$$

where

$$\psi(r, n, k, m, \nu) = \frac{n!}{\Gamma(m)(r-1)!(n-r)!} \left[e^{-\nu}\nu^m \sum_{i=0}^{\infty} \frac{\nu^i}{(m+i)}\right]^{r-1} \times \left[1 - e^{-\nu}\nu^m \sum_{i=0}^{\infty} \frac{\nu^i}{(m+i)!}\right]^{n-r} e^{-\nu}\nu^{m+k-1}$$

[Breiter and Krishnaiah (1968), p. 59]

[For $\sigma_{(r,s;n)}$ see Gupta (1960), p. 251.]

(2) Tables: For $\mu_{(r;n)}^{(k)}$: $n = 1(1)10$, $k = 1(1)4$, $1 \le r \le n$, $m = 1(1)5$,
$n = 11(1)15$, $k = 1(1)4$, $r = 1$, $m = 1(1)5$.

[Gupta (1960), p. 245-249]

For $\mu_{(r;n)}^{(k)}$: $n = 1(1)9$, $k = 1(1)4$, $1 \le r \le n$,
$m = 0.5(1)10.5$.

[Breiter and Krishnaiah (1968), pp. 61-71]

[Also, see Harter (1969), Vol. 2, pp. 522-545, 548.]

3.5.5 WEIBULL

$$F(x) = 1 - \exp(-x^c); \ x \ge 0, \ \alpha > 0, \ c > 0$$

(1)
$$\mu_{(r;n)}^{(k)} = n\binom{n-1}{r-1}\Gamma\left(1 + \frac{k}{c}\right)\sum_{i=0}^{r-1} (-1)^i\binom{r-1}{i} \times (n - r + i + 1)^{-[1+(k/c)]}$$

[For $\sigma_{(r,s;n)}$ see Govindarajulu (1968), p. 7.]

(2) Tables: For $\mu_{(1;n)}$: $n = 2(1)10$, $c = 1, 2, 2.5, 3(1)10$.

For $\sigma_{(r,s;n)}$: $n = 2(1)10$, $c = 1, 2, 2.5, 3(1)10$,
$1 \le r \le s \le n$.

[Govindarajulu (1968), pp. 2-4]

For $\mu_{(1;n)}$: $n = 5(5)20$, $c^{-1} = 0.1(.2)0.9, 1.0$.

For $\sigma_{(r,s;n)}$: $n = 5(5)20$, $c^{-1} = 0.1(0.2)0.9, 1.0$,
$1 \le r \le s \le n$.

[Weibull (1967), pp. 13-27]

[Also, see Harter (1969), Vol. 2, pp. 484-519, 548.]

3.5.6 POWER FUNCTION

$$F(x) = \left(\frac{x}{a}\right)^\nu; \ 0 < x < a, \ a > 0, \ \nu > 0$$

$$\mu_{(r;n)}^{(k)} = \frac{\Gamma(n + 1)\Gamma\left[\left(\frac{k}{\nu}\right) + r\right]a^k}{\Gamma(r)\Gamma\left[n + \left(\frac{k}{\nu}\right) + 1\right]}$$

$$\mu_{(r;n)}^{(k)} = \frac{r + \left(\frac{k}{\nu}\right) - 1}{(r - 1)} \mu_{(r-1;n)}^{(k)}, \quad k > 1$$

$$\mu_{(r,s;n)} = \frac{\Gamma(n + 1)\Gamma\left[\left(\frac{1}{\nu}\right) + r\right]\Gamma\left[\left(\frac{2}{\nu}\right) + s\right]a^2}{\Gamma(r)\Gamma\left[s + \left(\frac{1}{\nu}\right)\right]\Gamma\left[n + \left(\frac{2}{\nu}\right) + 1\right]}, \quad r < s$$

$$\mu_{(r,s;n)} = \frac{\left(\frac{2}{\nu}\right) + s - 1}{\left(\frac{1}{\nu}\right) + s - 1} \mu_{(r,s-1;n)}, \quad r < s$$

[Malik (1967), pp. 66, 68-69]

$$\phi_r(t) = \frac{\Gamma(n + 1)}{\Gamma(r)} \sum_{m=0}^{\infty} \frac{\Gamma\left[\left(\frac{m}{\nu}\right) + r\right] a^m}{\Gamma\left[n + \left(\frac{m}{\nu}\right) + 1\right]} \frac{(it)^m}{m!}$$

where ϕ_r is the characteristic function of $X_{(r)}$ [Malik (1967), p. 66].

3.5.7 UNIFORM

$$f(x) = 1; \quad 0 < x < 1$$

$$\mu_{(r;n)} = \frac{r}{n + 1}$$

$$\sigma_{(r,s;n)} = \frac{r(n - s + 1)}{(n + 2)(n + 1)^2}, \quad r \leq s$$

[Sarhan and Greenberg (1962), p. 383]

3.5.8 PARETO

$$F(x) = 1 - \left(\frac{m}{x}\right)^a; \quad x \geq m > 0, \ a > 0$$

(1) $$\mu_{(r;n)}^{(k)} = \frac{\Gamma(n + 1)\Gamma\left[n - r - \left(\frac{k}{a}\right) + 1\right]m^r}{\Gamma(n - r + 1)\Gamma\left[n - \left(\frac{s}{a}\right) + 1\right]}, \quad a > k$$

$$\mu_{(r-1;n)}^{(k)} = \frac{n - r - \left(\frac{k}{a}\right) + 1}{(n - r + 1)} \mu_{(r;n)}^{(k)}$$

$$\mu_{(r,s;n)} = \frac{\Gamma(n + 1)\Gamma\left[n - r - \left(\frac{2}{a}\right) + 1\right]\Gamma\left[n - s - \left(\frac{1}{a}\right) + 1\right]m^2}{\Gamma(n - s + 1)\Gamma\left[n - r - \left(\frac{1}{a}\right) + 1\right]\Gamma\left[n - \left(\frac{2}{a}\right) + 1\right]}$$

$$\mu_{(r,s;n)} = \frac{(n - s + 1)}{\left[n - s - \left(\frac{1}{a}\right) + 1\right]} \mu_{(r,s-1;n)}; \ r < s, \ a > 2$$

[Malik (1966), pp. 147-149]

(2) Tables: For $\mu_{(r;n)}$ and $\sigma_{(r,r;n)}$: $n = 1(1)8$, $a = 2.5(.5)5$, $1 \le r \le n$.

For $\mu_{(r,s;n)}$ and $\sigma_{(r,s;n)}$: $n = 2(1)8$, $a = 2.5(.5)5$, $1 \le r < s \le n$.

[Malik (1966), pp. 151-157]

3.5.9 *EXTREME-VALUE*

$$F(x) = \exp(-e^{-x}), \ -\infty < x < \infty$$

(1) $$\mu^{(k)}_{(r;n)} = \frac{n!}{(r - 1)!(n - r)!} \sum_{m=0}^{n-r} (-1)^m \binom{n - r}{m} \int_{-\infty}^{\infty} x^k e^{-x-(m+r)e^{-x}} \, dx$$

[For $\mu_{(r,s;n)}$ see Lieblein (1953), p. 283.]

(2) Tables: For $\mu_{(r;n)}$: $n - 1(1)10(5)60(10)100$, $r = 1(1)\min(n, 26)$.

[Lieblein and Salzer (1957), p. 205]

3.5.10 *LAPLACE*

$$f(x) = \frac{1}{2} \exp(-|x|), \ -\infty < x < \infty$$

(1) $$\mu^{(k)}_{(r;n)} = \frac{n!\Gamma(k + 1)}{(r - 1)!(n - r)!} \left[(-1)^k \sum_{m=0}^{n-r} (-1)^m \binom{n - r}{m} 2^{-(r+m+1)} \times (r + m)^{-(k+1)} + \sum_{m=0}^{r-1} (-1)^m \binom{r - 1}{m} 2^{-(n-r+2+m)} \times (n - r + 1 + m)^{-(k+1)}\right]$$

[Johnson and Kotz (1970b), p. 25]

$$E(R) = 2n\left[\sum_{m=0}^{n-1}(-1)^m\binom{n-1}{m}2^{-(m+2)}(m+1)^{-2} - 2^{-(n+1)}n^{-2}\right]$$

[Johnson and Kotz (1970b), p. 25]

$$\mu_{(r;n)} = -\mu_{(n-r+1;n)}$$

$$\mu_{([n/2]+1;n)} = 0 \quad \text{if } n \text{ is odd}$$

$$\mu_{(r;n-1)} = \frac{r\mu_{(r+1;n)} + (n-r)\mu_{(r;n)}}{n}$$

$$2^n\mu_{(r;n)} = \sum_{m=n-r+1}^{n}\binom{n}{m}s_1(m, n-r+1) - \sum_{m=r}^{n}\binom{n}{m}s_1(m, r)$$

where $s_1(j, k) = \sum_{n=j}^{k} k^{-1}$.

$\mu_{(r;n)}^{(2)}$ [Govindarajulu (1966a), p. 250]

$$\sigma_{(r,s;n)} = \sigma_{(s,r;n)}$$

$$\sigma_{(r,s;n)} = \sigma_{(n-s+1,n-r+1;n)}, \quad 1 \le r \le s \le n$$

$\mu_{(r,s;n)}$ [Govindarajulu (1966a), p. 250

(2) Tables: For $\mu_{(r;n)}$: $n = 2(1)20$, $r = 1 + \left[\frac{n+1}{2}\right], \ldots, n.$

For $\sigma_{(r,s;n)}$: $n = 2(1)20$, $1 \le r \le s \le n$,

$2 \le r + s \le n + 1.$

[Govindarajulu (1966a), pp. 250-254]

3.5.11 LOGISTIC

$$F(x) = [1 + \exp(-x)]^{-1}, \quad -\infty < x < \infty$$

(1) $\mu_{(r+1;n+1)}^{(k)} = \mu_{(r;n)}^{(k)} + \left(\frac{k}{r}\right)\mu_{(r;n)}^{(k-1)}$ [Shah (1970), p. 2150]

$\mu_{(r;n)}^{(2k-1)}$ and $\mu_{(r;n)}^{(2k)}$ [Gupta and Shah (1965), p. 911]

$$(n+1)\mu_{(r;n)} = (n+1)(n-m+1)\mu_{(r,m;n)} - (n-r+1)(n-m+1) \times \mu_{(r,m;n+1)} - r(n-m+1)\mu_{(r+1,m;n+1)}$$

$$1 < r < m \le n,\ m - r \ge 2$$

$$(n+1)\mu_{(m;n)} = -(n+1)r\mu_{(r,m;n)} + mr\mu_{(r+1,m+1;n+1)} + r(n-m+1)\mu_{(r+1,m;n+1)}$$

$$1 < r < m \le n,\ m - r \ge 2$$

$$mr\mu_{(r+1,m+1;n+1)} = (n+1)[\mu_{(r;n)} + \mu_{(m;n)}] + (n-r+1)(n-m+1)\mu_{(r,m;n+1)} - (n-m-r+1)\mu_{(r,m;n)};\ 1 < r < m \le n,\ m - r \ge 2$$

[Shah (1966), pp. 1006-1007]

$\mu_{(r,s;n)}$, [Shah (1966), p. 1005]

$$\phi_r(t) = \frac{\Gamma(r+it)\Gamma(n-r+1-it)}{\Gamma(r)\Gamma(n-r+1)}$$

where $\phi_r(t)$ is the characteristic function of $X_{(r;n)}$.

[Kendall and Stuart (1967), p. 532]

(2) Tables: For $\mu^{(k)}_{(r;n)}$: $n = 1(1)10$, $k = 1(1)4$,

$$r = \begin{cases} 1(1)\left(\frac{n}{2}\right) + 1 & \text{if } n \text{ odd} \\ 1(1)\ \frac{n}{2} & \text{if } n \text{ even.} \end{cases}$$

[Gupta and Shah (1965), pp. 908-909]

3.5.12 CHI (1 df)

$$f(x) = \left(\frac{2}{\pi}\right)^{1/2} \exp\left(-\frac{x^2}{2}\right),\ x > 0$$

(1) $$\mu_{(r-1,s-1;n-1)} = \frac{1}{n}\left[(r-1)\mu_{(r,s;n)} + (s-r)\mu_{(r-1,s;n)} + (n-s+r)\mu_{(r-1,s-1;n)}\right],\ 1 \le r \le s \le n$$

[Govindarajulu and Eisenstat (1965), p. 151]

(2) Tables: For $\mu_{(r;n)}$: $n = 1(1)100$, $1 \leq r \leq n$.

For $\sigma_{(r,s;n)}$: $n = 1(1)20$, $1 \leq r \leq s \leq n$.

[Govindarajulu and Eisenstat (1965), pp. 153-159]

3.5.13 TRIANGULAR

$$f(x) = \begin{cases} 4x, & 0 \leq x \leq \frac{1}{2} \\ 4(1 - x), & \frac{1}{2} \leq x \leq 1 \end{cases}$$

Tables: For $\mu_{(r;n)}$: (r, n) = (1, 2), (1, 3), (2, 3), (1, 4), (2, 4), (1.5), (2, 5), (3.5).

[Sarhan (1954), p. 320]

Chapter 4

FAMILIES OF DISTRIBUTIONS

In this chapter certain well-known families of distributions and some of their properties are considered.

4.1 PEARSON (CONTINUOUS) DISTRIBUTIONS

4.1.1 DEFINITION

For every member of the system, the pdf f satisfies a differential equation of the form

$$\frac{df}{dx} = \frac{(x - a)f}{b_0 + b_1 x + b_2 x^2}$$

where a, b_0, b_1, and b_2 are some constants. A good discussion of these distributions is in Johnson and Kotz (1970a) and also Ord (1972).

4.1.2 *PROPERTIES*

(1) Recurrence relations for moments and cumulants:

$$rb_0\mu'_{r-1} + \{(r+1)b_1 - a\}\mu'_r + \{(r+2)b_2 + 1\}\mu'_{r+1} = 0$$

$$\{1 + (r+2)b_2\}\kappa_{r+1} + rb_1\kappa_r + rb_2\sum_{j=1}^{r-2}\binom{r-1}{j}\kappa_{j+1}\kappa_{r-j} = 0$$

[Kendall and Stuart (1958), pp. 149, 176]

(2) The characteristic function $\phi(t)$ of Pearson distributions satisfies the relation:

$$b_2\theta\frac{d^2\phi}{d\theta^2} + (1 + 2b_2 + b_1\theta)\frac{d\phi}{d\theta} + (a + b_1 + b_0\theta)\phi = 0$$

where $\theta = it$ [Kendall and Stuart (1958), p. 176].

(3) The cumulant generating function $\eta(t)$ of Pearson distributions satisfies the relation:

$$b_2\theta\left\{\frac{d^2\eta}{d\theta^2} + \left(\frac{d\eta}{d\theta}\right)^2\right\} + (1 + 2b_2 + b_1\theta)\frac{d\eta}{d\theta} + (a + b_1 + b_0\theta) = 0$$

where $\theta = it$ [Kendall and Stuart (1958), p. 176].

(4) There may be 0, 1, or 2 points of inflection, depending on the form of the curve and the range of X, but if there are two such points they must be equidistant from the mode. If f(x) is twice differentiable on the interior of the range of x, the roots of $f''(x) = 0$ are

$$x = a \pm \left\{a^2 + \frac{ab_1 + b_0}{b_2}\right\}^{1/2}$$

or

$$x = \pm\left\{\frac{b_0}{b_2}\right\}^{1/2}$$

if the origin is at the mode [Ord (1972), p. 8].

(5) If a distribution defined for $x \in [a, b)$ is a Pearson distribution, then any truncated form of that distribution, defined for $x \in [c, d)$, $a \leq c < d \leq b$, is also a Pearson distribution.

[Ord (1972), p. 4]

(6)
$$a = b_1 = -\frac{\mu_3(\mu_4 + 3\mu_2^2)}{A}$$

$$b_0 = -\frac{\mu_2(4\mu_2\mu_4 - 3\mu_3^2)}{A}$$

$$b_2 = -\frac{2\mu_2\mu_4 - 3\mu_3^2 - 6\mu_2^3}{A}$$

where $A = 10\mu_4\mu_2 - 18\mu_2^3 - 12\mu_3^2$ [Kendall and Stuart (1958), p. 149].

(7) All the Pearson distributions are determined by the first four moments, except some of the degenerate types which are determined by fewer than four moments [Kendall and Stuart (1958), p. 152].

4.2 EXPONENTIAL FAMILY OF DISTRIBUTIONS

4.2.1 DEFINITIONS

(1) Continuous Distributions

(a) A one-parameter family of densities $f(x; \theta)$, $\theta \in \Omega$, is said to belong to the regular case of the exponential family if it can be expressed as

$$f(x; \theta) = \exp[Q(\theta)T(x) + S(x) + q(\theta)], \quad a < x < b$$

where

(i) neither a nor b depends on θ,

(ii) $Q(\theta)$ is a nontrivial continuous function of θ, for $\theta \in \Omega$,

(iii) each of $T'(x) \neq 0$ and $S(x)$ is a continuous function of x ($a < x < b$) [Hogg and Craig (1970), p. 231].

(b) A k-parameter family of densities $f(x;\ \theta_1, \theta_2, \ldots, \theta_k)$ is said to belong to the regular case of the exponential family if it can be expressed as

$$f(x;\ \theta_1, \theta_2, \ldots, \theta_k) = \exp\left[\sum_{j=1}^{k} Q_j(\theta_1, \theta_2, \ldots, \theta_k)T_j(x) + S(x) + q(\theta_1, \theta_2, \ldots, \theta_k)\right], \quad a < x < b$$

where

(i) a or b does not depend on any or all the parameters $\theta_1, \theta_2, \ldots, \theta_k$,

(ii) $Q_j(\theta_1, \theta_2, \ldots, \theta_k)$, $j = 1, 2, \ldots, k$, are nontrivial, functionally independent, continuous functions of θ_j $(\gamma_j < \theta_j < \delta_j,\ j = 1, 2, \ldots, k)$,

(iii) $T_j'(x)$ $(j = 1, 2, \ldots, k)$ are continuous for $a < x < b$, and no one is a linear homogeneous function of the others, $S(x)$ is a continuous function of x $(a < x < b)$.

[Hogg and Craig (1970), p. 239]

(2) Discrete Distributions

(a) A one-parameter family of probability functions $f(x, \theta)$, $\theta \in \Omega$, is said to belong to the regular case of exponential family if it can be expressed as

$$f(x;\ \theta) = \exp[Q(\theta)T(x) + S(x) + q(\theta)], \quad x = a_1, a_2, \ldots$$

where

(i) the set $\{x;\ x = a_1, a_2, \ldots\}$ does not depend on θ,

(ii) $Q(\theta)$ is a nontrivial continuous function of θ, $\theta \in \Omega$,

(iii) $T(x)$ is a nontrivial function of x on the set $\{x;\ x = a_1, a_2, \ldots\}$ [Hogg and Craig (1970), p. 231].

(b) A k-parameter family of probability functions $f(x;\ \theta_1, \theta_2, \ldots, \theta_k)$, $\theta \in \Omega$, is said to belong to the regular case of the exponential family if it can be expressed as

$$f(x;\ \theta) = \exp\left[\sum_{i=1}^{k} Q_j(\theta_1, \theta_2, \ldots, \theta_k)T_j(x) + S(x) + q(\theta_1, \theta_2, \ldots, \theta_k)\right], \quad x = a_1, a_2, \ldots$$

where

(i) the set $\{x | x = a_1, a_2, \ldots\}$ does not depend on $\theta_1, \theta_2, \ldots, \theta_k$,

(ii) $Q_j(\theta_1, \theta_2, \ldots, \theta_k)$ $(j = 1, 2, \ldots, k)$ are nontrivial, functionally independent, continuous functions of θ_j $(\gamma_j < \theta_j < \delta_j,\ j = 1, 2, \ldots, k)$,

(iii) $T_j(x)$ $(j = 1, 2, \ldots, k)$ are nontrivial functions of x on the set $\{x | x = a_1, a_2, \ldots\}$ and no one is a linear function of the others.

[Hogg and Craig (1970), p. 241]

In the following let $c(\theta) = \exp[q(\theta)]$.

4.2.2 PROPERTIES AND SOME USEFUL RESULTS

(1) If $T(X) = X$ and $Q(\theta) = \theta$,

Characteristic function: $\phi(t) = \dfrac{c(\theta)}{c(\theta + it)}$

Mean: $\mu = -\dfrac{c'(\theta)}{c(\theta)}$

(2) If $Q_j(\theta_1, \theta_2, \ldots, \theta_k) = \theta_j$ $(j = 1, 2, \ldots, k)$, then

$$E[T_j(X)] = -\frac{\partial \log c(\theta)}{\partial\theta_j}$$

$$\operatorname{cov}(T_i(X), T_j(X)) = -\frac{\partial^2 \log c(\theta)}{\partial\theta_i \partial\theta_j}, \quad i = 1, 2, \ldots, k$$

[Lehmann (1959), p. 58]

(3) (a) Let $X_1, \ldots, X_n$ be a random sample of size n from the pdf $f(x;\ \theta)$. Then a sufficient and complete statistic for θ is $\sum_{i=1}^{n} T(X_i)$.

(b) Let $X_1, \ldots, X_n$ be a random sample of size n from the pdf $f(x;\ \theta_1, \ldots, \theta_k)$. Let $S_j = \sum_{i=1}^{n} T_j(X_i)$. Then $S_1, \ldots, S_k$ are jointly sufficient and complete for $\theta_1, \ldots, \theta_k$ when $n > k$. The joint density of S_j $(j = 1, 2, \ldots, k)$ also belongs to the exponential family.

[Hogg and Craig (1970), pp. 232, 240]

(4) The minimum variance unbiased estimator (MVUE) of $\tau(\theta)$ is $\sum_i^n T(X_i)$ if

$$\frac{\partial \log L(\theta)}{\partial\theta} = Q(\theta)\left\{\sum_{i=1}^{n} T(x_i) - \tau(\theta)\right\}$$

[Kendall and Stuart (1967), p. 24]

(5) For members of the one-parameter exponential family there exist uniformly most powerful tests for certain hypotheses.

[Lehmann (1959), pp. 70, 88]

4.3 LINEAR EXPONENTIAL TYPE (CONTINUOUS) DISTRIBUTIONS (A Subclass of the Exponential Family)

4.3.1 DEFINITION

For every member of this family the pdf f can be written as

$$f(x;\ \theta) = \frac{a(x)e^{\theta x}}{g(\theta)}$$

where a(x) is a nonnegative function depending only on x, and θ ranges over an interval on the real line so that $g(\theta)$ is finite and differentiable.

4.3.2 PROPERTIES

(1) Moment generating function: $M(t) = \dfrac{g(\theta + t)}{g(\theta)}$

(2) $\mu'_r = \dfrac{1}{g(\theta)} \dfrac{d^r g(\theta)}{d\theta^r}$, $r = 1, 2, \ldots$

[Patil and Shorrock (1965), p. 94]

(3) A distribution is an exponential type iff

$$\kappa_{r+1} = \frac{d\kappa_r}{d\theta},\quad r = 1, 2, \ldots$$ [Patil (1963b), p. 206]

(4) Let $E(x^r) = m_r(\theta)$. Assume the moments exist. If the power series $\sum_0^\infty m_r(\theta)g(\theta)(t^r/r!)$ is uniformly convergent with respect to θ, then

$$m_{r+1}(\theta)g(\theta) = \frac{d}{d\theta}[m_r(\theta)g(\theta)], \quad r = 0, 1, 2, \ldots$$

with $m_0(\theta) = 1$, iff the distribution is of the linear exponential type [Wani (1968), p. 481].

(5) $\nu_1 = 2\mu_2 f(\mu; \theta) - \dfrac{2\partial F(\mu, \theta)}{\partial\theta}$, where F is the cdf corresponding to the pdf f.

Mean: $\mu = \dfrac{d}{d\theta}[\log g(\theta)]$

Variance: $\sigma^2 = \dfrac{d\mu}{d\theta}$ [Kamat (1965b), pp. 288-289]

4.4 PÓLYA TYPE (CONTINUOUS) DISTRIBUTIONS

4.4.1 DEFINITION

A family of distributions with pdf's $f(x; \theta)$, which are continuous in the real variables θ and x, is said to be of Pólya Type n (PT_n) if for all $x_1 < x_2 < \cdots < x_m$ and $\theta_1 < \theta_2 < \cdots < \theta_m$ and for every $1 \leq m \leq n$,

$$\begin{vmatrix} f(x_1; \theta_1) & \ldots & f(x_1; \theta_m) \\ \vdots & & \vdots \\ f(x_m; \theta_1) & \ldots & f(x_m; \theta_m) \end{vmatrix} \geq 0$$

and is strictly of Pólya Type n if strict inequality holds in the above determinant. If the family of distributions are Pólya Type n for every n, then the family is said to be of Pólya Type ∞.

[Karlin (1957), p. 282]

4.4.2 PROPERTIES

(1) For $n = 1$, all pdfs $f(x;\ \theta)$ are PT_1.

(2) For $n = 2$, $f(x;\ \theta)$ is PT_2 iff it has a monotone likelihood ratio (MLR) [Karlin (1957), p. 282].

(3) Exponential family, noncentral t, noncentral F, and the noncentral chi square distributions are all Pólya Type ∞. The Cauchy distribution is not of the Pólya Type $(n > 1)$.

[Karlin (1957), p. 282]

4.5 MONOTONE LIKELIHOOD RATIO DISTRIBUTIONS

4.5.1 DEFINITION

A family of distributions with pdf (pf) $f(x;\ \theta)$ ($\theta \in I$, I is an interval) is said to have a MLR in T, $T = t(x_1, x_2, \ldots, x_n)$, if the likelihood ratio $L(x_1, x_2, \ldots, x_n;\ \theta_1)/L(x_1, x_2, \ldots, x_n;\ \theta_2)$ is either a nonincreasing function of T for every $\theta_1 < \theta_2$ or a nondecreasing function of T for every $\theta_1 < \theta_2$.

[Mood et al. (1974), p. 423]

In the following we will let $T = x$.

4.5.2 PROPERTIES (CONTINUOUS DISTRIBUTIONS)

(1) $f(x;\ \theta)$ is log concave in x [Efron (1965), p. 272].

(2) $f(x;\ \theta)$ is unimodal [Barlow et al. (1963), p. 379].

(3) The one parameter exponential family of distributions has the MLR property, provided both $T(x)$ and $Q(\theta)$ are nondecreasing. This is also true for discrete distributions [Ferguson (1967), p. 209].

(4) Let $f(x)$ be defined on $[0, \infty)$. Then

$$\mu_r \le \Gamma(r + 1)\mu^r; \quad -1 < r < 0,\ r > 1$$

$$\left(\frac{\mu_r}{\Gamma(r+1)}\right)^{1/r} \leq \left(\frac{\mu_s}{\Gamma(s+1)}\right)^{1/s}, \quad r > s > 0$$

Strict inequality holds in both cases unless $f(x) = (1/\mu)\, e^{-x/\mu}$.

[Karlin et al. (1961), p. 1130]

4.5.3 SOME USEFUL RESULTS (CONTINUOUS DISTRIBUTIONS)

(1) Suppose $(\partial^2/\partial x \partial\theta) \log f(x;\theta)$ exists and f is strictly Pólya Type 1. Then f has MLR in x iff the mixed second derivative $(\partial^2/\partial x\partial\theta) \log f(x;\theta)$ exists, and this derivative is nonnegative for all θ and x. An equivalent condition is that

$$f(x;\theta)\,\frac{\partial^2 f(x;\theta)}{\partial\theta\partial x} \geq \frac{\partial f(x;\theta)}{\partial\theta}\,\frac{\partial f(x;\theta)}{\partial x} \quad \text{for all } \theta \text{ and } x$$

[Lehmann (1959), p. 111]

(2) The convolution of two Pólya Type 2 distributions is also a Pólya Type 2 distribution. If a Pólya Type 2 distribution is truncated, the truncated distribution is also Pólya Type 2.

[Efron (1965), p. 272]

(3) Suppose f is Pólya Type 2 with f(x) not necessarily zero for negative x. Then

(a) The distribution of the rth order statistic is also Pólya Type 2 for fixed r = 1, 2, ..., n.

(b) The distribution of the random variable $X_{(r)} - X_{(r-1)}$ is also Pólya Type 2 [Barlow and Proschan (1966), p. 1590].

(4) For MLR distributions there exist uniformly most powerful tests for certain hypotheses [Lehmann (1959), p. 68].

(5) For MLR distributions there exist uniformly most accurate confidence bounds for θ at each confidence level.

[Lehmann (1959), p. 80]

(6) Suppose f(x; θ) is defined on the real line and has a MLR in x.

(a) If ψ is a nondecreasing function of x, then $E_\theta\psi(X)$ is a nondecreasing function of θ. If $X_1, X_2, \ldots, X_n$ are independently distributed with pdf $f(x;\ \theta)$ and ψ_1 is a function of $x_1, x_2, \ldots, x_n$ which is nondecreasing in each of its arguments, then $E_\theta \psi_1(X_1, X_2, \ldots, X_n)$ is a nondecreasing function of θ.

(b) For any $\theta_1 < \theta_2$, the cdf of X under θ_1 and θ_2 satisfy $F_{\theta_2}(x) \leq F_{\theta_1}(x)$ for all x.

(c) Let ψ be a function with a single change of sign. More specifically, suppose there exists a value x_0 such that $\psi(x) \leq 0$ for $x < x_0$ and $\psi(x) \geq 0$ for $x \geq x_0$. Then there exists θ_0 such that $E_\theta \psi(x) \leq 0$ for $\theta < \theta_0$ and $E_\theta \psi(x) \geq 0$ for $\theta > \theta_0$, unless $E_\theta \psi(x)$ is either positive for all θ or negative for all θ [Lehmann (1959), p. 74].

4.6 GENERALIZED POWER SERIES (DISCRETE) DISTRIBUTIONS (GPSD)

4.6.1 DEFINITION

For every member of this family, the probability function may be written as

$$P(X = x) = f(x) = \frac{a(x)\theta^x}{A(\theta)}, \quad x \in T$$

where T is an arbitrary nonnull subset of nonnegative integers, and $a(x) \geq 0$ is a function of x over the set T or constant and $A(\theta) = \sum_{x \in T} a(x)\theta^x$. A good discussion of these distributions is given in Patil (1962a, b).

4.6.2 PROPERTIES

(1) Mean: $\theta \dfrac{d}{d\theta}[\log A(\theta)]$

Variance: $\mu + \theta^2 \dfrac{d^2}{d\theta^2}[\log A(\theta)]$

Probability generating function: $\dfrac{A(\theta t)}{A(\theta)}$ [Patil (1962b), p. 180]

(2) $$\mu'_{r+1} = \theta \frac{d\mu'_r}{d\theta} + \mu'_1\mu'_r$$

$$\mu'_r = \sum_{j=1}^{r} \binom{r-1}{j-1} \mu'_{r-j}\kappa_j$$

$$\mu_{r+1} = \theta \frac{d\mu_r}{d\theta} + r\mu_2\mu_{r-1}$$

$$\kappa_{r+1} = \theta \sum_{j=1}^{r} \binom{r-1}{j-1} \mu'_{r-j} \frac{d\kappa_j}{d\theta} - \sum_{j=2}^{r} \binom{r-1}{j-2} \mu'_{r+1-j}\kappa_j$$

[Noack (1950), pp. 127-129]

(3) $$\mu'_{r+1}A(\theta) = \theta \frac{d}{d\theta} \{\mu'_r A(\theta)\}$$ [Wani (1967), p. 50]

$$\kappa_{(r)} = \frac{d\kappa_{(r-1)}}{d\theta} - (r-1)\kappa_{(r-1)}$$ [Khatri (1959), p. 487]

$$\kappa_{(r)} = \theta^r \frac{d^r}{d\theta^r} \log A(\theta)$$ [Johnson and Kotz (1969), p. 34]

(4) $$\mu_{(r)} = \frac{\theta^r A^{(r)}(\theta)}{A(\theta)}$$

where $A^{(r)} = A(A-1) \ldots (A-r+1)$.

[Johnson and Kotz (1969), p. 34]

(5) $$\kappa_r = \theta \frac{d\kappa_{r-1}}{d\theta}$$ [Ord (1972), p. 117]

4.6.3 SOME USEFUL RESULTS

(1) If a generalized power series distribution (GPSD) is truncated, the truncated distribution is also a GPSD [Patil (1962b), p. 180].

(2) If the parameter space θ of a GPSD contains zero, then the range T of the distribution contains zero and the corresponding random variable takes the value zero with positive probabilities for all θ in the parameter space, and conversely [Patil (1962b), p. 180].

(3) The generating function and its logarithm of a GPSD are monotone nondecreasing functions of θ [Patil (1962b), p. 180].

(4) The mean $\mu = \mu(\theta)$ of a GPSD is a nonnegative monotone nondecreasing function of θ [Patil (1962b), p. 181].

(5) The equality of mean and variance is necessary and sufficient for a GPSD to become a Poisson distribution [Patil (1962b), p. 181].

(6) The first two cumulants (or moments) uniquely determine the distribution given that it is a GPSD [Khatri (1959), p. 487].

(7) For a GPSD,

(a) The maximum likelihood estimator of θ is $\hat{\theta} = \mu^{-1}(\bar{x})$ where $\mu = \theta A'(\theta)/A(\theta)$ and $\mathrm{var}(\hat{\theta}) = (\theta^2/n)/\mu_2(\theta)$ [Patil (1962a), p. 228].

(b) A complete and sufficient statistic for θ is $S = \sum_1^n X_i$. [Roy and Mitra (1957), pp. 371-372]

(c) The MVUE of θ^r is $U_r(S)$, $S = \sum_i^n X_i$, where

$$U_r(s) = \begin{cases} 0, & s < r \\ \dfrac{c(s - r, n)}{c(s, n)}, & s \geq r \end{cases}$$ [Roy and Mitra (1957), p. 372]

where $c(s, n)$ is defined by $P[S = s] = c(s, n)\theta^s\{A(\theta)\}^{-n}$.

4.7 MONOTONE FAILURE RATE (CONTINUOUS) DISTRIBUTIONS

4.7.1 DEFINITIONS

Let $F(x)$ and $f(x)$ be the cdf and pdf of a nonnegative random variable. The failure rate of $F(x)$ is defined for those values of X for which $F(x) < 1$ by $r(x) = f(x)/[1 - F(x)]$. Let $\gamma(x) = (1/x) \int_0^x r(y)\, dy$.

F(x) is known as

(1) an increasing failure rate (IFR) distribution if $r(x)$ is nondecreasing in x,

(2) a decreasing failure rate (DFR) distribution if $r(x)$ is nonincreasing in x,

(3) an increasing failure rate average (IFRA) distribution if $\gamma(x)$ is nondecreasing in x, and

(4) a decreasing failure rate average (DFRA) distribution if $\gamma(x)$ is nondecreasing in x.

A good discussion of IFR (DFR) distributions is in Barlow and Proschan (1965).

4.7.2 PROPERTIES

(1) If F(x) is IFR (DFR) then F(x) is IFRA (DFRA), but the converse is not true.

Example: $$F(x) = \begin{cases} (1 - e^{-x})(1 - e^{-kx}), & x \geq 0, \quad k > 1 \\ 0, & x < 0 \end{cases}$$

F(x) is IFRA but not IFR [Barlow and Proschan (1966), p. 1594].

(2) If F(x) is DFR then f(x) is decreasing in x.

[Barlow and Proschan (1965), p. 26]

(3) If F(x) is IFR then f(x) need not be unimodal.

Example: $$f(x) = \begin{cases} 1 + a - 4ax, & 0 \leq x \leq \frac{1}{2}, \; -1 \leq a \leq 2 - \sqrt{3} \\ 1 - 3a + 4ax, & \frac{1}{2} < x < 1, \quad -1 \leq a \leq 2 - \sqrt{3} \end{cases}$$

Hence f(x) is IFR but unimodal only for $-1 \leq a \leq 0$.

[Barlow et al. (1963), p. 379]

(4) IFR distributions have finite moments of all orders.

[Barlow and Proschan (1965), p. 33]

This is not true for DFR distributions.

Example: $$F(x) = 1 - \frac{1}{1 + x}, \quad x \geq 0$$

F(x) is DFR but does not have a mean.

(5) If F(x) is IFR

$$\mu'_r \leq \Gamma(r+1)\mu^r, \quad r = 1, 2, 3, \ldots$$

If $F(x)$ is DFR and the moments exist, the above inequality holds with the direction reversed [Barlow and Proschan (1965), p. 33].

4.7.3 SOME USEFUL RESULTS

(1) $F(x)$ is IFR (DFR) iff its hazard function $-\log[1 - F(x)]$ is monotone increasing (decreasing) and convex (concave).

[Barlow and Proschan (1965), p. 25]

(2) The IFR property is preserved under convolution but the DFR property is not.

$$\text{Example:}\quad f_1(x) = f_2(x) = \frac{x^{\alpha-1}e^{-x}}{\Gamma(\alpha)}, \quad x > 0, \ \frac{1}{2} < \alpha < 1$$

Distributions corresponding to $f_1(x)$, $f_2(x)$ are DFR but their convolution is IFR [Barlow and Proschan (1965), pp. 36, 37].

(3) Let $F_1(x)$, $F_2(x)$ be IFR distributions with failure rates $r_1(x)$ and $r_2(x)$ respectively. Let H denote their convolution and $r_h(x)$ be the corresponding failure rate. Then

$$r_h(x) \le \min\{r_1(x), r_2(x)\} \quad \text{[Barlow and Proschan (1965), p. 38]}$$

(4) The IFRA property is preserved under the formation of coherent systems, but the same is not true for DFR (or DFRA) distributions.

[Birnbaum et al. (1966), p. 816]

(5) If $F(x)$ is DFR, the random variable $X_{(r;n)} - X_{(r+1;n)}$ ($r = 1, 2, \ldots, n$) also has a DFR distribution. The same is not true for IFR distributions [Barlow and Proschan (1966), p. 1590].

(6) The maximum likelihood estimator of the failure rate of an IFR (DFR) distribution is given by Marshall and Proschan (1965, pp. 70, 76).

(7) For a discrete distribution $F(x)$ with probability function $f(x)$, the failure rate $r(x)$ can be defined as $r(x) = f(x)/[1 - F(x - 1)]$ $(0 < r(x) \le 1)$. $F(x)$ is IFR (DFR) iff $r(x)$ is nondecreasing (nonincreasing) in x [Barlow and Proschan (1965), p. 18].

4.8 NEW BETTER (WORSE) THAN USED (CONTINUOUS) DISTRIBUTIONS

4.8.1 DEFINITIONS

A distribution F(x) is new better (worse) than used (NBU (NWU)) iff

$$[1 - F(x + y)] \leq (\geq) [1 - F(x)][1 - F(y)] \quad \text{for} \quad x \geq 0,\ y \geq 0$$

This is equivalent to stating that the conditional survival probability $[1 - F(x + y)]/[1 - F(x)]$ of a unit of age x is less (greater) than the corresponding survival probability $[1 - F(y)]$ of a new unit.

A distribution F(x) is new better (worse) than used in expectation (NBUE (NWUE)) iff

$$\int_0^\infty [1 - F(y + x)]\, dx \leq (\geq) [1 - F(y)] \int_0^\infty [1 - F(x)]\, dx$$

$$\text{for } y \geq 0 \text{ and } F(y) < 1$$

[Haines and Singpurwalla (1974), p. 50]

[Barlow and Proschan (1975), p. 159]

4.8.2 PROPERTIES AND SOME USEFUL RESULTS

(1) IFR => IFRA => NBU => NBUE

DFR => DFRA => NWU => NWUE [Barlow and Proschan (1975), p. 159]

(2) F(x) is NBU iff its hazard function $H(x) = -\log[1 - F(x)]$ is superadditive (i.e., $H(x + y) \geq H(x) + H(y)$ for $x \geq 0$, $y \geq 0$) on $(0, \infty)$. F(x) is NWU iff its hazard function is subadditive (i.e., $H(x + y) \leq H(x) + H(y)$ for $x \geq 0$, $y \geq 0$) on $(0, \infty)$.

[Barlow and Proschan (1975), p. 161]

(3) NBUE distributions are closed under convolutions but the same is not true for NWUE distributions [Barlow and Proschan (1975), p. 184].

(4) The NBU property is preserved under the formation of coherent systems but the same is not true for NBUE, NWU, or NWUE property.

[Barlow and Proschan (1975), p. 183]

4.9 STABLE (CONTINUOUS) DISTRIBUTIONS

4.9.1 DEFINITION

Let X, X_1, X_2, ..., X_n be iid random variables with cdf F(x). Let $S_n = \sum_1^n X_i$. The distribution F is called stable if for each n there exist constants $c_n > 0$ such that S_n has the same distribution as $c_n X + \gamma_n$ and F(x) is not concentrated at the origin. Also, F(x) is called strictly stable if $\gamma_n = 0$ [Feller (1966), p. 166].

Alternately, a distribution F is called stable if to any positive a_1 and a_2 and any real b_1 and b_2 there correspond constants a > 0 and b such that the convolution of $F(a_1x + b_1)$ and $F(a_2x + b_2)$, denoted by $F(a_1x + b_1) * F(a_2x + b_2)$, satisfies the relation

$$F(a_1x + b_1) * F(a_2x + b_2) = F(ax + b)$$

[Kagan et al. (1973), p. 8]

A good discussion of these distributions and a good bibliography is in Holt and Crow (1973), and also in Cross (1974).

4.9.2 PROPERTIES

(1) F(x) is a stable distribution iff its characteristic function can be written in the form

$$\log \phi(t) = iat - c|t|^{\alpha}\left\{1 + \frac{ibt}{|t|}\,\omega(|t|, \alpha)\right\}$$

where a, b, c, α satisfy $-\infty < a < \infty$, $|b| \le 1$, $c \ge 0$, $0 < \alpha \le 2$, and

$$\omega(|t|, \alpha) = \begin{cases} \tan \dfrac{\pi\alpha}{2} & \text{if } \alpha \neq 1 \\ \dfrac{2}{\pi} \log |t| & \text{if } \alpha = 1 \end{cases}$$

α is called the characteristic exponent of the distribution. If b = 0, the distribution is symmetric [Moran (1968), p. 445].

[Holt and Crow (1973), pp. 146, 148]

(2) All stable distributions are infinitely divisible distributions.

[Feller (1966), p. 173]

(3) All stable distributions F are absolutely continuous.

[Holt and Crow (1973), p. 147]

(4) Every stable distribution with characteristic exponent α ($0 < \alpha < 2$) has finite absolute moments of order δ ($0 < \delta < \alpha$). Thus for $1 < \alpha < 2$ the stable distributions have first moments, and for $0 < \alpha \leq 1$ the stable distributions have no first moments.

[Holt and Crow (1973), p. 149]

(5) A stable distribution is concentrated on $[0, \infty)$ iff $\alpha < 1$, $b = 1$ and $a \geq 0$ [Feller (1966), p. 542].

(6) Every stable distribution is unimodal.

[Holt and Crow (1973), p. 148]

(7) Let $f(x, \alpha, b)$ be the pdf of a standard stable distribution ($a = 0$, $c = 1$). Then $f(-x; \alpha, -b) = f(x; \alpha, b)$.

[Holt and Crow (1973), p. 147]

(8) The derivatives of the stable pdf's with respect to x of all orders exist for all real x. They are bounded according to

$$\left|\frac{\partial^n f(x;\ \alpha,\ b)}{\partial x^n}\right| < \frac{1}{\pi\alpha}\,\Gamma\left(\frac{n+1}{\alpha}\right)$$ [Holt and Crow (1973), p. 147]

(9) If $0 < \alpha < 1$ and $\gamma = -\alpha$, then $f(x; \alpha, 1) = 0$ for $x > 0$. Also, $f(x; \alpha, -1) = 0$ for $x < 0$ and $0 < \alpha < 1$.

[Holt and Crow (1973), p. 149]

(10) In the definition of stable distributions, only the norming constants $c_n = n^{1/\alpha}$ are possible [Feller (1966), p. 166].

4.9.3 SOME USEFUL RESULTS

(1) If F is strictly stable with characteristic exponent α, then for arbitrary positive s and t, $s^{1/\alpha}X_1 + t^{1/\alpha}X_2$ is distributed as $(s + t)^{1/\alpha}X$ [Feller (1966), p. 167].

(2) For a characterization, let $X_1, X_2, \ldots, X_n$ be a random sample from a distribution F(x). Every linear statistic $L = \sum_i^n a_iX_i$ is distributed as $(\sum_i^n |a_i|^\alpha)^{1/\alpha}\ X_1$ iff F(x) is a symmetric stable distribution with characteristic exponent α.

[Lukacs and Laha (1964), p. 149]

(3) If F is stable with characteristic exponent $\alpha \neq 1$ then there exists a constant b such that $F(x + b)$ is strictly stable.

[Feller (1966), p. 168]

(4) The normal distribution ($\alpha = 2$) is stable (strictly stable if its mean is zero). It is the only stable distribution for which second and higher absolute moments exist.

[Fama and Roll (1968), p. 817]

(5) The Cauchy distribution ($\alpha = 1$, $b = 0$),

$$f(x) = \frac{1}{\pi} \frac{c}{c^2 + (x - \gamma)^2}$$

is strictly stable [Feller (1966), p. 170].

(6) The first passage time distribution for Brownian motion ($\alpha = 1/2$, $b = -1$)

$$f(x) = \frac{1}{\sqrt{2\pi x^3}} \exp\left(-\frac{1}{2x}\right)$$

is strictly stable [Feller (1966), p. 170].

(7) The standard pdf $f(x; \alpha, b)$ has been tabulated and graphed for selected values of α and b [Holt and Crow (1973), pp. 165-194].

4.10 INFINITELY DIVISIBLE DISTRIBUTIONS (IDD)

4.10.1 DEFINITION

A distribution F is called infinitely divisible if for every n there exists a distribution F_n such that $F = F_n^*$ where F_n^* is the n fold convolution of F_n. In other words F is IDD iff for each n it can be represented as the distribution of the sum $S_n = \sum_i^n X_i$ of n independent random variables with a common distribution F_n.

[Feller (1966), p. 173]

In terms of characteristic functions, a characteristic function is called infinitely divisible if for every n, there exists a characteristic function ϕ_n such that $\phi(t) = [\phi_n(t)]^n$ for all real t.

[Kagan et al. (1973), p. 7]

A good discussion of this class of distributions is in Feller (1966), and a good bibliography is in Fisz (1962).

4.10.2 PROPERTIES

(1) The characteristic function of an IDD never vanishes.

[Kagan et al. (1973), p. 7]

(2) The distribution function of the sum of a finite number of independent infinitely divisible random variables is itself infinitely divisible [Gnedenko and Kolmogorov (1954), p. 73].

(3) A distribution function which is the limit, in the sense of weak convergence, of IDD functions is itself infinitely divisible.

[Gnedenko and Kolmogorov (1954), p. 73]

(4) All stable distributions are IDD [Feller (1966), p. 73].

(5) The moment of order 2k of an IDD is finite iff the moment of G(u) (see 4.10.3(2)) of the same order is finite [Fisz (1962), p. 72].

4.10.3 SOME USEFUL RESULTS

(1) If ϕ is the characteristic function of an IDD, then $|\phi|$ and $\phi^{\alpha} = \exp(\alpha \log \phi)$ for any positive α are also characteristic functions of infinitely divisible distributions [Kagan et al. (1973), p. 8].

(2) In order that a distribution F(x) with a finite variance be infinitely divisible it is necessary and sufficient that $\log \phi(t)$ be written in the form

$$\log \phi(t) = iat + \int_{-\infty}^{\infty} \frac{e^{itx} - 1 - itx}{x^2}\, dG(x)$$

where a is a real constant, G(x) is a nondecreasing function of bounded variation, and the integrand at $x = 0$ equals $-(1/2)t^2$.

[Fisz (1962), p. 68]

(3) A nondegenerate bounded random variable can not be infinitely divisible [Fisz (1962), p. 72].

4.11 UNIMODAL DISTRIBUTIONS

4.11.1 DEFINITION

A continuous distribution $F(x)$ is said to be unimodal if there exists at least one value $x = a$ such that $F(x)$ is convex for $x < a$ and concave for $x > a$. The point $x = a$ is called a vertex of $F(x)$.

[Lukacs (1970), p. 91]

A discrete distribution $\{p_n\}$ with all support on the lattice of integers is said to be unimodal if there exists at least one integer m such that $p_n \geq p_{n-1}$ for all $n \leq m$ and $p_{n+1} \leq p_n$ for all $n \geq m$. A distribution $\{h_n\}$ is strongly unimodal if the convolution of $\{h_n\}$, with any unimodal $\{p_n\}$, is unimodal.

[Keilson and Gerber (1971), p. 386]

4.11.2 PROPERTIES

(1) A continuous distribution $F(x)$ is unimodal with vertex at $x = 0$ iff its characteristic function $\phi(t)$ can be represented as

$$\phi(t) = \frac{1}{t}\int_0^t g(z)\, dz, \quad -\infty < t < \infty$$

where $g(z)$ is a characteristic function of some other variable.

[Lukacs (1970), p. 92]

(2) In order that the continuous distribution $F(x)$ be unimodal (with vertex at $x = 0$), it is necessary and sufficient that the function $G(x) = F(x) - xF'(x)$ be a distribution function.

[Gnedenko and Kolmogorov (1954), p. 157]

(3) The convolution of two symmetric and unimodal continuous distributions is symmetric and unimodal [Lukacs (1970), p. 98].

(4) The convolution of two strongly unimodal discrete distributions is strongly unimodal [Keilson and Gerber (1971), p. 387].

(5) If a sequence of unimodal continuous distribution functions converges to a distribution, then the limiting distribution function is also unimodal [Laha (1961), p. 184].

(6) A necessary and sufficient condition that $\{h_n\}$ is strongly unimodal is that $h_n^2 \geq h_{n-1}h_{n+1}$ for all n.

[Keilson and Gerber (1971), p. 387]

(7) The limit of a convergent sequence of strongly unimodal discrete distributions is strongly unimodal.

[Keilson and Gerber (1971), p. 387]

4.11.3 SOME USEFUL RESULTS

(1) For any real α in the interval $0 < \alpha \leq 2$ the function $\phi(t) = 1/(1 + |t|^\alpha)$ is the characteristic function of a symmetric, absolutely continuous and unimodal distribution [Laha (1961), p. 181].

(2) A continuous distribution F is unimodal iff it is the distribution of X = YZ of two independent random variables such that Y is distributed uniformly in [0, 1] [Feller (1966), p. 155].

(3) The convolution of two unimodal continuous distributions may not be unimodal [Feller (1966), p. 164].

(4) A strongly unimodal discrete distribution is unimodal.

[Keilson and Gerber (1971), p. 386]

(5) The binomial and Poisson distributions are strongly unimodal.

[Keilson and Gerber (1971), p. 386]

4.12 CLASSIFICATION OF SOME USEFUL DISCRETE DISTRIBUTIONS

The classification corresponds to exponential, MLR, GPSD, monotone failure rate, IDD, and unimodal families. Note that "wrt" is used for "with respect to."

4.12.1 BINOMIAL

$$f(x) = \binom{n}{x} p^x q^{n-x}; \; x = 0, 1, \ldots, n, \; 0 < p < 1, \; q = 1 - p$$

(1) Exponential wrt p

(2) MLR in T(x), T(x) = x [Ferguson (1967), p. 209]

(3) GPSD [Patil (1963a), pp. 1054-1055]

(4) IFR [Barlow and Proschan (1965), pp. 17-18]

(5) Not IDD [Harris (1966), p. 250]

(6) Unimodal [Keilson and Gerber (1971), p. 386]

4.12.2 POISSON

$$f(x) = \frac{e^{-\lambda}\lambda^x}{x!}; \quad x = 0, 1, 2, \ldots, \quad \lambda > 0$$

(1) Exponential wrt λ

(2) MLR in T(x), T(x) = x [Ferguson (1967), p. 209]

(3) GPSD [Patil (1963a), pp. 1054-1055]

(4) IFR [Barlow and Proschan (1965), pp. 17-18]

(5) IDD [Moran (1968), p. 410]

(6) Unimodal [Keilson and Gerber (1971), p. 386]

4.12.3 NEGATIVE BINOMIAL

$$f(x) = \binom{s + x - 1}{x} q^x p^s; \quad x = 0, 1, 2, \ldots, \quad 0 < p < 1, \quad q = 1 - p, \; s > 0$$

(1) Exponential wrt p (s known)

Not exponential

(a) wrt s (p known)

(b) wrt both p and s

(2) MLR in T(x) (s known), T(x) = x [Ferguson (1967), p. 209]

(3) GPSD [Patil (1962b), p. 180]

(4) IFR ($s \geq 1$), DFR ($s \leq 1$), $r(x) = p$ ($s = 1$)

(5) IDD [Moran (1968), p. 410]

(6) Unimodal

4.12.4 HYPERGEOMETRIC

$$f(x) = \frac{\binom{\theta}{x}\binom{N-\theta}{n-x}}{\binom{N}{n}}, \quad \max(0, n - N + \theta) \leq x \leq \min(n, \theta)$$

(1) Not

(a) Exponential

(b) GPSD

(2) MLR in x (n, N known) [Ferguson (1967), p. 209]

4.12.5 LOGARITHMIC SERIES

$$f(x) = -\frac{1}{\log(1-\theta)} \frac{\theta^x}{x}; \; x = 1, 2, \ldots, \; 0 < \theta < 1$$

(1) Exponential wrt θ

(2) MLR in x

(3) GPSD [Patil (1962b), p. 180]

(4) DFR [Patel (1973), p. 284]

(5) IDD [Katti (1967), pp. 1307-1308]

(6) Unimodal

4.12.6 UNIFORM

$$f(x) = \frac{1}{\theta + 1}, \; x = 0, 1, 2, \ldots, \theta$$

(1) Not

(a) Exponential

(b) GPSD

(c) Unimodal

(2) MLR in x

(3) IFR, $r(x) = \dfrac{1}{\theta - x + 1}$ [Patel (1973), p. 284]

4.13 CLASSIFICATION OF SOME CONTINUOUS DISTRIBUTIONS

The classification corresponds to Pearson, exponential, MLR, monotone failure rate (only for nonnegative random variables), stable, IDD, and unimodal families.

4.13.1 NORMAL

$$f(x) = \frac{1}{\sigma\sqrt{2\pi}} \exp\left\{-\frac{(x-\mu)^2}{2\sigma^2}\right\}; \quad -\infty < x < \infty,\ -\infty < \mu < \infty,\quad \sigma > 0$$

(1) Pearson [Ord (1972), p. 6]

(2) Exponential family

(a) wrt μ (σ known)

(b) wrt σ^2 (μ known)

(c) wrt both μ and σ^2

(3) MLR in

(a) $T_1(x)$ (σ known), $T_1(x) = x$

(b) $T_2(x)$ (μ known), $T_2(x) = (x - \mu)^2$

Not MLR in x (μ known)

(4) IFR for a truncated (at origin) positive normal distribution [Barlow and Proschan (1965), p. 13]

(5) Stable, IDD [Feller (1966), p. 170]

(6) Unimodal

4.13.2 *LOGNORMAL*

$$f(x) = \frac{1}{x\sigma\sqrt{2\pi}} \exp\left\{-\frac{1}{2\sigma^2}(\log x - \mu)^2\right\}; \quad x > 0, -\infty < \mu < \infty, \sigma > 0$$

(1) Not Pearson

(2) Exponential family

(a) wrt μ (σ known)

(b) wrt σ^2 (μ known)

(c) wrt both μ and σ^2

(3) MLR in

(a) $T_1(x)$ (σ known), $T_1(x) = \log x$

(b) $T_2(x)$ (μ known), $T_2(x) = (\log x - \mu)^2$

Not MLR in x (μ known and $\mu \neq 0$)

(4) Not IFR, not DFR [Barlow and Proschan (1965), p. 13]

(5) Unimodal

(6) Unimodal

4.13.3 *INVERSE GAUSSIAN*

$$f(x) = \sqrt{\frac{\lambda}{2\pi x^3}} \exp\left\{-\frac{\lambda(x - \theta)^2}{2\theta^2 x}\right\}; \quad x > 0, \theta > 0, \lambda > 0$$

(1) Pearson [Johnson and Kotz (1970a), p. 12]

(2) Exponential

(a) wrt θ (λ known)

(b) wrt λ (θ known)

(c) wrt both θ and λ

(3) MLR in

(a) $T_1(x)$ (λ known), $T_1(x) = \lambda x$

(b) $T_2(x)$ (θ known), $T_2(x) = (x - \theta)^2/x$

Not MLR in x (θ known and $\theta \neq 0$)

(4) Not IFR, not DFR [Patel (1973), p. 283]

(5) IDD [Wasan (1968), p. 83]

(6) Unimodal

4.13.4 *CAUCHY*

$$f(x) = \frac{1}{\pi\beta[1 + \{(x - \alpha)/\beta\}^2]} ; \quad -\infty < x < \infty, -\infty < \alpha < \infty, \beta > 0$$

(1) Not Pearson

(2) Not Exponential

(a) wrt α (β known)

(b) wrt β (α known)

(c) wrt both α and β

(3) Not MLR

(a) in x (β known) [Ferguson (1967), p. 210]

(b) in x (α known)

(4) Stable, IDD [Feller (1966), p. 170]

(5) Unimodal

4.13.5 *GAMMA*

$$f(x) = \frac{x^{m-1}\theta^m \exp(-x\theta)}{\Gamma(m)} ; \quad x > 0, \theta > 0, m > 0$$

(1) Pearson [Ord (1972), p. 6]

(2) Exponential wrt θ (m known)

Not exponential

(a) wrt m (θ known)

(b) wrt both θ and m

(3) MLR in T(x) (m known), T(x) = x

(4) IFR ($m \geq 1$), DFR ($m \leq 1$), $r(x) = \theta$ ($m = 1$)

[Barlow and Proschan (1965), p. 13]

(5) IDD [Moran (1968), p. 410]

(6) Unimodal

4.13.6 WEIBULL

$$f(x) = \theta c x^{c-1} \exp(-\theta x^c); \quad x > 0,\ \theta > 0,\ c > 0$$

(1) Not Pearson (except for $c = 1$)

(2) Exponential wrt θ (c known)

Not exponential

(a) wrt c (θ known)

(b) wrt both θ and c

(3) MLR in $T(x)$ (c known), $T(x) = x^c$

(4) IFR ($c \geq 1$), DFR ($c \leq 1$), $r(x) = \theta c x^{c-1}$

[Barlow and Proschan (1965), p. 13]

(5) Unimodal

(6) Unimodal

4.13.7 BETA

$$f(x) = \frac{x^{a-1}(1 - x)^{b-1}}{B(a, b)}; \quad 0 < x < 1,\ a > 0,\ b > 0$$

(1) Pearson, [Ord (1972), p. 6]

(2) Exponential

(a) wrt a (b known)

(b) wrt b (a known)

(c) wrt both a and b

(3) MLR in

(a) $T_1(x)$ (b known), $T_1(x) = \log x$

(b) $T_2(x)$ (a known), $T_2(x) = \log(1 - x)$

(4) IFR ($a \geq 1$, $b = 1$), not IFR ($0 < a < 1$), not DFR ($0 < a < 1$),

$$r(x) = \frac{ax^{a-1}}{1 - x^a} \quad \text{for } b = 1$$

IFR ($a = 1$), $r(x) = \dfrac{b}{(1 - x)}$

(5) Unimodal ($a > 1$, $b > 1$)

Not unimodal ($a < 1$, $b < 1$ or $(a - 1)(b - 1) \leq 0$)

[Johnson and Kotz (1970b), p. 41]

4.13.8 POWER FUNCTION

$$f(x) = \theta k^{-\theta} x^{\theta-1}; \; 0 < x < k, \; \theta > 0$$

(1) Pearson

(2) Exponential wrt θ (k known)

Not exponential

(a) wrt k (θ known)

(b) wrt both k and θ

(3) MLR in

(a) $T(x)$ (k known), $T(x) = \log x$

(b) x (θ known)

(4) IFR ($\theta \geq 1$), not IFR ($0 < \theta < 1$), not DFR ($0 < \theta < 1$),

$$r(x) = \frac{\theta x^{\theta-1}}{k^\theta - x^\theta}$$

(5) Unimodal

4.13.9 UNIFORM

$$f(x) = \frac{1}{\theta}, \quad 0 < x < \theta$$

(1) Not

(a) Pearson

(b) Exponential

(c) Stable

(2) MLR in T(x), $T(x) = X_{(n;n)}$

(3) IFR, $r(x) = \dfrac{1}{\theta - x}$

4.13.10 PARETO

$$f(x) = \theta k^{\theta} x^{-(\theta+1)}; \quad x \geq k > 0, \quad \theta > 0$$

(1) Pearson

(2) Exponential wrt θ (k known)

Not exponential

(a) wrt k (θ known)

(b) wrt both θ and k

(3) MLR in

(a) T(x) (k known), $T(x) = \log x$

(b) x (θ known)

(4) DFR, $r(x) = \dfrac{\theta}{x}$

(5) Not stable

(6) Unimodal

4.13.11 EXTREME-VALUE

$$f(x) = \frac{1}{\beta} \exp\left\{ - \left(\frac{x - \alpha}{\beta}\right) - e^{-(x-\alpha)/\beta} \right\}; \quad -\infty < x < \infty, \ -\infty < \alpha < \infty, \ \beta > 0$$

(1) Not

(a) Pearson

(b) Exponential

(c) Stable

(2) MLR in x (β known)

Not MLR in x (α known)

(3) Unimodal

4.13.12 TRUNCATED EXTREME-VALUE

$$f(x) = \frac{1}{\theta} \exp\left\{x - \left(\frac{e^x - 1}{\theta}\right)\right\}; \quad x > 0,\ \theta > 0$$

(1) Not

(a) Pearson

(b) Stable

(2) Exponential wrt θ

(3) MLR in T(x), $T(x) = e^x - 1$

(4) IFR, $r(x) = \frac{e^x}{\theta}$ [Barlow and Proschan (1965), p. 13]

(5) Unimodal

4.13.13 LAPLACE

$$f(x) = \frac{1}{2\beta} \exp\left\{- \frac{|x - \alpha|}{\beta}\right\}; \quad -\infty < x < \infty,\ -\infty < \alpha < \infty,\ \beta > 0$$

(1) Not

(a) Pearson

(b) Stable

(2) Exponential wrt β (α known)

Not exponential

(a) wrt α (β known)

(b) wrt both α and β

(3) MLR in

(a) x (β known) [Ferguson (1967), p. 209]

(b) T(x) (α known), $T(x) = |x - \alpha|$

Not MLR in x (α known)

(4) Unimodal

4.13.14 LOGISTIC

$$f(x) = \frac{\exp\left(-\frac{x-\alpha}{\beta}\right)}{\beta\left[1 + \exp\left(-\frac{x-\alpha}{\beta}\right)\right]^2}; \quad -\infty < x < \infty,\ -\infty < \alpha < \infty,\ \beta > 0$$

(1) Not

(a) Pearson

(b) Exponential

(c) Stable

(2) MLR in x (β known) [Ferguson (1967), p. 215]

(3) Unimodal

4.13.15 CHI

$$f(x) = \frac{\left(\frac{x}{\theta}\right)^{\alpha-1} \exp\left\{-\frac{x^2}{2\theta^2}\right\}}{\theta 2^{(\alpha/2)-1}\Gamma\left(\frac{\alpha}{2}\right)}; \quad x > 0,\ \alpha > 0,\ \theta > 0$$

(1) Pearson

(2) Exponential

(a) wrt α (θ known)

(b) wrt θ (α known)

(c) wrt both α and θ

(3) MLR in

(a) $T_1(x)$ (θ known), $T_1(x) = \log x$

(b) $T_2(x)$ (α known), $T_2(x) = x^2$

(4) IFR ($\alpha = 1$, $\alpha \geq 2$), not DFR ($\alpha > 1$)

(5) Not stable

(6) Unimodal

Chapter 5

CHARACTERIZATION OF DISTRIBUTIONS

Characterization problems deal with the question of finding assumptions which determine the population distribution function at least to the extent that it belongs to a certain family of distribution functions. A good survey paper on this topic is Kotz (1974), pp. 39-65.

5.1 GENERAL CHARACTERIZATIONS

(1) An absolutely continuous random variable X has the cdf

$$F(x) = 1 - \exp\left(\frac{-h(x)}{h(b)}\right), \quad x \in [\alpha, \beta)$$

where b is a positive constant and $h(\cdot)$ is a strictly increasing differentiable function from $[\alpha, \beta)$ on to $[0, \infty)$ iff $E(h(X)|X > y) = h(y) + h(b)$ for $y \in [\alpha, \beta)$ [Hamdan (1972), p. 498].

(2) Let $X_1, X_2, \ldots, X_n$ be iid random variables with cdf F(x) such that each has finite moment of the third order. Let κ_1, κ_2 be the first two cumulants of F(x). Let $L_k = \sum_1^n X_i^k$ $(k = 1, 2, \ldots)$, $L_0 = n$, and $T = nL_4 + (n - 4)L_3L_1 + (3 - 2n)L_2^2 + L_2L_1^2 - nL_3 + (n + 1)L_2L_1 - L_1^3$.

Then the regression of T on L_1 is zero iff the characteristic function $\phi(t)$ of $F(x)$ has the form given by

$$\phi(t) = \left(\frac{\kappa_2}{\kappa_1} + \frac{\kappa_1 - \kappa_2}{\kappa_1} e^{it}\right)^{\kappa_1^2/(\kappa_1-\kappa_2)}$$

[Lukacs (1965), pp. 67-68]

(3) Let X and Y be independent discrete random variables and $c(x; x + y) = P(X = x|X + Y = x + y)$. If

$$\frac{c(x + y, x + y)\, c(0, y)}{c(x, x + y)\, c(y, y)} = \frac{h(x, y)}{h(x)h(y)}$$

where h is a nonnegative function, then $f(x) = f(0)h(x)e^{ax}$, $g(y) = g(0)k(y)e^{ay}$ where $0 < f(x) = P(X = x)$, $0 < g(y) = P(Y = y)$, and $k(y) = h(y)c(0, y)/c(y, y)$ [Kagan et al. (1973), p. 424].

(4) Let X and Y be independent random variables defined over the nonnegative integers $a \le X \le a + k$, $b \le Y \le b + m$, respectively. If $P(X = a) > 0$, $P(Y = b) > 0$ and $c(x, x + y)$ is the conditional distribution of X given X + Y, then

$$f(x) = P(X = x) = \frac{c_1(x)\theta^x}{\sum_{x=a}^{a+k} c_1(x)\theta^x},$$

$$g(y) = P(Y = y) = \frac{c_2(y)\lambda^y}{\sum_{y=b}^{b+m} c_2(y)\lambda^y}$$

where

$$\theta = \frac{g(b + 1)}{g(b)}, \quad \lambda = \frac{f(a + 1)}{f(a)}$$

and

$$c_1(x) = \prod_{i=1}^{x-a} \frac{c(a + i, a + b + i)}{c(a + i - 1, a + b + i)},$$

$$c_2(y) = \prod_{j=1}^{y-b} \frac{c(b + j, a + b + j)}{c(b + j - 1, a + b + j)}$$

[Patil and Seshadri (1964), p. 291]

(5) Let $X_1, X_2, \ldots, X_n$ be iid random variables with cdf $F(x)$, and denote by $p \geq 1$, $r \geq 1$ two positive integers. Assume that the moment of order $(p + r)$ of $F(x)$ exists. Then $F(x)$ has the characteristic function

$$\phi(t) = \exp\left\{\lambda_1(e^{it} - 1) + \delta_r\lambda_2(e^{-it} - 1) + c_1 it - \varepsilon_p c_2 \frac{t^2}{2}\right\}$$

where

$$\delta_r = \begin{cases} 0 & \text{if } r \text{ is an odd integer} \\ 1 & \text{if } r \text{ is an even integer} \end{cases}$$

$$\varepsilon_p = \begin{cases} 0 & \text{if } p = 1 \\ 1 & \text{if } p > 1 \end{cases}, \quad p \text{ an integer}$$

iff the k-statistic $k_{p+r} - k_p$ has constant regression on $k_1 = \bar{X}$, where λ_1, λ_2, c_1, c_2, are real constants such that $\lambda_1 \geq 0$, $\lambda_2 \geq 0$, $c_2 \geq 0$ [Lukacs (1965), p. 67].

(6) (a) Let $X_1, X_2, \ldots, X_n$ be iid random variables with cdf $F(x)$ with finite variance. Suppose the quadratic statistic $Q = \sum_1^n a_{ii}X_i^2$ satisfies $\sum_1^n a_{ii} \neq 0$. Then the sample mean $\bar{X}$ and the statistic Q are independent iff $F(x) = p\,\varepsilon(x - a) + (1 - p)\varepsilon(x + a)$, where

$$\varepsilon(X) = \begin{cases} 0 & \text{if } x < 0 \\ 1 & \text{if } x \geq 0 \end{cases}, \quad \text{and } 0 \leq p \leq 1$$

(b) Let $X_1, X_2, \ldots, X_n$ be iid random variables with cdf $F(x)$ with finite variance. The independence of $\bar{X}$ and $Q = \sum_{i=1}^n \sum_{j=1}^n a_{ij}X_iX_j$ determines $F(x)$ iff the following conditions are satisfied.

(i) $\sum_1^n a_{ii} \neq 0$ and

(ii) either $\sum_{j=1}^n a_{ij} = 0$ for $i = 1, 1, \ldots, n$ or $a_{ij} = 0$ for $i \neq j$ $(i, j = 1, 2, \ldots, n)$.

[Lukacs and Laha (1964), pp. 81-82]

(7) Let X and Y be two nonnegative independent random variables with F and G as their respective cdf's. Let $E(X) < \infty$ and F have an absolutely continuous part. Then G satisfies

$$G(t) = \int_0^\infty G(x + t)\, dF(x) + \int_0^\infty F(y + t)\, dG(y),\quad t \geq 0$$

iff G is absolutely continuous with pdf $g(y) = [1 - F(y)]/E(X)$ for all $y \geq 0$ [Puri and Rubin (1970), p. 2119].

(8) (a) Let X_0 and X be two real random variables with the corresponding cdf's F_0 and F_1. Assume that F_0 is continuous, and that there exists an interval [a, b] where $-\infty \leq a < b \leq +\infty$, such that $F(a + 0) = F_0(a) = 0$, $F(b - 0) = F_0(b) = 1$ and for each $a < X < b$ there is $0 < F_0(x) < 1$, $0 < F(x) < 1$.

Let h be a real function which maps the interval [a, b] on to $[\alpha, \beta]$ where $-\infty \leq \alpha < \beta \leq +\infty$, continuously differentiable, and let $h'(x) > 0$ for $a < x < b$. Assume that both $E[h(X_0)]$ and $E[h(X)]$ do exist and are finite. Then X_0 and X are identically distributed iff one of the following conditions is satisfied.

$$\text{(i)}\quad E[h(X)\,|\,X \leq y] = h(y) - \frac{\int_a^y F_0(x)\, dh(x)}{F_0(y)},\quad a < y \leq b$$

$$\text{(ii)}\quad E[h(X)\,|\,X > y] = h(y) + \frac{\int_y^b [1 - F_0(x)]\, dh(x)}{[1 - F_0(y)]},\quad a \leq y < b$$

(b) Let X_0 and X_1 be two real random variables with the corresponding cdf's F_0 and F_1, and a common support [a, b], where $-\infty \leq a < b \leq +\infty$. Assume that F_0 is everywhere continuous, that F, F_0 are strictly increasing on [a, b] and that $F(a + 0) = 0$, $F(b - 0) = 1$.

Let h be a real function which maps the interval [a, b] on to $[\alpha, \beta]$ where $-\infty \leq \alpha < \beta < +\infty$. Assume that h is continuously differentiable, and $h'(x) > 0$ for $a < x < b$. Then X and X_0 are identically distributed iff for every $a < y < z < b$ there is

$$E[h(X)\,|\,y < X \le z] = \frac{\int_y^z h(x)\, dF_0(x)}{F_0(z) - F_0(y)}$$

[Kotlarski (1972), pp. 463-464]

(9) Let X and Y be independent, discrete, nondegenerate random variables. Then $U = \min(X, Y)$ and $W = |X - Y|$ are independent iff the distributions of X and Y may, by a simultaneous change of location and scale, be put into one of the following four forms.

(a) For some $0 < r_1 < 1$ and $0 < r_2 < 1$

$$P(X = k) = (1 - r_1)r_1^k \quad \text{for } k = 0, 1, 2, \ldots$$

$$P(Y = k) = (1 - r_2)r_2^k \quad \text{for } k = 0, 1, 2, \ldots$$

(b) For integer $n \ge 1$, $0 < r < 1$ and $-1 \le \theta \le 1$

$$P(X = k) = \frac{(1 - r)r^k}{(1 + \theta r^n)}\begin{cases}1 & \text{for } k = 0, 1, \ldots, n - 1\\(1 + \theta) & \text{for } k = n, n + 1, \ldots\end{cases}$$

$$P(Y = k) = \frac{(1 - r)r^k}{(1 - \theta r^n)}\begin{cases}1 & \text{for } k = 0, 1, \ldots, n - 1\\(1 - \theta) & \text{for } k = n, n + 1\end{cases}$$

(c) For some $0 < r < 1$ and $0 < \theta < \infty$, either

$$P(X = k) = \frac{(1 - r)r^k}{(1 + \theta r^2)}\begin{cases}1 & \text{for } k = 0, 1\\(1 + \theta) & \text{for } k = 2, 3, \ldots\end{cases}$$

$$P(Y = k) = \begin{cases}(1 + \theta r)^{-1} & \text{for } k = 0\\1 - (1 + \theta r)^{-1} & \text{for } k = 1\end{cases}$$

or the same with X and Y interchanged.

(d) For some $0 < r < 1$ and $0 \le \theta \le \infty$

$$P(X = k) = (1 - r^2)r^k\begin{cases}(1 + \theta r)^{-1} & \text{for } k = 0, 2, 4, \ldots\\\theta(1 + \theta r)^{-1} & \text{for } k = 1, 3, 5, \ldots\end{cases}$$

$$P(Y = k) = (1 - r^2)r^k \begin{cases} \theta(\theta + r)^{-1} & \text{for } k = 0, 2, 4, \ldots \\ (\theta + r)^{-1} & \text{for } k = 1, 3, 5, \ldots \end{cases}$$

[Ferguson (1967b), p. 270]

(10) For characterizations of the exponential-type, monotone likelihood ratio type, generalized power series type, monotone failure rate type, stable and unimodal distributions type, see Chapter 4.

5.2 CHARACTERIZATION OF SOME USEFUL DISCRETE DISTRIBUTIONS

5.2.1 BINOMIAL

(1) If the conditional probability of X given X + Y is $\binom{m}{x}\binom{n}{y}/\binom{m+n}{x+y}$ then X and Y have binomial distributions with parameters (m, θ) and (n, θ), respectively.

[Kagan et al. (1973), p. 424]

(2) If in (2) of Sec. 5.1, $0 < \kappa_2/\kappa_1 = p < 1$ and $n = \kappa_1^2/(\kappa_1 - \kappa_2)$ is an integer, then $\phi(t) = (p + qe^{it})^n$, characterizes the binomial distribution [Lukacs (1965), p. 68].

5.2.2 POISSON

(1) Let $X_1, X_2, \ldots, X_n$ be a random sample from a certain distribution. The distribution is Poisson with parameter θ iff the statistic $S = \sum_1^n X_i$ has a Poisson distribution with parameter nθ.

[Lukacs (1956), p. 198]

(2) If the conditional probability of X given X + Y is $\binom{x+y}{x}[\theta/(1 - \theta)]^x(1 - \theta)^{x+y}$ then X and Y have Poisson distributions with parameters λ and [(1 - θ)/θ]λ, respectively [Kagan et al. (1973), p. 425].

(3) Let θ be a given parameter. If $\{\mu_s(\theta)\}$ is a sequence of constants which are functions of θ, then the necessary and sufficient condition that $\{\mu_s(\theta)\}$ be a sequence of moments of a unique distribution, which is Poisson with the parameter θ, is that $\mu_{s+1}(\theta) = \theta Q_s(\theta)$, where $Q_s(\theta)$ are monic polynomials of degrees s in θ given

by $Q_s(\theta) = \sum_0^s q(s, i)\theta^i$ $(s = 0, 1, 2, \ldots)$ with $q(s, i) = (i + 1) \times q(s - 1, i) + q(s - 1, i - 1)$ [Wani (1967), pp. 54-55].

(4) Let Z be a discrete random variable taking values 0, 1, 2, ... A random observation is obtained giving Z = n, and then n Bernoulli trials with probability p of success are conducted. Let X and Y denote the resulting number of successes and failures, respectively. Then Z has a Poisson distribution iff X and Y are independent.

[Srivastava (1971), p. 615]

(5) Let $X_1, X_2, \ldots, X_n$ be a random sample from a distribution F(x) and denote by $p \geq 1$, $r \geq 1$ two positive integers. Assume that

(a) the (p + r)th moment of F(x) exists,

(b) F(x) = 0 for x < 0 while F(x) > 0 for $x \geq 0$.

The distribution is a Poisson iff the k-statistic $k_{p+r} - k_p$ has constant regression on $k_1 = \bar{X}$ [Lukacs (1965), p. 67].

(6) Let $X_1, X_2, \ldots, X_n$ be a random sample from a distribution with a finite second moment. Let $S = \sum_1^n X_i$ and $Q = \sum_{j=1}^n \sum_{k=1}^m a_{jk}X_jX_k + \sum_1^n b_jX_j$. Suppose that $B_1 = \sum_1^n a_{jj} \neq 0$, $B_2 = \sum_{j=1}^n \sum_{k=1}^n a_{jk} = 0$ while $B_3 = \sum_1^n b_j \neq 0$. The distribution has the Poisson type characteristic function $\phi(t) = \exp[\lambda(e^{ipt} - 1) + i\mu t]$ iff Q has constant regression on S. Here $\lambda = B_1^2\sigma^2/B_3^2$, $p = -B_3/B_1$, $\mu = \alpha - (\sigma^2/p)$, where α and σ^2 are the mean and variance of the distribution, respectively.

[Lukacs and Laha (1964), p. 107]

(7) Let X be a nonnegative integer-valued random variable with distribution $\{g_j\}$ and Y be another random variable such that for every n with $g_n > 0$,

$$P(Y = r|X = n) = \binom{n}{r}p^r q^{n-r}, \quad r = 0, 1, 2, \ldots, n$$

where p is some number lying in (0, 1) and q = 1 - p.

$$P(Y = r) = P(Y = r|X = Y) = P(Y = r|X > Y), \quad r = 0, 1, \ldots$$

iff $\{g_j\}$ is Poisson [Shanbhag (1974), p. 211].

5.2.3 GEOMETRIC

(1) A necessary and sufficient condition that a discrete positive integer-valued random variable X have the geometric distribution $f(x) = pq^{x-1}$, $x = 1, 2, \ldots, p + q = 1, 0 < p \leq 1$, is that

$$P(X > a + b | X > a) = P(X > [a + b] - [a]) \quad \text{for all a and b}$$

[Shanbhag (1970), p. 1256]

(2) The positive integer-valued variable X has a geometric distribution $f(x) = pq^{x-1}$, $0 < p < 1$, $q = 1 - p$ iff

$$E(X | X > a) = [a] + 1 + E(X) \quad \text{for all a}$$

[Shanbhag (1970), p. 1256]

(3) Let X and Y be independent discrete random variables. Then $U = \min(X, Y)$ and $W = (X - Y)$ are independent iff both X and Y have geometric distributions with the same location and scale parameters.

[Ferguson (1965), p. 258]

(4) Let $\phi_1(t)$ be a characteristic function and Y be a random variable with cdf F(y). The solution $\phi(t)$ of $\phi(t) = \phi_1(t)E[\phi(ty)]$ is the characteristic function of the geometric distribution $P(X = x) = (1 - p)p^x$, $x = 0, 1, 2, \ldots$ iff $\phi_1(t)$ is the characteristic function of a geometric distribution and F(y) is such that $P(Y = 0) = a$, $P(Y = 1) = b$, $a + b = 1$, $0 < a \leq 1$.

[Paulson and Uppuluri (1972), p. 298]

(5) Let X and Y be mutually independent random variables taking nonnegative integer values. Then $P(X \leq n) - P(X + Y \leq n) = \theta P(X + Y = n)$ holds for $n = 0, 1, 2, \ldots$ for some positive constant θ iff Y is distributed as $P(Y = n) = [1/(1 + \theta)][\theta/(1 + \theta)]^n$, $n = 0, 1, 2, \ldots$ [Puri (1973), p. 63].

(6) If the conditional distribution of X given (X + Y) has the discrete uniform distribution for all given values of the total (X + Y), then both X and Y have identical geometric distributions.

[Kagan et al. (1973), p. 426]

(7) Let $X_1, X_2, \ldots, X_n$ be a random sample from a distribution whose second moment is finite. The distribution is geometric iff

the statistic $T_1 = [(n + 1)/(n - 1)]S_2 - [2/(n - 1)]S_1^2 - S_1$, $S_k = \sum_1^n X_i^k$ (k = 1, 2), has zero regression on S_1 [Lukacs (1965), p. 69].

(8) In (2) of Sec. 5.1, $0 < \kappa_1/\kappa_2 < 1$, $p = \kappa_1/\kappa_2$, $\kappa_2 = \kappa_1^2 + \kappa_1$ characterizes the geometric distribution with characteristic function $\phi(t) = p(1 - qe^{it})^{-1}$ [Lukacs (1965), p. 69].

(9) Let X be a nondegenerate random variable on the nonnegative integers with $P(X = i) \neq 0$ for all i = 0, 1, 2, ... The random variable X has the geometric distribution $P(X = i) = pq^i$, i = 0, 1, 2, ... $(0 < p < 1)$, iff $\mathrm{var}(X|X > c) = d$, for c = -1, 0, 1, ... , and d does not depend on c [Dallas (1974), p. 610].

5.2.4 *NEGATIVE-BINOMIAL*

If the conditional probability of X given X + Y is $\binom{x + y}{x} \times B(m + x, n + y)/B(m, n)$, where B(a, b) is the beta function (see Chapter 10, Sec. 3), then X and Y are negative binomial distributions with parameters (m, θ) and (n, θ), respectively.

[Kagan et al. (1973), p. 425]

5.2.5 *LOGARITHMIC-SERIES*

(1) Let X and Y be two independent discrete random variables each with its range containing unity. If the conditional distribution of X given X + Y = z is

$$P(X = x|X + Y = z) = \frac{\left(\frac{1}{x} + \frac{1}{z - x}\right)\beta^x}{\sum_{x=1}^{z-1}\left(\frac{1}{x} + \frac{1}{z - x}\right)\beta^x}$$

for $0 < \beta < \infty$ for every z = 2, 3, ..., ∞, then each X and Y has a logarithmic series distribution (see Chapter 1, Sec. 4.5) with parameters θ and λ, respectively, so that $\theta = \beta\lambda$.

[Patil and Wani (1965), p. 277]

(2) A distribution is the logarithmic series distribution with a parameter θ iff its moments μ_s are $\mu_1(\theta) = \alpha\theta/(1 - \theta)$, $\mu_{s+2}(\theta) = \alpha\theta c_s(\theta)/(1 - \theta)^{s+2}$ (s = 0, 1, 2, ...), where $\alpha = -1/\log(1 - \theta)$, and

$c_s(\theta)$ are monic polynomials of degrees s in θ given by $c_s(\theta) = \sum^s c(s, i)\theta^i$ $(s = 0, 1, 2, \ldots)$ such that $c(s, i) = (i + 1)c(s - 1, i) + (s - i + 1)c(s - 1, i - 1)$ with $c(0, 0) = 1$ and $c(s, i) = 0$ for $i < 0$.

[Wani (1967), p. 53]

5.3 CHARACTERIZATION OF SOME USEFUL CONTINUOUS DISTRIBUTIONS

5.3.1 NORMAL

(1) Let $X_1, X_2, \ldots, X_n$ be a random sample from a certain distribution and let $L = \sum_1^n a_i X_i$ be a linear statistic. The distribution is normal iff the statistic L is normally distributed.

[Lukacs (1956), p. 198]

(2) Let $X_1, X_2, \ldots, X_n$ be a random sample from a certain distribution and let $\bar{X}$ and S^2 be the sample mean and variance, respectively. A necessary and sufficient condition for the normality of the distribution is the stochastic independence of $\bar{X}$ and S^2.

[Lukacs (1956), p. 200]

(3) Let $X_1, X_2, \ldots, X_n$ be a random sample from a certain distribution. Let $L = \sum_1^n a_i X_i$ $\left(\sum_1^n a_i^2 = 1\right)$ and $S_1^2 = \sum_1^n X_i^2 - L^2$. A necessary and sufficient condition for the normality of the distribution is the stochastic independence of L and S_1^2.

[Kagan et al. (1973), pp. 105-106]

(4) If random variables X and Y are independent, then X + Y and X - Y are independent iff both X and Y have normal distribution with a common variance [Ferguson (1965), p. 256].

(5) Let $X_1, X_2, \ldots, X_n$ be a random sample from a certain distribution and let p be an integer greater than one. Assume that the pth moment of the distribution exists. The distribution is normal iff the k-statistic of order p is independent of $\bar{X}$.

[Lukacs (1956), p. 201]

(6) Let $X_1, X_2, \ldots, X_n$ be a random sample from a nondegenerate distribution, and assume that the second moment exists. Denote by $Q = \sum_{r=1}^{n} \sum_{s=1}^{n} a_{rs} X_r X_s$ such that $B_1 = \sum_1^n a_{rr} \neq 0$, $B_2 = \sum_{r=1}^{n} \sum_{s=1}^{n} a_{rs} = 0$. The distribution is normal iff the statistic Q has constant regression on $\bar{X}$ [Lukacs (1956), p. 205].

(7) Let $X_1, X_2, \ldots, X_n$ be a random sample from a certain distribution. Let $L_1 = \sum_1^n a_i X_i$ and $L_2 = \sum_1^n b_i X_i$ such that $\sum_1^n a_r b_r = 0$ while $\sum_1^n (a_r b_r)^2 \neq 0$. The distribution is normal iff L_1 and L_2 are independently distributed [Lukacs (1956), p. 203].

(8) Let $X_1, X_2, \ldots, X_n$ be a random sample from a certain distribution with finite variance. Let $\delta_k^2 = \sum_1^{n-k} (X_{i+k} - X_i)^2/2(n - k)$ $(k = 1, 2, \ldots, n - 1)$. A necessary and sufficient condition that the distribution is normal is that for any k, δ_k^2 and $\bar{X}$ be independent.
[Geisser (1956), p. 858]

(9) Let $\{F(x - \theta); -\infty < \theta < \infty\}$ be a translation parameter family of absolutely continuous distributions on the real line and the pdf f(x) be lower semi-continuous at x = 0. If for all random samples of sizes two and three, a maximum likelihood estimator of θ is $\bar{X}$, then F is a normal distribution with mean zero [Teicher (1961), p. 1215].

(10) Let $\{F(x/\sigma), \sigma > 0\}$ be a scale parameter family of absolutely continuous distributions with the pdf f(x) satisfying

(a) f is continuous on $(-\infty, \infty)$

(b) $\lim_{y \to 0} [f(\lambda y)/f(y)] = 1$, for all $\lambda > 0$

If for all samples sizes, a maximum likelihood estimator of σ is $[\sum_1^n X_i^2/n]^{1/2}$ then F is the normal distribution with mean zero and variance one [Teicher (1961), p. 1221].

(11) (a) Let $X_1, X_2, \ldots, X_n$ $(n \geq 4)$ be a random sample from a certain distribution. Let $Y = (X_1 - X_2)/S$, where $S^2 = \sum_1^n (X_i - \bar{X})^2/n$. If Y is stochastically independent of the pair $(\bar{X}, S)$, then each X_i has a normal distribution.

(b) Let $X_1, X_2, \ldots, X_n$ $(n \geq 4)$ be a random sample from a certain distribution with location parameter θ $(-\infty < \theta < \infty)$ and a scale parameter $\sigma(\sigma > 0)$. If $(\bar{X}, S^2)$ are sufficient statistics for (θ, σ^2) where $S^2 = \sum_1^n (X_i = \bar{X})^2/n$, then each X_i has a normal distribution.

(c) Let $X_1, X_2, \ldots, X_n$ $(n \geq 2)$ be independent random variables with a common scale parameter. Let F_i, the cdf of X_i, be absolutely continuous wrt Lebesgue measure in a neighborhood of the origin. At the point $x = 0$, let the F_i be nonzero and continuous. Then if $\sum_1^n X_i^2$ is sufficient for the scale parameter, each X_i has a normal distribution with mean zero.

(d) Let $X_1, X_2, \ldots, X_n$ $(n \geq 2)$ be independent nondegenerate random variables with cdf's $F_{X_i}(x) = F_i(x - \theta)$ $(i = 1, 2, \ldots, n)$, $-\infty < \theta < \infty$. A necessary and sufficient condition for $\sum_1^n b_i X_i$, where $\Pi_1^n b_i \neq 0$, to be a sufficient statistic for θ is that each X_i is a normal variable with variance a/b_i for some constant a.

[Kelkar and Matthes (1970), pp. 1086-1088]

(12) Let $X_0, X_1, X_2, \ldots, X_n$ be $(n + 1)$ independent random variables $(n \geq 2)$ satisfying $P(X_k = 0) = 0$ and having distributions symmetrical about zero. A necessary and sufficient condition for X_k to be identically normally distributed with mean zero and common standard derivation σ is that $Y_1, Y_2, \ldots, Y_n$ are independently distributed according to t-distributions with 1, 2, ..., n degrees of freedom, where

$$Y_1 = \frac{X_1\sqrt{1}}{|X_0|}, \quad Y_2 = \frac{X_2\sqrt{2}}{\sqrt{X_0^2 + X_1^2}}, \quad \ldots, \quad Y_n = \frac{X_n\sqrt{n}}{\sqrt{X_0^2 + X_1^2 + \cdots + X_{n-1}^2}}$$

[Kotlarski (1966), p. 603]

(13) Let $X_1, X_2, \ldots, X_n$ be a random sample from a certain distribution. Let $m_p = \sum_1^n (X_i - \bar{X})^p/n$. Suppose that $(p - 1)!$ is not divisibl by $(n - 1)$. Then m_p and $\bar{X}$ are independent iff the distribution is normal [Lukacs and Laha (1964), p. 101].

(14) Let $X_1, X_2, \ldots, X_n$ $(n \geq 3)$ be iid random variables with finite expectation $E(X_i) = 0$, and $E[\bar{X}|(X_1 - \bar{X}), \ldots, (X_n - \bar{X})] = 0$ then the random variables X_i $(i = 1, 2, \ldots, n)$ are normally distributed.

[Kagan et al. (1973), p. 155]

(15) Let $L_1, L_2, \ldots, L_n$ be linearly independent linear functions of the independent random variables $X_1, X_2, \ldots, X_n$ where all the

coefficients in the form L_1 are different from zero. Suppose that $E(X_i) = 0$ for all i. Then the condition $E(L_1|L_2, \ldots, L_n) = 0$ guarantees that the X_i (i = 1, 2, ..., n) are normal random variables provided $n \geq 3$ [Kagan et al. (1973), p. 156].

(16) Let $X_1, X_2, \ldots, X_k$ be independent random variables and a_i, b_i (i = 1, 2, ..., k) be nonzero constants satisfying the conditions $(a_i/b_i) + (a_j/b_j) \neq 0$ for any i, j, $i \neq j$. If the conditional distribution of $\sum_1^k a_i X_i$ given $\sum_1^k b_i X_i$ is symmetric, then the random variables X_i are normal (possibly degenerate). If the characteristic function of X_i is $\exp(itA_j - B_j t^2)$, with A_j real and $B_j \geq 0$, then $\sum_1^k A_i a_i = 0$ and $\sum_1^k B_i a_i b_i = 0$ [Kagan et al. (1973), p. 419].

(17) If, for iid random variables $X_1, X_2, \ldots, X_n$ with $n \geq 2$, the distribution of the statistic $T = \sum_1^n (X_i + a_i)^2$ depends on the a_i's only through $\sum_1^n a_i^2$, where the a_i are real, then the random variables X_i (i = 1, 2, ..., n) are normal [Kagan et al. (1973), p. 453].

(18) (a) The random variable W^2 is chi square with one degree of freedom ($\chi^2(1)$) iff the characteristic function of W satisfies $\phi_W(t) + \phi_W(-t) = 2\exp(-t^2/2)$.

(b) Let X be normally distributed with mean zero and variance one. Let X be independent of Y. Then $W^2 = (aX + bY)^2/(a^2 + b^2)$ for some $a, b \neq 0$ is $\chi^2(1)$ iff Y^2 is $\chi^2(1)$.

(c) Let X and Y be independent with X^2 and Y^2 each distributed as $\chi^2(1)$. Then $W^2 = (aX + bY)^2/(a^2 + b^2)$ is $\chi^2(1)$ for some $a, b \neq 0$ iff at least one of the pair X, Y is normally distributed with mean zero and variance one.

(d) Let X and Y be iid random variables. Then X and Y are normally distributed with mean zero and variance one iff $W_1^2 = (aX + bY)^2/(a^2 + b^2)$, $W_2^2 = (aX - bY)^2/(a^2 + b^2)$ for some $a, b \neq 0$ are $\chi^2_{(1)}$ [Geisser (1973), pp. 492-494].

5.3.2 INVERSE GAUSSIAN

Let $X_1, \ldots, X_n$ be iid random variables and let the expected values of X, X^2, X^{-1} and $(\sum_1^n X_i)^{-1}$ exist and be different from zero.

Then a necessary and sufficient condition that the random variables follow the Inverse Gaussian distribution, with pdf $f(x) = (\lambda/2\pi x^3)^{1/2} \exp\{-\lambda[(x - m)^2/2m^2x]\}$, $x > 0$, is that $Y = \sum_i^n X_i$ and $Z = \sum_1^n (X_i)^{-1} - n^2(Y)^{-1}$ are independently distributed.

[Khatri (1962a), p. 801]

5.3.3 *CAUCHY*

(1) A random variable X has the Cauchy distribution iff the mean of the sample has a Cauchy distribution [Lukacs (1956), p. 198].

(2) Let X be a symmetric random variable and X_i (i = 1, 2, ..., n) be iid. The following two conditions are necessary and sufficient for X to have a Cauchy distribution.

(a) For any real number c and positive integer n, there exist real numbers $a = a(n, c)$ and $b = b(n, c)$ for which $\sum_1^n (X_i + c)^{-1}$ is distributed as $a/(X + b)$.

(b) For some $c \neq 0$ the symmetric random variable $(X_1 + c)^{-1} + (X_2 - c)^{-1}$ is distributed as $a(c)/X$ for some number $a(c)$.

A corollary of this is the following. Let X, X_i (i = 1, 2, ..., be iid random variables. A necessary and sufficient condition that, for any real numbers $a_i \neq 0$, b_i (i = 1, 2, ...) and any positive integer n, there exist real numbers a and b for which $\sum_1^n (a_iX_i + b_i)^{-1}$ has the same distribution as $a/(X + b)$ is that X have the Cauchy distribution [Menon (1966), p. 289].

(3) (a) If for some real a, that is not the tangent of a rational multiple of π, $(1 + aX)/(a - X)$ is distributed the same as X, then X is Cauchy with pdf $f(x) = 1/\pi(1 + x^2)$.

(b) If $\rho^2/(2\rho \sin\theta - X)$ is distributed the same as X, where θ is not a rational multiple of π, then X is Cauchy with pdf $f(x) = \rho\cos\theta/\pi(\rho^2 - 2\rho x \sin\theta + x^2)$ [Williams (1969), pp. 1084, 1085].

(4) If X and Y are iid random variables, then a necessary and sufficient set of conditions for this to be a Cauchy distribution is as follows.

(a) The characteristic function $\phi(t) = E(e^{itX}) = E(e^{itY})$ has a finite nonzero right-hand derivative at $t = 0$, i.e. $\phi'(0) = \lambda \neq 0$.

(b) For any pair of positive real numbers a, b there is a positive real number c (depending on a and b) such that $aX + bY$ has the same distribution as cX (or cY) [Johnson and Kotz (1970a), p. 162].

(5) Let $X_1, X_2, \ldots, X_n$ be iid random variables. Every linear statistic $L = \sum_1^n a_i X_i$ is distributed the same as $\sum_1^n |a_i| X_1$ iff the distribution of X_i is a Cauchy [Lukacs (1956), p. 200].

(6) A necessary and sufficient condition for the random variable X to be Cauchy distributed with cdf $F(x) = (1/2) + (1/\pi)$ arctan x is that for every $-\infty < y < z < \infty$ there is

$$E(2X|y < X \leq z) = \frac{\log\left(\frac{1 + z^2}{1 + y^2}\right)}{\arctan\left(\frac{z - y}{1 + zy}\right)}$$ [Kotlarski (1972), p. 465]

(7) Let $X_1, X_2, \ldots, X_n$ with $n \geq 2$ be nondegenerate iid random variables. If X_i and $\sum_1^n a_i X_i$ are identically distributed then the random variables X_i follow a Cauchy distribution if $\sum_1^n |a_i|$ and at least one pair of the numbers $-\log|a_i|$ $(i \leq i \leq n)$ are mutually incommensurable.

[Kagan et al. (1973), p. 448]

5.3.4 EXPONENTIAL

(1) A necessary and sufficient condition that a random variable has the distribution $F(x) = 1 - \exp(-ax)$ for $x > 0$ and $a > 0$ is that $P\{X > x + y|X > y\} = P(X > x)$ for all x and y, $x > 0$, $y > 0$.

[Shanbhag (1970), p. 1256]

(2) Let X be a nonegative random variable such that $P(X > 0) > 0$. The random variable X has an exponential distribution iff $E(X|X > a) = a + E(X)$ for all $a \geq 0$ [Shanbhag (1970), p. 1256].

(3) Let X, X_1, X_2 be iid random variables with pdf f(x). Then X and $|X_1 - X_2|$ have the same distribution iff for some $\theta > 0$, $f(x) = \theta \exp(-\theta x)$, $x \geq 0$ [Puri and Rubin (1970), p. 2120].

(4) Let $X_{(1;n)}, X_{(2;n)}, \ldots, X_{(n;n)}$ be order statistics from a random sample of size $n \geq 2$ from a population with distribution F such that F(0) = 0. Let $U_1 = X_{(1;n)}$, $U_i = X_{(i;n)} - X_{(1;n)}$ (i = 2, 3, ..., n).

(a) The random variable U_1 and the vector $(U_2, \ldots, U_n)$ are independent iff $F(x) = 1 - \exp(-ax)$ for $x > 0$ and some $a > 0$.

(b) The random variables U_1 and $\sum_1^n U_i$ are independent iff $F(x) = 1 - \exp(-ax)$ for $x > 0$ and some $a > 0$.

(c) The random variables $X_{(i;n)}$ and $X_{(j+1;n)} - X_{(j;n)}$ $(i \leq j \leq n - 1)$ are independent iff $F(x) = 1 - \exp(-ax)$ for $x > 0$ and some $a > 0$ [Govindarajulu (1966b), pp. 133-135].

(5) Suppose F(x) is absolutely continuous and has finite expectation. Let $Y_k = X_{(k;n)} - X_{(k-1;n)}$ $(1 \leq k \leq n)$. The random variable Y_{k+1} $(k \geq 1)$ is independent of the random vector $(Y_1, Y_2, \ldots, Y_k)$ iff F(x) is given by $F(x) = 1 - \exp(-ax + b)$, $x > b/a$.

[Galambos (1972), p. 225]

(6) Let F be an absolutely continuous distribution of the random variable X with $F(\theta) = 0$, $\theta > 0$ and with pdf f(x). Then in order for the statistics $X_{(m+1;n)} - X_{(m;n)}$ and $X_{(m;n)}$ for fixed m $(1 \leq m < n)$ to be independent, it is necessary and sufficient that the random variable X has the pdf $f(x) = (1/\sigma) \exp[-(x - \theta)/\sigma]$, $X > \theta$, $\sigma > 0$.

[Srivastava (1967), p. 414]

(7) Suppose that the random variables X and Y are independent and have absolutely continuous distributions. Then, in order for U = min(X, Y) and V = X - Y to be independent, it is necessary and sufficient that both X and Y have exponential distributions with a common location parameter θ $(f(x) = (1/\sigma) \exp[-(x - \theta)/\sigma]$, $X > \theta)$.

[Ferguson (1964), p. 1204]

(8) If X_1 and X_2 are independent nondegenerate random variables, and if $\min(X_1, X_2)$ and $X_1 - X_2$ are independent then either

(a) both X_1 and X_2 have exponential distributions with common location but possibly different scale parameters or

(b) both X_1 and X_2 have geometric distributions with common location-scale parameters but possible different geometric parameters $(f(x) = (1 - p)p^{(x-\alpha)/\beta}, x = \alpha, \alpha + \beta, \ldots)$.

[Ferguson (1967b), p. 266]

(9) Suppose F does not degenerate at the origin.

(a) If the random variable $nX_{(1;n)}$ is identically distributed as X for some $n \geq 2$ and $E(nX_{(1;n)}) = E(X)$ for the other n's, then F is exponential.

(b) If there exist a real number λ and a positive integer k such that $E(X_{(k;n)}) = \lambda \sum_{j=1}^{k} [1/(n - j + 1)]$ for $n = n_1, n_2, \ldots$, where the n_i are distinct positive integers with $\sum_1^\infty (1/n_i) = \infty$, then F is exponential [Huang (1974), p. 607].

(10) A necessary and sufficient condition that a nonnegative absolutely continuous random variable X has the pdf $f(x) = a^{-1} \exp(-x/a)$, $x > 0$, $a > 0$, is that its kth order statistic $X_{(k;n)}$ can be expressed as $X_{(k;n)} = \sum_1^n [Y_i/(n - i + 1)]$ for any integer k such that $1 \leq k \leq n$, where the Y_i's $(i = 1, 2, \ldots, k)$ are iid as the random variable X.

[Ahsanullah and Rahman (1972), p. 458]

(11) Let X and Y be two mutually independent nonnegative random variables. Also let X + Y admit a pdf given by h(t) for $t \geq 0$. Then $P(X \leq t) - P(X + Y \leq t) = \theta h(t)$ holds for all $t \geq 0$, for some positive constant θ iff Y admits a pdf given by $f(y) = (1/\theta) \exp(-y/\theta)$, $y \geq 0$.

[Puri (1973), p. 62]

(12) If the conditional distribution of X given X + Y = z is the uniform distribution over (0, z) where X and Y are independent nonnegative random variables then both X and Y have the negative exponential distribution with the same scale parameters.

[Patil and Seshadri (1964), p. 290]

(13) Let $\{F(x/\sigma), \sigma > 0\}$ constitute a scale parameter family of absolutely continuous distributions with pdf f(x) satisfying

(a) f(x) is continuous on $(0, \infty)$

(b) $\lim_{y\to 0} [f(\lambda y)/f(y)] = 1$ for all $\lambda > 0$.

If, for all sample sizes, a maximum likelihood estimator of σ is the sample arithmetic mean $\bar{X}$, then F is the exponential distribution with $F(x) = 1 - \exp(-x)$, $x > 0$ [Teicher (1961), p. 1219].

(14) Let $F(x)$ be continuous and the constant coefficients of $L_{km} = \sum_k^m c_i X_{(i)}$ $(k < m \leq n)$ be subject to $\sum_k^m c_i = 0$, $c_k \neq 0$, $c_m \neq 0$. Then the independence of $X_{(k;n)}$ and L_{km} is necessary and sufficient for $F(x) = 1 - \exp(-ax - b)$, $x \geq (-b/a)$ where the numbers $a > 0$ and b are real [Rossberg (1972), p. 114].

(15) A random variable X is negative exponential iff $\mathrm{Var}(X|X > a)$ is constant for all $a > 0$ [Johnson and Kotz (1970a), p. 220].

5.3.5 GAMMA

(1) Let X and Y be two nondegenerate and positive random variables and assume that they are independently distributed. The random variables $U = X + Y$ and $V = X/Y$ are independently distributed iff both X and Y have gamma distributions with the same scale parameter.

[Lukacs (1956), p. 208]

(2) Let $X_1, X_2, \ldots, X_n$ be a random sample from a nondegenerate distribution with a finite second moment. Let $Q = \sum_{r=1}^n \sum_{s=1}^n a_{rs} X_r X_s$ such that $EQ = 0$ and $B_1 = \sum_1^n a_{rr} \neq 0$, $B_2 = \sum_{r=1}^n \sum_{s=1}^n a_{rs} \neq 0$ (a_{rs} are real numbers). The distribution is gamma iff the statistic Q has a constant regression on $S = \sum_1^n X_i$ [Lukacs (1956), p. 205].

(3) Let $X_1, X_2, \ldots, X_n$ be a random sample from a nondegenerate distribution with a finite second moment. Let $S = \sum_1^n X_i$ and $Q = \sum_{r=1}^n \sum_{s=1}^n a_{rs} X_r X_s$ with a_{rs} real numbers. Let $B_1 = \sum_1^n a_{rr}$ and $B_2 = \sum_{r=1}^n \sum_{s=1}^n a_{rs}$ and suppose $B_2 \neq nB_1$. The distribution is gamma iff the statistic Q/S^2 has a constant regression on S.

[Lukacs (1956), p. 207]

(4) Let $X_1, X_2, \ldots, X_n$ be a random sample from a nondegenerate distribution with a finite second moment. The distribution is gamma iff $T = \sum_1^n a_i X_i/S$ and S are independently distributed ($S = \sum_1^n X_i$).

[Lukacs (1956), p. 208]

(5) Let $X_1, X_2, \ldots, X_n$ $(n \geq 3)$ be independent, positive, and in general not identically distributed random variables with EX_i finite for all i. If the regression of $\sum_1^n X_i$ on the vector $(X_2/X_1, \ldots, X_n/X_1)$ is constant, then the X_i have gamma distributions with parameters (α, m_i) for $i = 1, 2, \ldots, n$ and α is the scale parameter.

[Kagan et al. (1973), p. 197]

(6) Let $X_1, X_2, \ldots, X_n$ $(n \geq 3)$ be independent but not necessarily identically distributed random variables such that $E(1/X_i)$ exists for all i, and is nonzero, and further $E(X_1^{-1} + \cdots + X_n^{-1} | (X_2 - X_1), \ldots, (X_n - X_1)) = \text{constant}$. The random variables X_i (or $-X_i$) for all i have gamma distributions with parameters (α_i, m) for all i and $m > 1$, and α is the scale parameter [Kagan et al. (1973), p. 198].

(7) Let $X_1, X_2, \ldots, X_n$ be iid positive random variables. If $E(X_1 \log X_1)$ is finite and $E(a_1X_1 + \cdots + a_nX_n | X_1^{b_1} \cdots X_n^{b_n}) = \text{constant}$, where $\sum a_ib_i = 0$, $|b_n| > \max\{|b_1|, \ldots, |b_{n-1}|\}$ and $a_ib_i/a_nb_n < 0$ for $i = 1, 2, \ldots, n - 1$, then the random variables have a gamma distribution [Kagan et al. (1973), p. 198].

(8) Let $X_1, X_2, \ldots, X_n$ be iid random variables. If $E(1/X_1)$ exists and is nonzero, and $E\left(\sum_1^n a_iX_i^{-1} | \sum_1^n b_iX_i\right) = \text{constant}$, where $\sum a_ib_i = 0$, $|b_n| > \max(|b_1|, \ldots, |b_{n-1}|)$, and $a_ib_i/a_nb_n < 0$ for $i = 1, 2, \ldots, n - 1$, then the random variables X_i (or $-X_i$) have gamma distribution with parameters (α, m) for some $m > 1$, and α is the scale parameter.

[Kagan et al. (1973), p. 199]

(9) The distribution of a random variable X^2 is gamma with parameters α and m where α is a scale parameter, iff the density of X is $g(x) = h(x)|x|^{2m-1} \exp(-\alpha x^2)$, where $h(x) + h(-x) = \text{constant}$ for all x.

[Roberts and Geisser (1966), p. 276]

(10) Let $X_1, X_2, \ldots, X_n$ $(n \geq 2)$ be independent random variables involving a common scale parameter, i.e., $F_{X_i}(x) = F_i(X/\sigma)$, $i = 1, 2, \ldots, n$, $\sigma > 0$. Let X_i^2 be nondegenerate. Then a necessary and sufficient condition for $\sum_1^n X_i^2$ to be sufficient for σ is that each X_i^2

has a gamma distribution with a common scale parameter and that for each i, either $P(X_i > 0) = 1$, or $P(X_i < 0) = 1$, or $P(X_i < -|x|) = cP(X_i > |x|)$ for some constant c [Kelker and Matthes (1970), p. 1087].

5.3.6 WEIBULL

(1) Let $X_1, X_2, \ldots, X_n$ be iid random variables from a Weibull distribution with parameters α, β and γ (i.e., pdf $f(X) = \gamma\beta^{-1}(x - \alpha)^{\gamma-1} \exp[-\beta^{-1}(x - \alpha)^{\gamma}]$, $x \geq \alpha$, $-\infty < \alpha < \infty$, $\beta > 0$, $\gamma > 0$). Then $X_{(1;n)}$ has a Weibull distribution with parameters α, (β/n), γ. Conversely, if $X_{(1;n)}$ has a Weibull distribution with parameters μ, σ and λ, then all X_i have the Weibull distribution with parameters μ, nσ and λ [Dubey (1966), p. 3].

(2) A necessary and sufficient condition for a random variable with support $[0, \infty)$ to be distributed with $F(x) = 1 - \exp\left[-\left(x/x_0\right)^c\right]$ is that $E(X^c | X > y) = y^c + x_0^c$, $c > 0$, $0 \leq y < \infty$.

[Kotlarski (1972), p. 463]

5.3.7 BETA

(1) Let $X_1, X_2, \ldots, X_n$ be iid random variables from a uniform distribution defined over the unit interval, then $X_{(1;n)}$ has the beta distribution with parameters 1 and n (i.e., pdf $f(x) = n(1 - x)^{n-1}$, $0 \leq x \leq 1$). Conversely, if $X_{(1;n)}$ has the uniform distribution over the unit interval, then each X_i has the beta distribution with parameters 1 and 1/n.

(2) Let $X_1, X_2, \ldots, X_n$ be iid random variables from the beta distribution with parameters α and 1 (i.e., pdf $f(x) = \alpha x^{\alpha-1}$, $0 \leq x \leq 1$). Then $X^{\alpha}_{(1;n)}$ has the beta distribution with parameters 1 and n. Conversely, if $X_{(1;n)}$ has the beta distribution with parameters β and 1, then each X_i^{β} has the beta distribution with parameters 1 and 1/n.

[Dubey (1966), pp. 14, 15]

5.3.8 POWER FUNCTION

(1) Let X_1 and X_2 be iid random variables with cdf F(x). Let $Z_1 = X_{(1;2)}/X_{(2;2)}$ and $Z_2 = X_{(2;2)}$. If F(x) is an absolutely continuous distribution with F(0) = 0, then the pdf $f(x) = (m + 1)x^m/b^{m+1}$, $0 \le x \le b$, $m \ge 0$, iff Z_1 and Z_2 are independent [Fisz (1958), p. 65].

(2) Let F be an absolutely continuous cdf and F(0) = 1. Then $X_{(2;n)}/X_{(1;n)}$ and $X_{(1;n)}$ are independent iff $f(x) = AX^a$, $-\infty < b \le x \le 0$. A, a, b are finite real numbers [Galambos (1972), p. 229].

(3) Let $X_1, X_2, \ldots, X_n$ be iid random variables with cdf F(x) as the right continuous distribution on (0, 1).

(a) $X_{(i;n)}/X_{(n;n)}$ (i = 1, 2, ..., n - 1) and $X_{(n;n)}$ are stochastically independent iff $F(x) = x^a$ for some a > 0.

(b) $X_{(m-1;n)}/X_{(m;n)}$ and $X_{(k;n)}$ $(2 \le m \le k \le n)$ are stochastically independent iff $F(x) = x^a$ for some a > 0.

[Govindarajulu (1966b), pp. 134, 135]

(4) (a) Let X be a real-valued random variable with absolutely continuous distribution F(x) on (0, b). Let $Z = X_{(m;n)}/X_{(m+1;n)}$ for fixed m $(1 \le m \le n - 1)$. Then a necessary and sufficient condition that Z and $X_{(m+1;n)}$ be stochastically independent is that $F(x) = (x/b)^c$, c > 0, b is finite.

(b) Let X be a real-valued random variable with absolutely continuous distribution F(x) on the interval $-\infty$ to a, a < 0. Let $Z = X_{(m+1;n)}/X_{(m;n)}$ for fixed m $(1 \le m \le n - 1)$. Then a necessary and sufficient condition that Z and $X_{(m+1;n)}$ be stochastically independent is that $F(x) = (x/a)^c$, $x \le a$, and 1 for x > a, where a is finite and c < 0 [Rogers (1963), pp. 857-858].

(5) A necessary and sufficient condition for a random variable X defined on [0, 1] to be distributed according to $F(X) = x^a$, a > 0, is that $E(X^p|X \le b) = [a/(a + p)]b^p$, $0 < b \le 1$.

[Kotlarski (1972), p. 462]

(6) Let $X_{(1;n)}, X_{(2;n)}, \ldots, X_{(n;n)}$ be order statistics from a continuous distribution F. If $E(X_{(m;n)}|X_{(m+1;n)} = x) = ax - b$, for

some $m < n$, then the distribution F has the following form, to within a shift and a change of scale:

(a) $F(x) = e^x$ for $x < 0$ if $a = 1$

(b) $F(x) = x^\theta$ for $0 < x < 1$ if $0 < a < 1$

(c) $F(x) = (-x)^\theta$ for $x < -1$ if $a > 1$

where $\theta = a/[m(1 - a)]$ [Kagan et al. (1973), p. 446].

5.3.9 *PARETO*

(1) Let X be a random variable with an absolutely continuous distribution $F(x)$, $\theta \le x < \infty$, $\theta > 0$. A necessary and sufficient condition that X follows the Pareto distribution $F(x) = 1 - (\theta/x)^a$, $x \ge \theta$, $a > 0$, is that for some r and s ($1 \le r < s \le n$) the statistics $X_{(r;n)}$ and $X_{(s;n)}/X_{(r;n)}$ are independent [Ahsanullah and Kabir (1973), p. 109].

(2) Let F be an absolutely continuous distribution of a random variable X with $F(x) = 0$ for $x \le k$, $k > 0$. In order that the statistics $X_{(m+1;n)}/X_{(m;n)}$ and $X_{(m;n)}$ for fixed m ($1 \le m \le n - 1$) be independent, it is necessary and sufficient that the random variable X has the Pareto distribution $F(x) = 1 - (k/x)^a$, $x \ge k$, $a > 0$, $k > 0$.

[Malik (1970), p. 115]

(3) Let $X_1, X_2, \ldots, X_n$ be a random sample from a distribution F.

(a) The vector of random variables

$$\left(\frac{X_{(2;n)}}{X_{(1;n)}}, \frac{X_{(3;n)}}{X_{(1;n)}}, \ldots, \frac{X_{(n;n)}}{X_{(1;n)}}\right)$$

and $X_{(1;n)}$ are independent iff $F(x) = 1 - (k/x)^a$, $x \ge k$, $a > 0$.

(b) The random variables $X_{(j+1;n)}/X_{(j;n)}$ and $X_{(i;n)}$, $i \le j$, $1 \le j \le n - 1$, are independent iff $F(x) = 1 - (k/x)^a$, $x \ge k$, $a > 0$.

[Samanta (1972), p. 192]

(4) Let $Y = X - U$, $0 < U < \max(0, X - k)$ and $E(U|X = x) = b(x - k) = a + bx$ where $0 < b < 1$ and $a = -bk$. Then for $E(U|X > y) = \alpha + \beta y$ with $\beta > b > 0$, it is necessary and sufficient that X have a Pareto distribution with cdf $1 - [(k + c)/(x + c)]^\theta$; $x > k$, $\theta > 1$.

[Revankar et al. (1974), p. 600]

(5) Let X be a random variable having an absolutely continuous cdf $F(x)$, $\theta < x < \infty$, $\theta > 0$. A necessary and sufficient condition that X follows the Pareto distribution $F(x) = 1 - (\theta/x)^a$, $x \geq \theta$, is that for some r_1, r_2, and r_3 $(1 \leq r_1 < r_2 < r_3 \leq n)$ the statistics $X_{(r_1;n)}$ and $X_{(r_3;n)}/X_{(r_2;n)}$ are independent [Ahsanullah and Kabir (1974), p. 954].

5.3.10 EXTREME-VALUE

Let $X_1, X_2, \ldots, X_n$ be iid random variables from an extreme-value distribution with parameters α, μ and σ (i.e., pdf $f(x) = \alpha \exp[(x - \mu)/\sigma] \exp\{-\alpha\sigma \exp[(x - \mu)/\sigma]\}$, $-\infty < x < \infty$, $-\infty < \mu < \infty$, $\alpha > 0$, $\sigma > 0$). Then $X_{(1;n)}$ has the extreme-value distribution with parameters $n\alpha$, μ and σ. Conversely, if $X_{(1;n)}$ has an extreme-value distribution with parameters β, γ and δ then each X_i has an extreme-value distribution with parameters β/n, γ and δ [Dubey (1966), pp. 6, 7].

5.3.11 LAPLACE

Let $\{F(x - \theta), -\infty < \theta < \infty\}$ be a family of absolutely continuous distributions on the real line, depending on a location parameter θ. Suppose that the density $f(x) = F'(x)$ is lower semicontinuous at $x = 0$. If the sample median is the maximum likelihood estimator for θ for $n = 4$, then $f(x) = (1/2)a \exp(-a|x|)$ [Kagan et al. (1973), p. 413].

Chapter 6

POINT ESTIMATION

6.1 INTRODUCTION

Point estimation is concerned with inference about the unknown parameter(s) of a distribution from a sample. It provides a single value for each unknown parameter.

6.1.1 *SOME DEFINITIONS*

(1) Statistic. A statistic is a function of observable random variables which does not contain any unknown parameters. A statistic is itself an observable random variable.

(2) Estimator. Any statistic which is used to estimate $\tau(\theta)$, where $\tau(\theta)$ is some function of a parameter θ, is defined to be an estimator of $\tau(\theta)$. The experimentally determined value of the estimator is referred to as the estimate of $\tau(\theta)$.

6.1.2 *UNBIASEDNESS*

An estimator $T = t(X_1, X_2, \ldots, X_n)$ is defined to be an unbiased estimator of $\tau(\theta)$ iff $E(T) = \tau(\theta)$ for all $\theta \in \Omega$ where Ω is the parameter space. An estimator which is not unbiased is called a biased estimator.

The term $E(T) - \tau(\theta)$ is called the bias of the estimator T. For a biased estimator, an estimator is called an asymptotically unbiased estimator of $\tau(\theta)$ iff $\lim_{n\to\infty} E(T) = \tau(\theta)$.

6.1.3 COMMENTS

(1) An unbiased estimator is not unique.

Example:

Uniform: $f(x;\ \theta) = \frac{1}{\theta}$, $0 < x < \theta$

Both $T_1 = [(n + 1)/n]X_{(n;n)}$ and $T_2 = 2\bar{X}$ are unbiased estimators of θ.

(2) An unbiased estimator may not exist.

Examples:

(a) Hypergeometric: $$f(x;\ \theta) = \frac{\binom{m}{x}\binom{\theta - m}{n - x}}{\binom{\theta}{n}};\quad x = 0, 1, 2, \ldots, n,$$

$$\theta = m, m + 1, \ldots$$

No unbiased estimator of θ exists [Wasan (1970), p. 109].

(b) Binomial: $f(x;\ \theta) = \binom{n}{x}\theta^x(1 - \theta)^{n-x}$, $x = 0, 1, 2, \ldots, n$

No unbiased estimator of $1/\theta$ exists (for sample of size 1).

[Mood et al. (1974), p. 330]

(3) An unbiased estimator may be meaningless.

Example:

Poisson: $f(x;\ \theta) = \frac{e^{-\theta}\theta^x}{x!}$, $x = 0, 1, 2, \ldots$

An unbiased estimator of $\tau(\theta) = \exp(-3\theta)$ is $T = (-2)^X$; $\tau(\theta)$ is always positive but T can sometimes be negative.

[Wasan (1970), p. 108]

(4) For every distribution, $\bar{X} = \sum_i^n X_i/n$ is an unbiased estimator of μ and $S^2 = \sum_i^n(X_i - \bar{X})^2/(n - 1)$ is an unbiased estimator of σ^2, provided that σ^2 exists [Kendall and Stuart (1967), p. 5].

(5) An unbiased estimator is not necessarily consistent.

Example:

$$f(x) = \frac{1}{2} \exp[-|x - \theta|], \quad -\infty < x < \infty, \quad -\infty < \theta < \infty$$

An unbiased estimator of θ is $T = (X_{(1;n)} + X_{(n;n)})/2$, but it is not consistent. ($\text{var}(T) = \pi^2/12$.)

[Kendall and Stuart (1958), p. 341]

6.1.4 CONSISTENCY

Consistency is a limiting property of an estimator.

Let $\{T_n\}$, $n = 1, 2, \ldots$, be a sequence of estimators of $\tau(\theta)$, where $T_n = t_n(X_1, X_2, \ldots, X_n)$ is based on a sample of size n. The sequence $\{T_n\}$ is said to be a (mean-squared error) consistent sequence of estimators of $\tau(\theta)$ if $\lim_{n\to\infty} E(T_n - \tau(\theta))^2 = 0$ for all $\theta \in \Omega$.

[Mood et al. (1974), p. 295]

A consistent estimator of $\tau(\theta)$ is T_n, if T_n is an unbiased estimator of $\tau(\theta)$ and $\text{var}(T_n) \to 0$ as $n \to \infty$.

6.1.5 COMMENTS

(1) A consistent estimator may be meaningless.

Example: Let

$$T_n' = \begin{cases} 0 & \text{for } n \le 10^{10} \\ T_n & \text{for } n > 10^{10} \end{cases}$$

If T_n is a consistent estimator then T_n' is also a consistent estimator, but T_n' is meaningless in any practical situation.

[Rao (1973), p. 344]

(2) A consistent estimator is not unique.

Example:

If T_n is a consistent estimator then for fixed a and b, $T_n' = [(n - a)/(n - b)]T_n$ is also consistent.

(3) A consistent estimator is not necessarily unbiased.

Example:

Uniform: $f(x;\ \theta) = \frac{1}{\theta}, \quad 0 < x < \theta$

A consistent estimator of θ is $X_{(n;n)}$, but it is not unbiased.

(4) A consistent estimator with finite mean value must tend to be unbiased in large samples, provided $\lim_{n\to\infty} |E(T_n)| < \infty$.

[Kendall and Stuart (1967), p. 5]

6.1.6 EFFICIENCY

The ratio of the Cramér-Rao lower bound (see Sec. 6.5.3) to the actual variance of any unbiased estimator for a parameter is called the efficiency of that estimator. An estimator with efficiency equal to 1 is called an efficient estimator. If the efficiency of an estimator approaches 1 as the sample size goes to infinity, the estimator is called an asymptotically efficient estimator.

6.2 METHODS OF FINDING ESTIMATORS

6.2.1 MAXIMUM-LIKELIHOOD ESTIMATION

Let $X_1, X_2, \ldots, X_n$ be iid random variables with pdf $f(x;\ \theta)$. Then the likelihood function $L(\theta) = L(\theta;\ x_1, x_2, \ldots, x_n)$ is defined by

$$L(\theta) = \prod_1^n f(x_i;\ \theta)$$

If $\hat{\theta} = \hat{\theta}(x_1, x_2, \ldots, x_n)$ is the value of θ in Ω which maximizes $L(\theta)$ then $\hat{\theta} = \hat{\theta}(X_1, X_2, \ldots, X_n)$ is known as a maximum-likelihood estimator (MLE) of θ.

If the likelihood function contains k parameters, that is, if

$$L(\theta_1, \theta_2, \ldots, \theta_k) = \prod_1^n f(x_i;\ \theta_1, \theta_2, \ldots, \theta_k)$$

then the joint maximum-likelihood estimators are $\hat{\theta}_1 = \hat{\theta}_1(X_1, \ldots, X_n)$, $\hat{\theta}_2 = \hat{\theta}_2(X_1, \ldots, X_n)$, ..., $\hat{\theta}_k = \hat{\theta}_k(X_1, \ldots, X_n)$ of $\theta_1, \theta_2, \ldots, \theta_k$ in Ω which maximize $L(\theta_1, \theta_2, \ldots, \theta_k)$.

6.2.2 *PROPERTIES*

(1) In a single parameter case, if $\hat{\theta}$ exists and is an interior point of Ω and $(\partial L/\partial\theta)$ exists for all $\theta \in \Omega$, then $\hat{\theta}$ is a root of likelihood equation $(\partial L/\partial\theta) = 0$ (or equivalently $\hat{\theta}$ is a root of $(\partial \log L/\partial\theta) = 0$).

(2) A maximum-likelihood estimator is not unique.

Example:

Uniform: $f(x; \theta) = 1, \quad \theta < x < \theta + 1, \quad -\infty < \theta < \infty$

Both $\hat{\theta}_1 = X_{(1;n)}$ and $\hat{\theta}_2 = X_{(n;n)} - 1$ are MLE of θ.

[Zacks (1971), p. 223]

(3) If an estimator attains the Cramér-Rao lower bound (see Sec. 6.5.3), then the likelihood equation has a unique root.

[Wasan (1970), p. 157]

(4) If a single sufficient statistic T exists for a parameter θ, then MLE of θ must be a function of T.

[Kendall and Stuart (1967), p. 36]

(5) *Invariance Property.* Let $\hat{\theta}$ be a MLE of θ. If $\tau(\cdot)$ is a function with a single-valued inverse, then the MLE of $\tau(\theta)$ is $\tau(\hat{\theta})$.

[Mood et al. (1974), p. 284]

(6) Suppose the pdf $f = f(x; \theta)$ satisfies the following regularity conditions.

(a) For almost all x, $(\partial \log f/\partial\theta)$, $(\partial^2 \log f/\partial\theta^2)$, and $(\partial^3 \log f/\partial\theta^3)$ exist for every $\theta \in \Omega$.

(b) For all $\theta \in \Omega$,

$$\left|\frac{\partial f}{\partial\theta}\right| < A_1(x), \quad \left|\frac{\partial^2 f}{\partial\theta^2}\right| < A_2(x), \quad \text{and} \quad \left|\frac{\partial^3 \log f}{\partial\theta^3}\right| < B(x),$$

the functions A_1 and A_2 being integrable over $(-\infty, \infty)$ and $\int_{-\infty}^{\infty} B(x)f(x;\ \theta)\ dx < m$, where m does not depend on θ.

(c) For all $\theta \in \Omega$, the integral $\int_{-\infty}^{\infty} (\partial \log f/\partial\theta)^2 f(x;\ \theta)\ dx$ is finite and positive [Norden (1972), p. 335].

If $\hat{\theta}_n$ is the MLE of θ for a random sample of size n from $f(x;\ \theta)$, which satisfies the above regularity conditions, then $\sqrt{n}(\hat{\theta}_n - \theta)$ is asymptotically normally distributed with mean 0 and variance $1/E[(\partial/\partial\theta) \log f(x;\ \theta)]^2$. Also, $\hat{\theta}_n$ is an asymptotically efficient and consistent estimator of θ.

(7) A MLE need not be consistent.

Example:

$$f(x;\ \theta) = \begin{cases} \theta^x(1-\theta)^{1-x} & \text{if } \theta \text{ is rational} \quad (0 < \theta < 1,\ x = 0, 1) \\ (1-\theta)^x\theta^{1-x} & \text{if } \theta \text{ is irrational} \end{cases}$$

A MLE of θ is $\hat{\theta}_n = \bar{X}$. But

$$\hat{\theta}_n \xrightarrow{\text{a.s.}} \begin{cases} \theta & \text{if } \theta \text{ is rational} \\ 1-\theta & \text{if } \theta \text{ is irrational} \end{cases}$$

Hence $\hat{\theta}_n$ is not a consistent estimator of θ.

[Zacks (1971), pp. 235-236]

(8) The regularity conditions in (6) are not necessary conditions.

Example:

Laplace: $f(x;\ \theta) = \frac{1}{2}\exp\{-|x - \theta|\}$; $-\infty < x < \infty$, $-\infty < \theta < \infty$

For $\theta = x$, $(\partial/\partial\theta)f(x;\ \theta)$ does not exist. Also $(\partial^2/\partial\theta^2) \log f(x, \theta) = 0$ a.s. Thus condition (a) in (6) is not satisfied. Nevertheless, the MLE of θ, the sample median, is an asymptotically normal and efficient estimator [Zacks (1971), p. 243].

(9) A MLE may not be unbiased.

Example:

Uniform: $f(x;\ \theta) = \frac{1}{\theta}$, $0 < x < \theta$

A MLE of θ is $\hat{\theta}_n = X_{(n;n)}$, but it is not unbiased, since $E(X_{(n;n)}) = \theta[n/(n+1)]$.

6.2.3 *METHOD-OF-MOMENTS*

Let $X_1, X_2, \ldots, X_n$ be iid random variables with pdf $f(x; \theta_1, \theta_2, \ldots, \theta_k)$ having k parameters $\theta_1, \theta_2, \ldots, \theta_k$. Let $\mu_r'(\theta_1, \theta_2, \ldots, \theta_k) = \mu_r' = EX^r$ be the rth population moment (if it exists) and let $M_r' = \sum_1^n X_i^r/n$ be the rth sample moment. Form the k equations,

$$M_r' = \mu_r'(\theta_1, \theta_2, \ldots, \theta_k), \quad r = 1, 2, \ldots, k$$

in the k variables $\theta_1, \theta_2, \ldots, \theta_k$, and let $\hat{\theta}_1, \hat{\theta}_2, \ldots, \hat{\theta}_k$ be the solution of this system of equations (if there is a unique solution). Then $(\hat{\theta}_1, \hat{\theta}_2, \ldots, \hat{\theta}_k)$, where $\hat{\theta}_j$ estimates θ_j, is the method-of-moments estimator of $(\theta_1, \theta_2, \ldots, \theta_k)$ [Mood et al. (1974), p. 274].

6.2.4 *COMMENTS*

(1) Method-of-moments estimators are not uniquely defined.

[Mood et al. (1974), p. 276]

(2) Under suitable conditions, this method provides consistent estimators but they are generally not efficient. The method is not applicable when the population moments do not exist.

[Rao (1973), p. 351]

(3) Method-of-moment estimators may not be functions of sufficient or complete statistics.

Example:

Uniform: $f(x; \theta_1, \theta_2) = \dfrac{1}{2\theta_2}; \quad \theta_1 - \theta_2 < x < \theta_1 + \theta_2, \ \theta_2 > 0$

Method-of-moment estimators for (θ_1, θ_2) are $(\bar{X}, \sqrt{3\sum(X_i - \bar{X})^2/n})$, but sufficient and complete statistics are $(X_{(1;n)}, X_{(n;n)})$.

6.3 SUFFICIENT STATISTICS

"A sufficient statistic contains all the relevant information in a sample."

6.3.1 EQUIVALENT DEFINITIONS OF SUFFICIENCY

(1) A Single Sufficient Statistic. Let $X_1, X_2, \ldots, X_n$ be iid random variables with pdf $f(x; \theta)$, where θ may be a vector.

(a) A statistic $T = t(X_1, X_2, \ldots, X_n)$ is a sufficient statistic iff the conditional distribution of $X_1, X_2, \ldots, X_n$ given $T = t$ does not depend on θ for any value t of T.

(b) A statistic $T = t(X_1, X_2, \ldots, X_n)$ is defined to be a sufficient statistic iff the conditional distribution of S given T does not depend on θ for any statistic $S = s(X_1, X_2, \ldots, X_n)$.

[Mood et al. (1974), pp. 301, 306]

(2) Jointly Sufficient Statistics. Let $X_1, X_2, \ldots, X_n$ be iid random variables with pdf $f(x; \theta)$. The statistics $T_1, T_2, \ldots, T_r$ are defined to be jointly sufficient iff the conditional distribution of $X_1, X_2, \ldots, X_n$ given $T_1 = t_1, T_2 = t_2, \ldots, T_r = t_r$ does not depend on θ.

[Mood et al. (1974), p. 306]

(3) Minimal Sufficient Statistics. A set of jointly sufficient statistics is defined to be minimal sufficient iff it is a function of every other set of sufficient statistics.

[Mood et al. (1974), p. 312]

6.3.2 COMMENTS

(1) A single sufficient statistic does not always exist.

Example:

Uniform: $f(x; \theta) = \frac{1}{\theta}; \quad k\theta \le x \le (k + 1)\theta, \quad k > 0$

No single sufficient statistic exists for θ. Here $(X_{(1;n)}, X_{(n;n)})$ is jointly sufficient for θ [Kendall and Stuart (1967), p. 30].

(2) If $T_1, T_2, \ldots, T_r$ is a set of jointly sufficient statistics, then any set of one-to-one functions or transformations of $T_1, T_2, \ldots, T_r$ is also jointly sufficient [Mood et al. (1974), p. 307].

(3) Let $X_1, X_2, \ldots, X_n$ be iid random variables from a continuous distribution. Then the set of order statistics $(X_{(1;n)}, X_{(2;n)}, \ldots, X_{(n;n)})$ from $f(x; \theta)$, is sufficient for θ [Lehmann (1959), p. 48].

(4) No other sufficient statistic condenses the data more than a minimal sufficient statistic.

6.3.3 FACTORIZATION CRITERION

(1) Single Sufficient Statistic. Let $X_1, X_2, \ldots, X_n$ be iid random variables with pdf $f(x; \theta)$, where θ may be a vector. A statistic $T = t(X_1, X_2, \ldots, X_n)$ is sufficient iff the joint density of $X_1, X_2, \ldots, X_n$, which is $\prod_1^n f(x_i; \theta)$, factors as

$$\prod_1^n f(x_i; \theta) = g[t(x_1, x_2, \ldots, x_n); \theta]h(x_1, x_2, \ldots, x_n)$$

where the function $h(x_1, x_2, \ldots, x_n)$ is nonnegative and does not involve θ, and the function $g(t(x_1, \ldots, x_n); \theta)$ is nonnegative and depends on $X_1, X_2, \ldots, X_n$ only through the function $t(X_1, X_2, \ldots, X_n)$ [Mood et al. (1974), p. 307].

(2) Joint Sufficient Statistic Let $X_1, X_2, \ldots, X_n$ be iid random variables with pdf $f(x; \theta)$, where θ may be a vector. A set of statistics $T_1 = t_1(X_1, X_2, \ldots, X_n), \ldots, T_r = t_r(X_1, X_2, \ldots, X_n)$ is jointly sufficient iff the joint density $\prod_1^n f(x_i; \theta)$ factors as

$$\prod_1^n f(x_i; \theta) = g[t_1(x_1, x_2, \ldots, x_n), \ldots, t_r(x_1, x_2, \ldots, x_n); \theta] \times h(x_1, x_2, \ldots, x_n)$$

where the function $h(\cdot)$ is nonnegative and does not involve the parameter θ, and the function $g(\cdot)$ is nonnegative and depends on $x_1, x_2, \ldots, x_n$ only through the functions $t_1, \ldots, t_r$.

[Mood et al, (1974), p. 307]

6.3.4 SOME USEFUL RESULTS

(1) If $f(x; \theta)$ belong to the regular case of a one-parameter exponential family (see Chapter 4), then $\sum_1^n T(X_i)$ is a minimal sufficient statistic for θ. If $f(x; \theta_1, \theta_2, \ldots, \theta_k)$ belongs to the regular case

of k-parameter exponential family (see Chapter 4), then $\sum_1^n T_1(X_i)$, $\sum_1^n T_2(X_i)$, ..., $\sum_1^n T_k(X_i)$ are minimal sufficient statistics for θ_1, θ_2, ..., θ_k [Mood et al. (1974), pp. 313-314].

(2) Sufficient statistics when the range of a distribution depends on the parameters are as follows. Let $f(x;\ \theta)$ be factored as $f(x;\ \theta) = g(x)/h(\theta)$.

(a) Given $f(x;\ \theta)$, $a(\theta) \le x \le b$, where $a(\theta)$ is monotone in θ, then $X_{(1;n)}$ is sufficient for θ.

(b) Given $f(x;\ \theta)$, $a \le x \le b(\theta)$, where $b(\theta)$ is monotone in θ, then $X_{(n;n)}$ is sufficient for θ.

(c) Given $f(x;\ \theta)$, $a(\theta) \le x \le b(\theta)$, and if $a(\theta)$ and $b(\theta)$ are both increasing (or decreasing) functions of θ, then no single sufficient statistic exists, but both $X_{(1;n)}$ and $X_{(n;n)}$ are jointly sufficient for θ.

(d) Given $f(x;\ \theta)$, $a(\theta) \le x \le b(\theta)$, and if $a(\theta)$ is an increasing and $b(\theta)$ is a decreasing function of θ, then $T = \min\{a^{-1}(X_{(1;n)}), b^{-1}(X_{(n;n)})\}$ is sufficient for θ.

(e) Given $f(x;\ \theta)$, $a(\theta) \le x \le b(\theta)$, and if $a(\theta)$ is a decreasing and $b(\theta)$ is an increasing function of θ, then $T = \max\{a^{-1}(X_{(1;n)}), b^{-1}(X_{(n;n)})\}$ is sufficient for θ [Kendall and Stuart (1967), p. 29].

(3) The most general continuous distribution for which the MLE for a parameter θ is the geometric mean of the sample is

$$f(x;\ \theta) = \left(\frac{x}{\theta}\right)^{\theta A'(\theta)} \exp\{A(\theta) + B(x)\}$$

The most general continuous distribution for which the MLE for a parameter θ is the harmonic mean of the sample is

$$f(x;\ \theta) = \exp[\frac{1}{x}\{\theta A'(\theta) - A(\theta)\} - A'(\theta) + B(x)]$$

In each case the MLE of θ is also sufficient for θ.

[Kendall and Stuart (1967), p. 68]

6.4 COMPLETE FAMILIES AND COMPLETE STATISTICS

6.4.1 DEFINITIONS

Let $X_1, X_2, \ldots, X_n$ be iid random variables with pdf $f(x; \theta)$, $\theta \in \Omega$, and let $T = t(X_1, X_2, \ldots, X_n)$ be a statistic. The family of densities of T is defined to be complete iff $E[h(T)] \equiv 0$, for all $\theta \in \Omega$, implies that $P[h(T) = 0] \equiv 1$, for all $\theta \in \Omega$, where $h(T)$ is a statistic. The statistic T is said to be complete iff its family of densities is complete. If the above hold for all bounded h, then the family of densities of T is called boundedly complete.

For iid random variables $X_1, X_2, \ldots, X_n$, with pdf $f(x; \theta_1, \theta_2, \ldots, \theta_k)$, let $(T_1, T_2, \ldots, T_m)$ be a set of statistics. Then $T_1, T_2, \ldots, T_m$ are defined to be jointly complete iff $Eh(T_1, T_2, \ldots, T_m) \equiv 0$, for all $\theta \in \Omega$, implies that $P[h(T_1, T_2, \ldots, T_m) = 0] \equiv 1$, for all $\theta \in \Omega$, where $h(T_1, T_2, \ldots, T_m)$ is a statistic.

[Mood et al. (1974), pp. 324, 354]

6.4.2 COMMENTS

(1) The statistic T is complete iff the only unbiased estimator of 0 that is a function of T is the statistic that is identically 0 with probability 1.

Example:

Bernoulli: $f(x; \theta) = \theta^x(1 - \theta)^{1-x}$; $x = 0, 1$, $0 < \theta < 1$

Here, $T = (X_1 - X_2)$ is not complete since $E(T) = 0$ and $X_1 - X_2$ is not zero with probability 1 [Mood et al. (1974), p. 324].

(2) A consequence of the completeness of a statistic T is that only one function of that statistic can have a given expected value. Completeness thus confers a uniqueness property upon an estimator.

[Kendall and Stuart (1967), p. 190]

(3) Bounded completeness implies minimal sufficiency but the minimal sufficiency does not imply bounded completeness.

Examples:

(a) Two Normal Distributions. Let X_i ($i = 1, 2, \ldots, m$) and Y_i ($i = 1, 2, \ldots, n$) be independently normally distributed with the same mean θ and variances σ_1^2 and σ_2^2, respectively. Then $T_1 = (\bar{X}, S^2, \bar{Y}, T^2)$ is minimal sufficient but not boundedly complete, where $S^2 = \sum_1^n [(X_i - \bar{X})^2/n]$ and $T^2 = \sum_1^n [(Y_i - \bar{Y})^2/n]$.

(b) Let $P(X = -1) = \theta$, $P(X = x) = (1 - \theta)^2\theta^x$; $x = 0, 1, \ldots,$ $0 < \theta < 1$. Then X is minimal sufficient for θ but it is not complete ($E(X) = 0$) [Rao (1973), p. 379].

(4) Let $X_1, X_2, \ldots, X_n$ be iid random variables from a continuous distribution. Then the set of order statistics $(X_{(1;n)}, \ldots, X_{(2;n)})$ is complete [Lehmann (1959), p. 133].

(5) If T is complete it is also boundedly complete. The converse is not true.

Example:

$$f(x;\ \theta) = \begin{cases} \theta & \text{if } x = -1 \\ (1 - \theta)^2\theta^x & \text{if } x = 0, 1, 2, \ldots \end{cases}, \quad 0 < \theta < 1$$

Here, X is a boundedly complete (sufficient) statistic for θ but it is not a complete (sufficient) statistic for θ.

[Ferguson (1967), p. 137]

(6) There cannot be more than one boundedly complete sufficient statistic for a parameter [Kendall and Stuart (1967), p. 194].

(7) If T is a boundedly complete sufficient statistic for θ, and U is a minimal sufficient statistic for θ, then T is equivalent to U, except possibly for a zero-measure set.

[Kendall and Stuart (1967), p. 194]

6.4.3 SOME USEFUL RESULTS

(1) If $f(x;\ \theta)$ belongs to the regular case of one-parameter exponential family (see Chapter 4, Sec. 2), then $\sum_1^n T(X_i)$ is a complete and minimal sufficient statistic. If $f(x;\ \theta_1, \theta_2, \ldots, \theta_k)$ belongs to a regular case of a k-parameter exponential family (see Chapter 4,

Sec. 2), then $(\sum_1^n T_1(X_i), \sum_1^n T_2(X_i), \ldots, \sum_1^n T_k(X_i))$ is jointly complete and sufficient [Mood et al. (1974), pp. 326, 355].

(2) Completeness for distributions which have ranges depending on θ is as follows. (Let $f(x; \theta) = g(x)/h(\theta)$.)

(a) If a single terminal of $f(x; \theta)$ is a function of θ, the corresponding extreme order-statistic is complete and sufficient.

(b) If both terminals of $f(x; \theta)$ are functions of θ, and the upper terminal $b(\theta)$ is a monotone decreasing function of the lower terminal θ, then $T = \min\{X_{(1;n)}, b^{-1}(X_{(n;n)})\}$ is complete and sufficient for θ [Kendall and Stuart (1967), pp. 191-192].

(3) If T is complete for θ, then any statistic T_1 depending on x only through T is also complete for θ [Wasan (1970), p. 58].

6.5 UNIFORMLY MINIMUM-VARIANCE UNBIASED ESTIMATOR (UMVUE)

6.5.1 *DEFINITION*

Let $X_1, X_2, \ldots, X_n$ be iid random variables with pdf $f(x; \theta)$. An estimator $T = t(X_1, X_2, \ldots, X_n)$ of $\tau(\theta)$ is defined to be a uniformly minimum-variance unbiased estimator (UMVUE) of $\tau(\theta)$ iff

(a) T is unbiased

(b) $\mathrm{var}(T) \leq \mathrm{var}(S)$ for any other unbiased estimator $S = s(X_1, X_2, \ldots, X_n)$ of $\tau(\theta)$ for all $\theta \in \Omega$ [Mood et al. (1974), p. 315].

6.5.2 *COMMENTS*

(1) A UMVUE may not exist even though an unbiased estimator does exist.

Examples:

(a) Let $P(X = -1) = \theta$ and $P(X = n) = (1 - \theta)^2\theta^n$, $n = 0, 1, 2, \ldots$, $0 < \theta < 1$. No UMVUE of θ exists even though unbiased estimators of θ exist. For example, T = 1 if x = -1 and T = 0, otherwise, is an unbiased estimator of θ. Also T = 1 if x = 0 and T = 0, otherwise, is a UMVUE of $(1 - \theta)^2$ for all θ [Rao (1973), p. 379].

(b) Uniform: $f(x; \theta) = 1, \theta < x < \theta + 1$

No UMVUE for θ exists but $\bar{X} - (1/2)$ is an unbiased estimator of θ [Mood et al. (1974), p. 330].

(2) (a) The correlation between a UMVUE and any unbiased estimator is nonnegative.

(b) If there are two unbiased estimators with the same minimum variance, their correlation coefficient is unity; that is, they are the same except for a set of samples of probability measure zero.

(c) If T_1, T_2 are UMVUE's of $g_1(\theta)$, $g_2(\theta)$, then $b_1T_1 + b_2T_2$ is a UMVUE for $b_1g_1(\theta) + b_2g_2(\theta)$ when b_1 and b_2 are fixed constants.

6.5.3 SOME USEFUL RESULTS

(1) Cramér-Rao Inequality. Let $X_1, X_2, \ldots, X_n$ be a random sample from $f(x; \theta)$, $\theta \in \Omega$. Assume Ω is a subset of the real line. Let $T = t(X_1, X_2, \ldots, X_n)$ be an unbiased estimator of $\tau(\theta)$. Assume $f(x; \theta)$ satisfies the following regularity conditions.

(a) $\frac{\partial}{\partial\partial} \log f(x; \theta)$ exists for all x and all θ

(b) $$\frac{\partial}{\partial\theta} \int \cdots \int \prod_1^n f(x_i; \theta)\, dx_1, \ldots, dx_n = \int \cdots \int \frac{\partial}{\partial\theta} \prod_1^n f(x_i; \theta)\, dx_1, \ldots, dx_n$$

(c) $$\frac{\partial}{\partial\theta} \int \cdots \int t(x_1, x_2, \ldots, x_n) \prod_1^n f(x_i; \theta)\, dx_1, \ldots, dx_n = \int \cdots \int t(x_1, x_2, \ldots, x_n) \frac{\partial}{\partial\theta} \prod_1^n f(x_i; \theta)\, dx_1, \ldots, dx_n$$

(d) $0 < E[\frac{\partial}{\partial\theta} \log f(X; \theta)]^2 < \infty$ for all θ in Ω

Then

$$\text{var}(T) \geq \frac{(\tau'(\theta))^2}{nE\left[\frac{\partial}{\partial\theta} \log f(X; \theta)\right]^2}$$ [Mood et al. (1974), pp. 315-316]

(2) Comments

(a) If an unbiased estimator of $\tau(\theta)$ whose variance coincides with the right side of the inequality for var(T) (known as the Cramér-Rao lower bound) can be found then this estimator is an UMVUE.

The Cramér-Rao lower bound becomes equality iff $(\partial/\partial\theta) \log[\prod_1^n f(x_i; \theta)] = k(\theta, n)[T - \tau(\theta)]$. Thus, if there exists an estimator $T = t(X_1, X_2, \ldots, X_n)$ such that this condition holds, then T is sufficient and is the UMVUE of $\tau(\theta)$, with $\text{var}(T) = |\tau'(\theta)/k(\theta, n)|$ [Mood et al. (1974), p. 318].

[Kendall and Stuart (1967), pp. 10, 24]

(b) Under certain assumptions involving the existence of second derivatives and the validity of interchanging the order of differentiations and integrations,

$$E\left[\frac{\partial}{\partial\theta} \log f(X; \theta)\right]^2 = -E\left[\frac{\partial^2}{\partial\theta^2} \log f(X; \theta)\right]$$

[Mood et al. (1974), p. 320]

(c) A UMVUE may not attain the Cramér-Rao lower bound.

Example:

$$\text{Poisson:} \quad f(x; \theta) = \frac{e^{-\theta}\theta^x}{x!}; \quad x = 0, 1, 2, \ldots, \theta > 0$$

A statistic $T_n = \sum_1^n X_i$ is complete and sufficient for θ. The UMVUE of $e^{-\theta}$ is $[1 - (1/n)]^{T_n}$, with variance $= e^{-2\theta}(e^{\theta/n} - 1)$. The Cramér-Rao lower bound for $[1 - (1/n)]^{T_n}$ is $e^{-2\theta}(n/\theta)$.

[Zacks (1971), p. 188]

(d) If an unbiased estimator has the Cramér-Rao lower bound as its variance, it must be a sufficient statistic for the parameter.

[Hogg and Craig (1970), p. 250]

(3) Rao-Blackwell Theorem. Let $X_1, X_2, \ldots, X_n$ be iid random variables with pdf $f(x; \theta)$, and let $S_1 = s_1(X_1, X_2, \ldots, X_n), \ldots, S_k = s_k(X_1, X_2, \ldots, X_n)$ be a set of jointly sufficient statistics. Let the statistic $T_1 = t_1(X_1, X_2, \ldots, X_n)$ be an unbiased estimator of $\tau(\theta)$. Define T by $T = E[T_1|S_1, S_2, \ldots, S_k] = t(s_1, s_2, \ldots, s_k)$.

Then

(a) T is an unbiased estimator of $\tau(\theta)$.

(b) $\text{var}(T) \leq \text{var}(T_1)$ for every θ, and $\text{var}(T) < \text{var}(T_1)$ for some θ unless T is equal to T_1 with probability 1.

[Mood et al. (1974), p. 321]

What the theorem says is that, given an unbiased estimator, another unbiased estimator that is a function of sufficient statistics can be obtained and it will not have larger variance.

(4) Let U_g be the class of all unbiased estimators of $g(\theta)$, and U_0 be the class of all functions with zero expectation. A necessary and sufficient condition that an estimator $T \in U_g$ has minimum variance at the value $\theta = \theta_0$ is that $\text{cov}(T, S|\theta_0) = 0$ for every $S \in U_0$ such that $\text{var}(S|\theta_0) < \infty$ provided $\text{var}(T|\theta_0) < \infty$. Also, T is called locally MVUE of θ at θ_0.

If we restrict estimators to a particular class of functions G, such as the class of linear or continuous functions, then besides being unbiased, the necessary and sufficient condition is $E(TS|\theta_0) = 0$ for all $S \in U_0 \cap G$, and $\text{var}(S|\theta_0) < \infty$ [Rao (1973), pp. 317-318].

(5) Lehmann-Scheffé Theorem. Let $X_1, X_2, \ldots, X_n$ be iid random variables with pdf $f(x; \theta)$. If $S = s(X_1, X_2, \ldots, X_n)$ is a complete sufficient statistic and if $T = t(s)$, a function of S, is an unbiased estimator of $\tau(\theta)$, then T is the UMVUE of $\tau(\theta)$.

[Mood et al. (1974), p. 326]

(6) The most general form of distribution, differentiable in θ, for which the MLE of θ is the arithmetic mean $\bar{X}$ is $f(x; \theta) = \exp\{A(\theta) + A'(\theta)(x - \theta) + B(x)\}$, and $\bar{X}$ is a sufficient statistic for θ with the Cramér-Rao lower bound equal to $\{nA''(\theta)\}^{-1}$.

[Kendall and Stuart (1967), p. 67]

(7) Let $X_1, X_2, \ldots, X_n$ be a random sample from a distribution $F(x; \theta)$, where θ may be a vector. Let $T = t(X_1, X_2, \ldots, X_n)$ be a scalar or vector statistic sufficient and complete for θ. Then the conditional distribution function of X_1 given T, $\phi(a, T) = P(X_1 \leq a|T)$ is the UMVUE of $F(a; \theta)$, where a is a known constant.

[Patil and Wani (1966), p. 39]

(8) Let $X_1, X_2, \ldots, X_n$ be iid random variables having a density $f(x;\ \theta) = k_1(\theta)h_1(x);\ a < \theta \leq x < b,\ -\infty < a < b < \infty$. Let $g(\theta)$ be an absolutely continuous function over (a, b). Then the UMVUE of $g(\theta)$ is $g(T_1) - [g'(T_1)/nk_1(T_1)h_1(T_1)]$, where $T_1 = X_{(1;n)}$.

[Zacks (1971), p. 137]

(9) Let $X_1, X_2, \ldots, X_n$ be iid random variables having a density $f(x;\ \theta) = k_2(\theta)h_2(x);\ a < x \leq \theta \leq b,\ -\infty \leq a < b \leq \infty$. Let $g(\theta)$ be an absolutely continuous function over (a, b). Then the UMVUE of $g(\theta)$ is $g(T_2) + [g'(T_2)/nk_2(T_2)h_2(T_2)]$, where $T_2 = X_{(n;n)}$.

[Zacks (1971), p. 139]

6.6 COMPLETE SUFFICIENT STATISTICS AND UMVUE'S (DISCRETE)

In the following, several useful univariate parametric families of distributions are identified as being complete, boundedly complete, or not complete. Complete sufficient statistics and UMVUE's for parameters of each of these families, when convenient and possible, are listed. The listing is by no means exhaustive. Statistics are based on a random sample of size n, and limits for summation $\sum$ are from 1 to n. A family of probability functions is denoted by $f = f(x;\ \theta),\ \theta \in \Omega$, where the set Ω is the parameter space. Most of the following results are from a survey paper by Patel (1973).

6.6.1 BINOMIAL

$$f(x;\ p) = \binom{N}{x}p^x q^{N-x};\ x = 0, 1, 2, \ldots, N,\ q = 1 - p,\ 0 \leq p \leq 1$$

(1) f is complete wrt p.

(2) $T = \sum X_i$ is complete and sufficient for p.

(3) $\dfrac{T}{n}$ is UMVUE for $\mu = Np$.

$\dfrac{T}{Nn}$ is UMVUE for p.

$\dfrac{T(T - 1)}{Nn(Nn - 1)}$ is UMVUE for p^2.

$\dfrac{T(Nn - T)}{n(Nn - 1)}$ is UMVUE for $\sigma^2 = Npq$.

(4) The UMVUE for $P[a < x < b]$ (a and b known) is

$$\sum_{a<k<b} \frac{\binom{N}{k}\binom{N(n - 1)}{T - k}}{\binom{Nn}{T}} \qquad \text{[Johnson and Kotz (1969), p. 58]}$$

(5) If

$$f(x;\ \theta) = \binom{\theta}{x}\left(\frac{1}{2}\right)^{\theta};\ x = 0, 1, 2, \ldots, \theta,\ \theta = 0, 1, 2, \ldots$$

then $T = X$ is complete and sufficient for θ, and T is UMVUE for $\mu = \theta/2$ [Arnold (1972), p. 35].

6.6.2 POISSON

$$f(x;\ \theta) = \frac{e^{-\theta}\theta^{x}}{x!}\ ;\ x = 0, 1, 2, \ldots,\ \theta > 0$$

(1) f is complete wrt θ.

(2) $T = \sum X_i$ is complete and sufficient for θ.

(3) T/n is UMVUE for $\mu = \sigma^2 = \theta$.

The UMVUE of θ^r (r known) is

$$\begin{cases} 0 & \text{if } T < r \\ \dfrac{T!}{(T - r)!\,n^r} & \text{if } T \geq r \end{cases} \qquad \text{[Zacks (1971), p. 110]}$$

(4) The UMVUE for $P[a < x < b]$ (a and b known) is

$$\sum_{a<k<b} \binom{T}{k}\left(\frac{1}{n}\right)^{k}\left(1 - \frac{1}{n}\right)^{T-k} \qquad \text{[Johnson and Kotz (1969), p. 95]}$$

6.6.3 *NEGATIVE BINOMIAL*

$$f(x;\ p,\ r) = \binom{r + x - 1}{x} p^r (1 - p)^x;\ x = 0, 1, 2, \ldots, r > 0, \quad 0 \le p \le 1$$

(When r = 1, f is known as the geometric distribution.)

(1) f is complete wrt p (r known).

(2) $T = \sum X_i$ is complete and sufficient for p (r known).

(3) $\dfrac{(n - 1)}{(n + T - 1)}$ is UMVUE for p (r = 1)

$\dfrac{T}{nr}$ is UMVUE for $\mu = \dfrac{r(1 - p)}{p}$ (r known).

$\dfrac{(n + T)T}{(n + 1)n}$ is UMVUE for $\sigma^2 = \dfrac{(1 - p)}{p^2}$ (r = 1).

[Guttman (1958), pp. 566-567]

(4) The UMVUE for f(k; p, r) (k and r known) is

$$\frac{\binom{r + k - 1}{k}\binom{nr - r + T - k - 1}{T - k}}{\binom{nr + T - 1}{T}}$$ [Patil (1963a), p. 1055]

6.6.4 *HYPERGEOMETRIC*

$$f(x;\ \theta) = \frac{\binom{\theta}{x}\binom{N - \theta}{n - x}}{\binom{N}{n}};\ x = 0, 1, 2, \ldots, \theta = 0, 1, 2, \ldots, N$$

(1) f is complete wrt θ [Lehmann and Scheffé (1950), p. 315].

(2) T = X is complete and sufficient for θ for one sample.

(3) T is UMVUE for $\mu = \frac{n}{N}\theta$.

6.6.5 LOGARITHMIC SERIES

$$f(x;\ \theta) = -\frac{1}{\log(1-\theta)}\frac{\theta^x}{x};\ x = 1, 2, \ldots,\ 0 < \theta < 1$$

(1) f is complete wrt θ.

(2) $T = \sum X_i$ is complete and sufficient for θ.

(3) $\frac{T}{n}$ is UMVUE for $\mu = -\frac{1}{\log(1-\theta)}\left(\frac{\theta}{1-\theta}\right)$.

(4) The UMVUE of $f(k;\ \theta)$ (k known) is

$$\left[\frac{T!}{nk(T-k)!}\right]\left[\frac{|S_{T-k}^{n-1}|}{|S_T^n|}\right]$$

where S_T^n is the Stirling number of the first kind (see Chapter 10, Sec. 7) [Patil (1963a), p. 1056].

6.6.6 UNIFORM

$$f(x;\ N) = \frac{1}{N};\ x = 1, 2, \ldots, N,\ N = 1, 2, \ldots$$

(1) f is complete wrt N.

(2) $T = x_{(n;n)}$ is complete and sufficient for N.

[Wasan (1970), p. 60]

(3) $T_1 = \frac{T^{n+1} - (T-1)^{n+1}}{T^n - (T-1)^n}$ is UMVUE for N [Wasan (1970), p. 112].

$\frac{T_1 + 1}{2}$ is UMVUE for $\mu = \frac{N+1}{2}$.

6.6.7 GENERALIZED POWER SERIES

$$f(x;\ \nu,\ \lambda) = \frac{a(x)\lambda^x}{h(\nu,\ \lambda)},\quad x = \nu,\ \nu + 1,\ \ldots$$

(1) Let $T_1 = X_{(1;n)}$ and $T_2 = \sum X_i$. Then, (T_1, T_2) is jointly complete and sufficient for (ν, λ) [Park (1973), pp. 395-396].

(2) The UMVUE of λ is

$$\frac{g_n(T_1,\ T_2 - 1) - g_n(T_1 + 1,\ T_2 - 1)}{g_n(T_1,\ T_2) - g_n(T_1 + 1,\ T_2)} \qquad \text{[Park (1973), p. 396]}$$

The UMVUE of ν is

$$T_1 - \frac{g_n(T_1 + 1,\ T_2)}{g_n(T_1,\ T_2) - g_n(T_1 + 1,\ T_2)} \qquad \text{[Park (1973), p. 396]}$$

where $g_n(\nu, t)$ is defined by

$$[h(\nu,\ \lambda)]^n = \sum_{t=\nu n}^{\infty} \lambda^t g_n(\nu,\ t)$$

6.7 COMPLETE SUFFICIENT STATISTICS AND UMVUE'S (CONTINUOUS)

In the following, several useful univariate parametric families of distributions are identified as being complete, boundedly complete, or not complete. Complete sufficient statistics and UMVUE's for parameters of each of these families, when convenient and possible, are given. This listing is by no means exhaustive. Statistics are based on a random sample of size n. Limits for summation $\sum$ are from 1 to n. A family of pdf's is denoted by $f = f(x;\ \theta)$, $\theta \in \Omega$, where the set Ω is the parameter space. Most of the following results are from a survey paper by Patel (1973).

6.7.1 NORMAL

$$f(x;\ \theta_1,\ \theta_2) = \frac{1}{\sqrt{2\pi\theta_2}} \exp\left\{-\frac{(x-\theta_1)^2}{2\theta_2}\right\},\ \theta_2 > 0$$

(1) f is complete wrt θ_1 (θ_2 known) but not even boundedly complete wrt θ_2 (θ_1 known).

(2) $T_1 = \sum X_i$ is complete sufficient for θ_1 (θ_2 known).

Let $T_2 = \sum X_i^2$.

$T_3 = \sum (X_i - \theta_1)^2$ is complete sufficient for θ_2 (θ_1 known).

(T_1, T_2) are jointly complete and sufficient for (θ_1, θ_2).

(3) $\frac{T_1}{n}$ is UMVUE for $\mu = \theta_1$.

$\frac{T_3}{n}$ is UMVUE for $\sigma^2 = \theta_2$ (θ_1 known).

$\frac{nT_2 - T_1^2}{n(n-1)} = \sum \frac{(X_i - \bar{X})^2}{(n-1)}$ is UMVUE for σ^2 (θ_1 unknown).

$\frac{T_1^2 - n\theta_2}{n^2}$ is UMVUE for θ_1^2 (θ_2 known).

$\exp\left(-\frac{(2T_1 + \theta_2)}{2n}\right)$ is UMVUE for $\exp(-\theta_1)$ (θ_2 known).

Let $\theta_2 = \theta_1 = \theta > 0$.

T_2 is the complete minimal sufficient statistic for θ.

The UMVUE of θ is

$$\left(\frac{T_2}{n}\right)^{1/2} \frac{\int_{-1}^{1} x(1-x^2)^{(n-3)/2} e^{\sqrt{nT_2}\,x}\,dx}{\int_{-1}^{1} (1-x^2)^{(n-3)/2} e^{\sqrt{nT_2}\,x}\,dx}$$

[Feldman and Fox (1968), p. 154]

(4) (a) The UMVUE of $F(b; \theta_1, \theta_2)$ (b and θ_2 known) is

$$\Phi\left(\frac{nb - T_1}{\sqrt{n(n-1)\theta_2}}\right)$$

where Φ is the standard normal cdf [Hogg and Craig (1970), p. 236].

(b) The UMVUE of $F(b; \theta_1, \theta_2)$ (b known and $\theta_1 = 0$) is

$$\begin{cases} \frac{1}{2} I_A\left(\frac{1}{2}, \frac{n-1}{2}\right) & \text{if } b < 0 \\ \frac{1}{2} & \text{if } b = 0 \\ 1 - \frac{1}{2} I_A\left(\frac{1}{2}, \frac{n-1}{2}\right) & \text{if } b > 0 \end{cases}$$

where $A = b^2/T_2$, $I_A(m, n)$ is the incomplete beta function ratio.

[Patil and Wani (1966), pp. 41-42]

(c) The UMVUE of $F(b; \theta_1, \theta_2)$ (b known) is

$$\begin{cases} \frac{1}{2} I_A\left(\frac{1}{2}, \frac{n-2}{2}\right) & \text{if } nb < T_1 \\ \frac{1}{2} & \text{if } nb = T_1 \\ 1 - \frac{1}{2} I_A\left(\frac{1}{2}, \frac{n-2}{2}\right) & \text{if } nb > T_1 \end{cases}$$

where $A = n^2(b - T_1/n)^2/\{(n-1)(nT_2 - T_1^2)\}$, and $I_A(m, n)$ is defined as above [Patil and Wani (1966), pp. 42-43].

(d) The UMVUE of $P(X \leq 0) = \Phi(-\theta_1/\sqrt{\theta_2})$ is

$$\begin{cases} I_A\left(\frac{n}{2} - 1, \frac{n}{2} - 1\right) & \text{if } 0 \leq A \leq 1 \\ 1 \text{ if } A > 1 \\ 0 \text{ if } A < 0 \end{cases}$$

where $a = (1/2)\{1 - [T_1/\sqrt{(n-1)(nT_2 - T_1^2)}]\}$ and $I_A(m, n)$ and Φ are as defined above [Zacks (1971), pp. 101-102].

(e) The UMVUE of $f(b; \theta_1, \theta_2)$ (b known, $\theta_2 = 1$) is

$$\left[2\pi\left(1 - \frac{1}{n}\right)\right]^{-(1/2)} \exp\left\{-\frac{(nb_1 - T_1)^2}{2n(n-1)}\right\}, \quad n \geq 2$$

[Zacks (1971), p. 132]

(f) For UMVUE of any analytic function of μ and σ^2 refer to Gray et al. (1973), pp. 285-320.

6.7.2 LOG NORMAL

$$f(x; \theta_1, \theta_2) = \frac{1}{x\sqrt{2\pi\theta_2}} \exp\left\{-\frac{(\log x - \theta_1)^2}{2\theta_2}\right\}; \quad x > 0, \; \theta_2 > 0$$

(1) f is complete wrt θ_1 (θ_2 known).

(2) $T_1 = \sum \log X_i$ is complete and sufficient for θ_1 (θ_2 known).

Let $T_2 = \sum(\log X_i)^2$.

Let $T_3 = \sum(\log X_i - \theta_1)^2$ is sufficient for θ_2 (θ_1 known).

(T_1, T_2) is jointly complete and sufficient for (θ_1, θ_2).

(3) $\dfrac{T_1}{n}$ is UMVUE for θ_1.

$\dfrac{T_3}{n}$ is UMVUE for θ_2 (θ_1 known).

$\dfrac{nT_2 - T_1^2}{n(n-1)}$ is UMVUE for θ_2 (θ_1 known).

$\exp\left(\dfrac{2T_1 + (n-1)\theta_2}{2n}\right)$ is UMVUE for $\mu = \exp\left(\theta_1 + \dfrac{\theta_2}{2}\right)$ (θ_2 known).

$[\exp(\theta_2) - 1]\exp\left(\dfrac{2T_1 + (n-2)\theta_2}{n}\right)$ is UMVUE for $\sigma^2 = [\exp(\theta_2) - 1]\exp(2\theta_1 + \theta_2)$ (θ_2 known).

6.7.3 INVERSE GAUSSIAN

$$f(x;\ \theta,\ \lambda) = \sqrt{\frac{\lambda}{2\pi x^3}}\ \exp\left\{-\frac{\lambda(x - \theta)^2}{2\theta^2 x}\right\};\ x > 0,\ \theta > 0,\ \lambda > 0$$

(1) f is complete wrt θ (λ known) and also complete wrt λ (θ known).

(2) $T_1 = \sum X_i$ is complete and sufficient for θ (λ known).

$T_2 = \sum \frac{(X_i - \theta)^2}{X_i}$ is complete and sufficient for λ (θ known).

Let $T_3 = \sum \frac{1}{X_i}$.

(T_1, T_3) are jointly complete and sufficient for (θ, λ).

(3) $\frac{T_1}{n}$ is UMVUE for $\mu = \theta$ (λ known).

$\frac{T_2}{n\theta^2}$ is UMVUE for $\frac{1}{\lambda}$ (θ known).

$\left(\frac{1}{n - 1}\right)\left(T_3 - \frac{n^2}{T_1}\right)$ is UMVUE for $\frac{1}{\lambda}$ (θ unknown).

[Johnson and Kotz (1970a), p. 143]

(4) The UMVUE of $F(b;\ \theta,\ \lambda)$ (λ and b known) is

$$\begin{cases} 0 \text{ if } b \leq 0 \\ 1 \text{ if } b > T_1 \\ \Phi(\omega_0) + \left(\frac{n - 2}{n}\right) \exp\left\{\frac{2(n - 1)\lambda}{T_1}\right\} \Phi(-\omega_0'), \text{ otherwise} \end{cases}$$

where

$$\omega_0 = \frac{\sqrt{n\lambda}\ (b - T_1/n)}{\sqrt{bT_1(T_1 - b)}},\quad \omega_0' = \frac{\sqrt{\lambda}\ [T_1 + (n - 2)b]}{\sqrt{bT_1(T_1 - b)}}$$

and ϕ is the standard normal cdf.

The UMVUE of $F(b;\ \theta,\ \lambda)$ (θ and b known) is

$$\begin{cases} 0 & \text{if } b \leq \frac{1}{2}\left[(2\theta + T_2) - \sqrt{4\theta T_2 + T_2^2}\right] \\ 1 & \text{if } b \geq \frac{1}{2}\left[(2\theta + T_2) + \sqrt{4\theta T_2 + T_2^2}\right] \\ F_{t,n-1}(\omega_0) + \left[\dfrac{T_2 + 4\theta}{T_2}\right]^{(n-2)/2} F_{t,n-1}(-\omega_0'), & \text{otherwise} \end{cases}$$

where

$$\omega_0 = \frac{\sqrt{(n - 1)}(b - \theta)}{\sqrt{T_2 b - (b - \theta)^2}}, \quad \omega_0' = \frac{\sqrt{(n - 1)}(b + \theta)}{\sqrt{T_2 b - (b - \theta)^2}}$$

and $F_{t,n-1}$ is the cdf of a t-distribution with (n - 1) degrees of freedom [Chhikara and Folks (1974), pp. 252, 254].

6.7.4 CAUCHY

$$f(x;\ \theta,\ \sigma) = \frac{\sigma}{\pi[\sigma^2 + (x - \theta)^2]}; \quad -\infty < x < \infty,\ -\infty < \theta < \infty,\ \sigma > 0$$

(1) f is complete wrt θ ($\sigma = 1$) but not even boundedly complete wrt σ^2 ($\theta = 0$).

[Ghosh and Singh (1966), p. 1673]

[Lehmann and Scheffé (1950), p. 314]

(2) $T = \sum_1^n X_i^2$ is complete for σ^2 ($\theta = 0$).

[Lehmann and Scheffé (1950), p. 314]

6.7.5 TRUNCATED EXPONENTIAL

$$f(x;\ \theta,\ \alpha) = \frac{1}{\alpha} \exp\left\{-\left(\frac{x - \theta}{\alpha}\right)\right\}; \quad x \geq \theta,\ \alpha > 0$$

(1) f is complete wrt θ (α known) and also complete wrt α (θ known).

(2) $T_1 = X_{(1;n)}$ is complete and sufficient for θ (α known).

$T_2 = \sum X_i$ is complete and sufficient for α (θ known).

(T_1, T_2) are jointly complete and sufficient for (θ, α).

(3) $T_1 + \alpha\left(1 - \frac{1}{n}\right)$ is UMVUE for $\mu = \theta + \alpha$ (α known).

$\frac{T_2}{n}$ is UMVUE for $\mu = \theta + \alpha$ (θ known).

$$\left\{T_1^r\left[1 + \frac{r}{n - 1}\right] - \frac{rT_2T_1^{r-1}}{n(n - 1)}\right\}$$ is UMVUE of θ^r $(r \geq 0)$.

[Tate (1959), p. 360]

(4) The UMVUE of $[1 - \{F(b; \theta, \alpha)\}]^r$ (α known), $r \leq n$, is

$$\begin{cases} 1 & \text{if } b < T_1 \\ \left(1 - \frac{r}{n}\right)\exp\left\{-\frac{r(b - T_1)}{\alpha}\right\} & \text{if } b > T_1 \end{cases}$$

[Sathe and Varde (1969), p. 713]

The UMVUE of $[1 - \{F(b; \theta, \alpha)\}]^r$ (θ known), $r \leq n$, is

$$\begin{cases} 1 & \text{if } b < \theta \\ \left[1 - \frac{r(b - \theta)}{(T_2 - n\theta)}\right]^{r-1} & \text{if } \theta \leq b \leq \frac{T_2 - (n - r)\theta}{r} \\ 0 & \text{if } b > \frac{T_2 - (n - r)\theta}{r} \end{cases}$$

[Sathe and Varde (1969), p. 713]

The UMVUE of $[1 - \{F(b; \theta, \alpha)\}]^r$, $r \leq n$, is

$$\begin{cases} 1 & \text{if } b < T_1 \\ \left(1 - \frac{r}{n}\right)\left[1 - \frac{r(b - T_1)}{T_2 - nT_1}\right]^{n-2} & \text{if } T_1 \leq b \leq \frac{T_2 - (n - r)T_1}{r} \\ 0 & \text{if } b > \frac{T_2 - (n - r)T_1}{r} \end{cases}$$

[Sathe and Varde (1969), p. 713]

6.7.6 GAMMA

$$f(x;\ \theta) = \frac{\theta^m x^{m-1} e^{-\theta x}}{\Gamma(m)};\ x > 0,\ \theta > 0,\ m > 0$$

(When m = 1, f is known as exponential distribution.)

(1) f is complete wrt θ (m known).

(2) $T = \sum X_i$ is complete and sufficient for θ (m known).

(3) $\frac{T}{mn}$ is UMVUE for $\mu = \frac{1}{\theta}$ (m known).

$\frac{\Gamma(mn)}{\Gamma(mn - k)} \frac{1}{T^k}$ is UMVUE for θ^k (m known) for any k ($k \leq mn - 1$ and $mn > 1$).

(4) The UMVUE of F(b; θ) (m and b known) is $I_p(m,\ mn - m)$, where $I_p(c,\ d)$ is the incomplete beta ratio function, and p = b/T.

[Patil and Wani (1966), p. 44]

6.7.7 WEIBULL

$$f(x;\ \theta,\ \alpha) = \alpha\theta x^{\alpha-1} e^{-\theta x^{\alpha}};\ x > 0,\ \theta > 0,\ \alpha > 0$$

(1) f is complete wrt θ (α known).

(2) $T = \sum X_i^{\alpha}$ is complete and sufficient for θ (α known).

(3) $\frac{\Gamma(n)}{\Gamma\left(n + \frac{1}{\alpha}\right)} \Gamma\left(\frac{1}{\alpha} + 1\right) T^{1/\alpha}$ is UMVUE for $\mu = \theta^{\alpha}\Gamma\left(\frac{1}{\alpha} + 1\right)$ (α known).

For any k ($k \leq n - 1$ and $n > 1$), $\frac{\Gamma(n)}{\Gamma(n - k)} \frac{1}{T^k}$ is UMVUE for θ^k (α known).

(4) The UMVUE of $F(b;\ \theta,\ \alpha)$ (α known) is

$$\begin{cases} 1 - \left(1 - \dfrac{b^{\alpha}}{T}\right)^{n-1} & \text{if } T > b^{\alpha} \\ 0 \quad \text{if } T < b^{\alpha} \end{cases}$$

[Sathe and Varde (1969), p. 712]

6.7.8 BETA

$$f(x;\ p,\ q) = \frac{\Gamma(p + q)}{\Gamma(p)\Gamma(q)}\, x^{p-1}(1 - x)^{q-1};\quad 0 < x < 1,\ p > 0,\ q > 0$$

(1) f is complete wrt p (q known) and also complete wrt q (p known).

(2) $T_1 = \sum \log X_i$ is complete and sufficient for p (q known).
$T_2 = \sum \log (1 - X_i)$ is complete and sufficient for q (p known).
$(T_1,\ T_2)$ is jointly complete and sufficient for (p, q).

(3) $\dfrac{(1 - n)}{T_1}$ is UMVUE for p (q = 1), n > 1.

$\dfrac{(1 - n)}{T_2}$ is UMVUE for q (p = 1), n > 1.

For n = 1, $\dfrac{(q - 1)e^{T_1}}{1 - e^{T_1}}$ is UMVUE for p (q known), q > 1.

For n = 1, $\dfrac{(p - 1)e^{T_2}}{1 - e^{T_2}}$ is UMVUE for q (p known), p > 1.

6.7.9 POWER FUNCTION

$$f(x;\ \theta,\ \alpha) = \frac{\theta x^{\theta-1}}{\alpha^{\theta}};\quad 0 < x < \alpha,\ \theta > 0$$

(1) f is complete wrt θ (α known) and also complete wrt α (θ known).

(2) $T_1 = \sum_1 \log X_i$ is complete and sufficient for θ (α known).
$T_2 = X_{(n;n)}$ is complete and sufficient for α (θ known).

(3) $\left(\frac{n\theta + 1}{n\theta}\right)T_2$ is UMVUE for α (θ known).

$\left(\frac{\theta}{\theta + 1}\right)\left(\frac{n\theta + 1}{n\theta}\right)T_2$ is UMVUE for $\mu = \left(\frac{\theta}{\theta + 1}\right)\alpha$ (θ known).

$\log \alpha - \frac{T_1}{n}$ is UMVUE for $\frac{1}{\theta}$ (α known).

6.7.10 UNIFORM

(1) $f(x; \theta) = \frac{1}{\theta}$; $0 < x < \theta$, $\theta > 0$

(a) f is complete wrt θ.

(b) $T = X_{(n;n)}$ is complete and sufficient for θ.

(c) $\left(\frac{n + 1}{2n}\right)T$ is UMVUE for $\mu = \frac{\theta}{2}$.

$\left(\frac{n + r}{n}\right)T^r$ is UMVUE for θ^r.

The UMVUE of θ^r ($\alpha < \theta < \infty$, α known) is

$$\begin{cases} \alpha^r & \text{if } T \leq \alpha \\ \left(\frac{n + r}{n}\right) T^r & \text{if } T > \alpha \end{cases}$$

[Morimoto and Sibuya (1967), p. 17]

The UMVUE of θ^r ($\theta = 1, 2, 3, \ldots$) is

$$\frac{(S + 1)^{n+r} - S^{n+r}}{(S + 1)^n - S^n}, \quad S = [T]$$

[Morimoto and Sibuya (1967), p. 21]

(d) The UMVUE of $F(b; \theta)$ is

$$\begin{cases} 0 & \text{if } b < 0 \\ \left(\frac{n - 1}{n}\right)\frac{b}{T} & \text{if } 0 < b \leq T \\ 1 & \text{if } b > T \end{cases}$$

[Zacks (1971), p. 140]

(2) $f(x, \theta_1, \theta_2) = \frac{1}{\theta_2 - \theta_1}$; $\theta_1 < x < \theta_2$, $-\infty < \theta_1 < \theta_2 < \infty$

(a) f is complete wrt θ_1 (θ_2 known) and also complete wrt θ_2 (θ_1 known).

(b) $T_1 = X_{(1;n)}$ is complete and sufficient for θ_1 (θ_2 known).

$T_2 = X_{(n;n)}$ is complete and sufficient for θ_2 (θ_1 known).

(T_1, T_2) is jointly complete and sufficient for (θ_1, θ_2).

(c) $T_3 = \dfrac{(n+1)T_1 - \theta_2}{n}$ is UMVUE for θ_1 (θ_2 known).

$T_4 = \dfrac{(n+1)T_2 - \theta_1}{n}$ is UMVUE for θ_2 (θ_1 known).

$\dfrac{(\theta_2 - T_3)}{2}$ is UMVUE for $\mu = \dfrac{(\theta_2 - \theta_1)}{2}$ (θ_2 known).

$\dfrac{(T_4 - \theta_1)}{2}$ is UMVUE for μ (θ_1 known).

$\left(\dfrac{n+1}{n-1}\right)\left(\dfrac{T_2 - T_1}{2}\right)$ is UMVUE for μ.

$\dfrac{1}{(n-1)}(nT_1 - T_2)$ is UMVUE of θ_1.

$\dfrac{1}{(n-1)}(nT_2 - T_1)$ is UMVUE of θ_2.

(d) The UMVUE of $F(b; \theta_1, \theta_2)$ (b and θ_1 known) is

$$\begin{cases} \left(1 - \dfrac{1}{n}\right) \dfrac{b}{T_2} & \text{if } b < T_2 \\ 1 & \text{if } b \geq T_2 \end{cases}$$

[Patil and Wani (1966), p. 46]

The UMVUE of $F(b; \theta_1, \theta_2)$ (b known) is

$$\begin{cases} 0 & \text{if } b < T_1 \\ \dfrac{1}{n} & \text{if } b = T_1 \\ \dfrac{1}{n} + \dfrac{(n-2)(b - T_1)}{n(T_2 - T_1)} & \text{if } T_1 < b < T_2 \\ 1 & \text{if } b \geq T_2 \end{cases}$$

[Patil and Wani (1966), p. 46]

(3) $f(x; \theta_1, \theta_2) = \dfrac{1}{\theta_2}$; $\theta_1 - \dfrac{\theta_2}{2} \leq x \leq \theta_1 + \dfrac{\theta_2}{2}$, $-\infty < \theta_1 < \infty$, $\theta_2 > 0$

(a) f is not even boundedly complete wrt θ_2 (θ_1 known).

(b) $T = (X_{(1;n)}, X_{(n;n)})$ is jointly complete and sufficient for (θ_1, θ_2).

(c) $\frac{1}{2}(X_{(n;n)} + X_{(1;n)})$ is UMVUE for $\mu = \theta_1$.

$\left(\frac{n+1}{n-1}\right)(X_{(n;n)} + X_{(1;n)})$ is UMVUE for θ_2.

(4) $f(x;\theta) = 1;\ \theta - \frac{1}{2} < x < \theta + \frac{1}{2},\ -\infty < \theta < \infty$

(a) $T = (X_{(1;n)}, X_{(n;n)})$ is sufficient but not even boundedly complete for θ

(b) $\frac{1}{2}(X_{(1;n)} + X_{(n;n)})$ is MVU linear estimator for $\mu = \theta$.

(5) $f(x;\theta) = 1;\quad \theta < x < \theta + 1,\ -\infty < \theta < \infty$

(a) f is not even boundedly complete wrt θ.

[Kendall and Stuart (1967), p. 193]

(b) $T = (X_{1;n)}, X_{(n;n)})$ is jointly sufficient for θ.

(c) $\left(\frac{X_{(1;n)} + X_{(n;n)} - 1}{2}\right)$ is MVU linear estimator for θ.

(6) $f(x;\theta) = \frac{1}{2\theta};\ -\theta < x < \theta,\ \theta > 0$

(a) f is not even boundedly complete wrt θ.

(b) $T = \max[-X_{(1;n)}, X_{(n;n)}]$ is complete and sufficient for θ.

[Kendall and Stuart (1967), p. 30]

(c) $\left(\frac{n+1}{n}\right) T$ is UMVUE for θ.

6.7.11 PARETO

$$f(x;\alpha,\beta) = \frac{\alpha\beta^{\alpha}}{x^{\alpha+1}};\ x \geq \beta > 0,\quad \alpha > 1$$

(1) f is complete wrt α (β known) and also complete wrt β (α known).

(2) $T_1 = \sum \log X_i$ is complete and sufficient for α (β known).

$T_2 = X_{(1;n)}$ is complete and sufficient for β (α known).

(3) $\left(\frac{\alpha}{\alpha - 1}\right)\left(\frac{n\alpha - 1}{n\alpha}\right) T_2$ is UMVUE for $\mu = \left(\frac{\alpha}{\alpha - 1}\right) \beta$ (α known).

$\frac{n - 1}{T_1 - n \log \beta}$ is UMVUE for α (β known), $n > 1$.

6.7.12 TRUNCATED EXTREME-VALUE

$$f(x;\ \theta) = \frac{1}{\theta} \exp\left[x - \frac{e^x - 1}{\theta}\right]; \quad x > 0,\ \theta > 0$$

(1) f is complete wrt θ.

(2) $T = \sum\left(e^{X_i} - 1\right)$ is complete and sufficient for θ.

(3) $\frac{T}{n}$ is UMVUE for θ.

6.7.13 CHI

$$f(x;\ \theta) = \frac{x^{\alpha-1} e^{-x^2/2\theta}}{\theta^{\alpha/2} 2^{(\alpha/2)-1} \Gamma\left(\frac{\alpha}{2}\right)}; \quad x > 0,\ \theta > 0,\ \alpha > 0$$

(When $\alpha = 1$, f is known as truncated normal distribution, and when $\alpha = 2$, f is known as Rayleigh distribution.)

(1) f is complete wrt α (θ known).

(2) $T_1 = \sum X_i^2$ is complete and sufficient for θ (α known).

$T_2 = \sum \log X_i$ is complete and sufficient for α (θ known).

$(T_1,\ T_2)$ are jointly complete and sufficient for $(\theta,\ \alpha)$.

(3) $\frac{T_1}{n\alpha}$ is UMVUE for θ (α known).

$$\frac{\Gamma\left(\frac{\alpha + 1}{2}\right)}{\Gamma\left(\frac{\alpha}{2}\right)} \frac{\Gamma\left(\frac{n\alpha}{2}\right)}{\Gamma\left(\frac{n\alpha + 1}{2}\right)} \sqrt{T_1} \text{ is MVUE for } \mu = \frac{\Gamma\left(\frac{\alpha + 1}{2}\right)}{\Gamma\left(\frac{\alpha}{2}\right)} \sqrt{2\theta} \quad (\alpha \text{ known}).$$

6.7.14 BURR

$$f(x;\ \alpha,\ \beta) = \frac{\alpha\beta x^{\alpha-1}}{(1 + x^{\alpha})^{\beta+1}}\ ;\quad x \geq 0,\ \beta > 0,\ \alpha > 0$$

(1) f is complete wrt β (α known).

(2) $T = \sum \log(1 + X^{\alpha})$ is complete and sufficient for β (α known).

(3) For $n > 1$, $\frac{(n - 1)}{T}$ is UMVUE for β (α known).

Chapter 7

CONFIDENCE INTERVALS

7.1 INTRODUCTION

A confidence interval (CI) is a random interval which covers the true value of the parameter with some measure of assurance.

7.1.1 DEFINITIONS

(1) A Random Interval. A random interval is a finite or infinite interval, where at least one of the end-points is a random variable.

(2) One-sided Confidence Intervals. Let $X_1, X_2, \ldots, X_n$ be a random sample from a one-parameter pdf (or pf) $f(x; \theta)$. Let $T_1 = t_1(X_1, X_2, \ldots, X_n)$ be a statistic for which $P[T_1 \leq \theta] \geq 1 - \alpha$ for all θ. Then T_1 is called a lower confidence bound for θ with confidence level $(1 - \alpha)$. The random interval $[T_1, \infty)$ is called a lower one-sided $(1 - \alpha)$ CI for θ. Similarly, if $T_2 = t_2(X_1, X_2, \ldots, X_n)$ is a statistic for which $P[\theta \leq T_2] \geq 1 - \alpha$ for all θ then T_2 is called an upper confidence bound for θ with confidence level $(1 - \alpha)$, and the random interval $(-\infty, T_2]$ is called an upper one-sided $(1 - \alpha)$ CI for θ.

(3) Two-sided Confidence Interval. Let $X_1, X_2, \ldots, X_n$ be a random sample from a one-parameter pdf (or pf) $f(x; \theta)$. Let $T_1 = t_1(X_1, X_2, \ldots, X_n)$ and $T_2 = t_2(X_1, X_2, \ldots, X_n)$ be two statistics satisfying $T_1 \le T_2$, for which $P[T_1 \le \theta \le T_2] \ge 1 - \alpha$. Then the random interval $[T_1, T_2]$ is called a two-sided $(1 - \alpha)$ CI for θ.

If in definitions (2) and (3), an equality is achieved in the probability statement, $(1 - \alpha)$ is called the confidence coefficient.

(4) The Length of a Confidence Interval. The length $\delta = \delta(X_1, X_2, \ldots, X_n)$ of a CI $[T_1, T_2]$ is $\delta = T_2 - T_1$.

7.1.2 COMMENTS

(1) If $[T_1, T_2]$ is a two-sided $(1 - \alpha)$ CI for θ, it means that the random interval $[T_1, T_2]$ contains the unknown parameter θ with probability at least $(1 - \alpha)$. A similar interpretation can be given for one-sided CI's.

(2) If a $(1 - \alpha)$ two-sided CI $[T_1, T_2]$ for θ is available, and if $h(\theta)$ is a strictly monotone function of θ, then a $(1 - \alpha)$ two-sided CI for $h(\theta)$ is $[h(T_1), h(T_2)]$ or $[h(T_2), h(T_1)]$, depending on whether h is strictly increasing or strictly decreasing. Similar statements hold for one-sided CI's.

(3) Confidence intervals are not unique. This is because of one or the other of the following two conditions.

(a) Different statistics are available to obtain $(1 - \alpha)$ CI's.

Example: $f(x; \theta) = \frac{1}{\theta} e^{-x/\theta}; \quad x \ge 0, \ \theta > 0$

$$P\left[\frac{2n\bar{X}}{\chi^2_{(1-\alpha;2n)}} \le \theta\right] = 1 - \alpha, \quad P\left[\frac{2nX_{(1;n)}}{\chi^2_{(1-\alpha;2)}} \le \theta\right] = 1 - \alpha$$

where $\chi^2_{(1-\alpha,m)}$ is the $100(1 - \alpha)$ lower percentage point of a chi square distribution with m degrees of freedom.

(b) Different multiples of the same statistic in a two-sided CI can be used.

Example: $f(x;\ \theta) = \frac{1}{\theta} e^{-x/\theta};\quad x \geq 0,\ \theta > 0$

$$P\left[\frac{2n\bar{X}}{\chi^2_{[1-(\alpha/2);2n]}} \leq \theta \leq \frac{2n\bar{X}}{\chi^2_{(\alpha/2;2n)}}\right] = 1 - \alpha$$

$$P\left[\frac{2n\bar{X}}{\chi^2_{[1-(3\alpha/4);2n]}} \leq \theta \leq \frac{2n\bar{X}}{\chi^2_{(\alpha/4;2n)}}\right] = 1 - \alpha$$

7.1.3 CRITERIA FOR SELECTING CONFIDENCE INTERVALS

If more than one CI for θ exist, it is necessary to consider whether any particular interval can be regarded as better than the others in some useful sense.

(1) Length (or Expected Length) of Confidence Intervals

(a) Minimize the length $\delta = T_2 - T_1$ of a CI $[T_1, T_2]$. A weakness of this criterion is that in some cases, δ could be a random variable.

(b) Minimize the expected length $E(\delta) = E(T_2 - T_1)$. A weakness of this criterion is that minimization of $E(\delta)$ depends on the unknown true value of θ.

In large samples, the CI's based on $(\partial \log L)/\partial\theta$, where L is the likelihood function, have minimum expected length.

[Kendall and Stuart (1967), p. 117]

(2) A random interval $[T_1, T_2]$ is said to be unbiased if

$$\begin{aligned} P(\theta, \theta') = P[T_1 \leq \theta' \leq T_2] &\geq 1 - \alpha \quad \text{if } \theta' = \theta \\ &\leq 1 - \alpha \quad \text{if } \theta' \neq \theta \end{aligned}$$

[Guenther (1971a), p. 51]

(3) Most Accurate Confidence Bounds. A $(1 - \alpha)$ lower confidence bound for θ, T_1 is called uniformly most accurate if

$$P[T_1 \leq \theta'] \leq P[T^* \leq \theta']$$

for all $\theta' < \theta$, where T^* is any other $(1 - \alpha)$ lower confidence bound for θ. Similarly a uniformly most accurate upper confidence bound can be defined [Zacks (1971), p. 500].

7.1.4 METHODS OF FINDING CONFIDENCE INTERVALS

(1) Pivotal Quantity Method. Let $X_1, X_2, \ldots, X_n$ be a random sample from a one-parameter pdf $f(x; \theta)$. Let $T = t(X_1, X_2, \ldots, X_n; \theta)$ be a function of $X_1, X_2, \ldots, X_n$ and θ. If the distribution of T does not depend on θ, T is called a pivotal quantity.

[Mood et al. (1974), p. 379]

(a) Let $X_1, X_2, \ldots, X_n$ be a random sample from a continuous distribution function $F(x; \theta)$. Assume that $F(x; \theta)$ is monotone in θ. Then the statistic $T = -\sum_{i=1}^{n} \log F(X_i, \theta)$ is a pivotal quantity and has a gamma distribution with parameters 1 and n; 1 being a scale parameter. Now

$$P\left[a \leq \prod_{i=1}^{n} F(X_i; \theta) \leq b\right] = P[-\log b \leq T \leq -\log a]$$

Noting that $a \leq \prod_{i=1}^{n} F(X_i; \theta) \leq b$ iff $T_1 \leq \theta \leq T_2$, which defines T_1 and T_2, and setting a and b in terms of the appropriate percentage point of the gamma distribution, the desired CI's can be obtained.

[Mood et al. (1974), pp. 387-388]

(b) If θ is a location parameter, then $X - \theta$ has a distribution independent of θ. Similarly, if θ is a scale parameter then X/θ has a distribution independent of θ. Hence the pivotal quantities could be $\sum_1^n (X_i - \theta)$ or $\sum_1^n X_i/\theta$ according as θ is a location or scale parameter.

(2) Let $X_1, X_2, \ldots, X_n$ be a random sample from a one-parameter pdf (or pf) $f(x; \theta)$. Suppose the parameter space is some interval. Let T be some statistic of interest, and suppose the pdf (or pf) of T is known to be $g(t; \theta)$. Let $G(t; \theta)$ be the corresponding cdf. For a given value of T say t_0, let $S_1 = S_1(X_1, X_2, \ldots, X_n)$ be found by solving for θ in $G(t_0; \theta) \leq \alpha_1$ and $S_2 = S_2(X_1, X_2, \ldots, X_n)$ be found by solving for θ in the equation $G(t_0; \theta) \leq 1 - \alpha_2$. Let $\alpha_1 + \alpha_2 = \alpha$. Then a $(1 - \alpha)$ CI for θ is

$$P[S_1 \leq \theta \leq S_2] \geq 1 - \alpha \quad \text{[Mood et al. (1974), pp. 389-393]}$$

(3) Large-sample Confidence Intervals. If a sequence of estimators T_n are available which are asymptotically ($n \to \infty$) normally distributed, with mean θ and variance $\sigma_n^2(\theta)$ where $\sigma_n^2(\theta)$ may be a function of θ, then an approximate $(1 - \alpha)$ CI for θ can be obtained from

$$P\left[-Z_{1-(\alpha/2)} \le \frac{T_n - \theta}{\sigma_n(\theta)} \le Z_{1-(\alpha/2)}\right] \approx 1 - \alpha$$

where $Z_{1-(\alpha/2)}$ is the $100[1 - (\alpha/2)]$ lower percentage point of a standard normal cdf.

The MLE, T_n, of θ is asymptotically normally distributed with mean θ and variance $= 1/\{-nE[\partial^2 \log f(X;\ \theta)/\partial\theta^2]$.

[Mood et al. (1974), pp. 393-394]

7.1.5 SOME USEFUL RESULTS

(1) Let the family of densities $f(x;\ \theta)$, $\theta \in \Omega$ have MLR in $T(x)$ and suppose that the cdf $F(t;\ \theta)$ of $T = T(X)$ is a continuous function of t for each θ. Then

(a) There exists a uniformly most accurate lower confidence bound $\underline{\theta}(x)$ for θ at each confidence level $(1 - \alpha)$.

(b) If x denotes the observed value of X and $t = t(x)$, and if the equation $F(t;\ \theta) = 1 - \alpha$ has a solution $\theta = \hat{\theta}$ in Ω, then this solution is unique and $\underline{\theta}(x) = \hat{\theta}$. A similar result holds for an upper confidence bound [Lehmann (1959), p. 80].

(2) Let $f(x,\ \theta)$, $\theta \in \Omega$ be a MLR family of density functions of an integer-valued discrete random variable X. Let R be an independent random variable having a rectangular distribution on (0, 1). Then the uniformly most accurate lower confidence limit for θ is the root $\underline{\theta}$ of the equation

$$RF(x;\ \theta) + (1 - R)F(x - 1;\ \theta) = 1 - \alpha$$

where $F(x;\ \theta)$ is the cdf of X [Zacks (1971), p. 504].

(3) If $f(x;\ \theta) = g(x)/h(\theta)$, $a(\theta) \le x \le b(\theta)$, where $b(\theta)$ is a monotone decreasing function of $a(\theta)$, then a single sufficient statistic for θ is

$$\hat{\theta} = \min\left\{a^{-1}(X_{(1;n)}),\ b^{-1}(X_{(n;n)})\right\}$$

Let $\psi = h(\hat{\theta})/h(\theta)$. Then $P\{\alpha^{1/n} \leq \psi \leq 1\} = 1 - \alpha$, from which a CI for θ can be obtained. This interval is shorter than other intervals based on the distribution of ψ [Kendall and Stuart (1967), p. 132].

(4) If $f(x;\ \theta) = g(h)/h(\theta)$, $a(\theta) \leq x \leq b(\theta)$, where $a(\theta)$ is monotone increasing and $b(\theta)$ is monotone decreasing in θ, then

$$P\left[h^{-1}\left\{\frac{h(\hat{\theta})}{\alpha^{1/n}}\right\} \leq \theta \leq \hat{\theta}\right] = 1 - \alpha$$

where $\hat{\theta} = \min\{a^{-1}(X_{(1;n)}),\ b^{-1}(X_{(n;n)})\}$ [Huzurbazar (1955), p. 89].

7.2 CONFIDENCE INTERVALS FOR SOME USEFUL DISCRETE DISTRIBUTIONS

The following CI's, unless otherwise specified, are based on a complete (not truncated or censored) random sample. In the following, let $Z_{(\gamma)}$, $\chi^2_{(\gamma;m)}$, $t_{(\gamma;n)}$ denote 100γ lower percentage points of a standard normal distribution, a chi square distribution with m degrees of freedom and a t distribution with n degrees of freedom, respectively. Let $0 < \alpha_1, \alpha_2 < 1$, $\alpha_1 + \alpha_2 = \alpha$, and $0 < \alpha < 1$. Also let $X_1, X_2, \ldots, X_n$ denote a random sample from a given population.

7.2.1 BINOMIAL

$$f(x;\ m,\ p) = \binom{m}{x} p^x q^{m-x};\ x = 0, 1, 2, \ldots, m,\ 0 < p < 1,\quad q = 1 - p$$

(1) CI for p (m known). [Tables of shortest interval are given by Crow (1956, pp. 428-433) and Pachares (1960, pp. 524-533)].

(2) CI for p (m known).

$$P[p_L \leq p \leq p_u] = 1 - \alpha$$

where $p_u = m_1F_{(\lambda;m_1,m_2)}/(m_2 + m_1F_{(\lambda;m_1,m_2)})$, $p_L = m_4/(m_4 + m_3F_{(\lambda;m_3,m_4)})$, and $m_1 = 2(X + 1)$, $m_2 = 2(n - X)$, $m_3 = 2(n - X + 1)$, $m_4 = 2X$, $\lambda = \alpha/2$.

[Satterthwaite (1957), p. 57]

(3) Asymptotic ($n \to \infty$) CI for p (m known).

$$P[T_1 \le p \le T_2] \approx 1 - \alpha$$

where

$$T_1 = \left(\frac{N}{k^2 + N}\right)\left\{\bar{X} + \frac{k^2}{2N} - k\left(\frac{\bar{X}(1 - \bar{X})}{N} + \frac{k^2}{4N^2}\right)^{1/2}\right\} \approx \bar{X} - k\left(\frac{\bar{X}(1 - \bar{X})}{N}\right)^{1/2}$$

$$T_2 = \left(\frac{N}{k^2 + N}\right)\left\{\bar{X} + \frac{k^2}{2N} + k\left(\frac{\bar{X}(1 - \bar{X})}{N} + \frac{k^2}{4N^2}\right)^{1/2}\right\} \approx \bar{X} + k\left(\frac{\bar{X}(1 - \bar{X})}{N}\right)^{1/2}$$

with $N = nm$ and $k = Z_{[1-(\alpha/2)]}$, is the $100[1 - (\alpha/2)]$ lower percentage point of the standard normal cdf where $\bar{X} = \sum_1^n (X_i/n)$.

(4) Asymptotic ($m \to \infty$) CI for p is the same as in case (3) with n = 1.

(5) Two binomial populations with proportions p_1, p_2. CI for p_1p_2.

[Buehler (1957), p. 488]

7.2.2 *POISSON*

$$f(x;\ \theta) = \frac{e^{-\theta}\theta^x}{x!}; \quad x = 0, 1, 2, \ldots, \theta > 0$$

(1) CI for θ [Crow and Gardner (1959), pp. 441-453].

(2) CI for θ

$$P[\theta_L \le \theta \le \theta_U] = 1 - \alpha$$

where $\theta_U = \chi^2_{(\lambda_2;m_2)}/2$, $\theta_L = \chi^2_{(\lambda_1;m_1)}/2$, $m_1 = 2X$, $m_2 = 2(X + 1)$, $\lambda_1 = 1 - (\alpha/2)$, $\lambda_2 = \alpha/2$ [Satterthwaite (1957), p. 57].

(3) Asymptotic ($n \to \infty$) CI for θ

$$P[T_1 \le \theta \le T_2] \approx 1 - \alpha$$

where

$$T_1 = \bar{X} + \frac{k^2}{2n} - k\left(\frac{\bar{X}}{n} + \frac{k^2}{4n^2}\right)^{1/2}, \quad T_2 = \bar{X} + \frac{k^2}{2n} + k\left(\frac{\bar{X}}{n} + \frac{k^2}{4n^2}\right)^{1/2}$$

with $k = Z_{[1-(\alpha/2)]}$ as defined in the binomial distribution (Sec. 7.2.1(3)) and $\bar{X} = \sum_1^n (X_{i/n})$.

(4) Asymptotic CI for large θ is the same as in case (3) with n replaced by 1.

7.2.3 *NEGATIVE BINOMIAL*

$$f(x;\ p,\ r) = \binom{r + x - 1}{x} p^r q^x; \quad x = 0, 1, 2, \ldots, r > 0,$$
$$0 \le p \le 1, \; q = 1 - p$$

CI for mean q/p ($r = 1$) [Clemans (1959), pp. 260-263].

7.2.4 *MULTINOMIAL*

$$f(n_1, n_2, \ldots, n_k;\ p_1, p_2, \ldots, p_k)$$

$$= \frac{n!}{\prod_1^k (n_i!)} \prod_1^k (p_i)^{n_i}; \quad 0 < p_i < 1, \sum_1^k p_i = 1, \sum_1^k n_i = n$$

Confidence region for $p_1, p_2, \ldots, p_k$,

$$P[L_{1i} \le p_i \le L_{2i},\ i = 1, 2, \ldots, k] \approx 1 - \alpha$$

where

$$L_{1i} = \frac{C + 2n_i - \left[C\left\{C + 4n_i\left(\frac{n - n_i}{n}\right)\right\}\right]^{1/2}}{2(n + C)}$$

$$L_{2i} = \frac{C + 2n_i + \left[C\left\{C + 4n_i\left(\frac{n - n_i}{n}\right)\right\}\right]^{1/2}}{2(n + C)}$$

and $C = \chi^2_{(1-\alpha;\, k-1)}$ [Quesenberry and Hurst (1964), p. 193].
[Also see Goodman (1965), pp. 247-254.]

7.3 CONFIDENCE INTERVALS FOR SOME CONTINUOUS DISTRIBUTIONS

The following CI's, unless otherwise specified are based on a complete (not truncated or censored) random sample. In the following, let $Z_{(\gamma)}$, $\chi^2_{(\gamma;m)}$, $t_{(\gamma;n)}$ denote 100γ lower percentage points of a standard normal distribution, a chi square distribution with m degrees of freedom and a t distribution with n degrees of freedom, respectively. Let $0 < \alpha_1, \alpha_2 < 1$, $\alpha_1 + \alpha_2 = \alpha$, and $0 < \alpha < 1$. Also let $X_1, X_2, \ldots, X_n$ denote a random sample from a given population.

7.3.1 NORMAL

$$f(x;\, \mu,\, \sigma^2) = \frac{1}{\sigma\sqrt{2\pi}} \exp\left\{-\frac{(x - \mu)^2}{2\sigma^2}\right\}; \quad -\infty < x < \infty,\ -\infty < \mu < \infty,\ \sigma > 0$$

(1) Single Population Case

(a) CI for μ (σ known)

$$P\left[\bar{X} - Z_{[1-(\alpha/2)]}\frac{\sigma}{\sqrt{n}} \le \mu < \bar{X} + Z_{[1-(\alpha/2)]}\frac{\sigma}{\sqrt{n}}\right] = 1 - \alpha$$

where $\bar{X} = (\sum_1^n X_i)/n$ [Guenther (1971a), p. 52].

(b) CI for μ (σ unknown)

$$P\left[\bar{X} - t_{[1-(\alpha/2);n-1]}\frac{S}{\sqrt{n}} \le \mu \le \bar{X} + t_{[1-(\alpha/2);n-1]}\frac{S}{\sqrt{n}}\right] = 1 - \alpha$$

where $\bar{X} = \sum_1^n (X_i/n)$, and $S^2 = \sum_1^n [(X_i - \bar{X})^2/(n - 1)]$.

[Guenther (1969), p. 23; (1971), p. 52]

(c) CI for σ^2 (μ known)

$$P\left[\frac{\sum_1^n (X_i - \mu)^2}{\chi^2_{[1-(\alpha/2);n]}} \leq \sigma^2 \leq \frac{\sum_1^n (X_i - \mu)^2}{\chi^2_{[(\alpha/2);n]}}\right] = 1 - \alpha$$

(d) CI for σ^2 (μ unknown)

$$P\left[\frac{(n - 1)S^2}{\chi^2_{[1-(\alpha/2);n-1]}} \leq \sigma^2 \leq \frac{(n - 1)S^2}{\chi^2_{[(\alpha/2);n-1]}}\right] = 1 - \alpha$$

where S^2 is as defined in (b). [For reference see Greenwood and Sandomire (1950), pp. 257-260; Guenther (1969), p. 23 and (1971), p. 52; Tate and Klett (1959), pp. 674-682; Graybill and Morrison (1960), pp. 636-641; Thompson and Endriss (1961), pp. 22-23.]

(2) Two Populations (Unpaired) Case. Let $X_1, X_2, \ldots, X_n$ and $Y_1, Y_2, \ldots, Y_m$ be independent random samples from two normal populations with means μ_1 and μ_2 and variances σ_1^2 and σ_2^2, respectively.

(a) CI for $(\mu_1 - \mu_2)$ (σ_1^2, σ_2^2 known)

$$P\left[(\bar{X} - \bar{Y}) - Z_{[1-(\alpha/2)]}\sqrt{\frac{\sigma_1^2}{n} + \frac{\sigma_2^2}{m}}\right.$$

$$\left.\leq (\mu_1 - \mu_2) \leq (\bar{X} - \bar{Y}) + Z_{[1-(\alpha/2)]}\sqrt{\frac{\sigma_1^2}{n} + \frac{\sigma_1^2}{m}}\right] = 1 - \alpha$$

where $\bar{X} = \sum_1^n (X_i/n)$, $\bar{Y} = \sum_1^n (Y_i/m)$.

(b) CI for $(\mu_1 - \mu_2)$ ($\sigma_1 = \sigma_2 = \sigma$ unknown)

$$P\left[(\bar{X} - \bar{Y}) - t_{[1-(\alpha/2);n+m-2)}S_p\sqrt{\frac{1}{n} + \frac{1}{m}}\right.$$

$$\left.\leq (\mu_1 - \mu_2) \leq (\bar{X} - \bar{Y}) + t_{[1-(\alpha/2);n+m-2]}S_p\sqrt{\frac{1}{n} + \frac{1}{m}}\right] = 1 - \alpha$$

where $S_p^2 = [(n-1)S_1^2 + (m-1)S_2^2]/(n+m-2)$, $S_1^2 = [\sum_{i=1}^n (X_i - \bar{X})^2]/(n-1)$ and $S_2^2 = \sum_{i=1}^n [(Y_i - \bar{Y})^2/(m-1)]$ [Roussas (1973), p. 346].

(c) CI for σ_1^2/σ_2^2 (μ_1, μ_2 unknown)

$$P\left[\frac{S_1^2}{S_2^2}\frac{1}{F_{[1-(\alpha/2);n-1,m-1]}} \le \frac{\sigma_1^2}{\sigma_2^2} \le \frac{S_1^2}{S_2^2}\frac{1}{F_{[(\alpha/2);n-1,m-1]}}\right] = 1 - \alpha$$

where S_1^2 and S_2^2 are as defined in (b) and $F_{(\gamma;n,m)}$ is the $100(\gamma)$ lower percentage point of an F-distribution with degrees of freedom n and m.

[Roussas (1973), p. 346]

(3) Two Populations (Paired) Case. Let $X_1, X_2, \ldots, X_n$ and $Y_1, Y_2, \ldots, Y_n$ be a paired sample from normal populations with means μ_1 and μ_2 and variances σ_1^2 and σ_2^2, respectively.

CI for $(\mu_1 - \mu_2)$ (σ_1, σ_2 unknown)

$$P\left[(\bar{X} - \bar{Y}) - t_{[1-(\alpha/2);n-1]}\frac{S_d}{\sqrt{n}} \le (\mu_1 - \mu_2) \le (\bar{X} - \bar{Y}) + t_{[1-(\alpha/2):n-1]}\frac{S_d}{\sqrt{n}}\right] = 1 - \alpha$$

where $S_d^2 = \sum_1^n[(d_i - \bar{d})^2/(n-1)]$, $d_i = (X_i - Y_i)$, and $\bar{d} = (\bar{X} - \bar{Y}) = (\sum_1^n X_i/n) - (\sum_1^n Y_i/n)$.

(4) Miscellaneous

(a) Simultaneous confidence region for (μ, σ^2)

$$P\left[\left(\frac{\bar{X} - \mu}{\frac{\sigma}{\sqrt{n}}}\right)^2 \le c^2,\ \frac{(n-1)S^2}{b} \le \sigma^2 \le \frac{(n-1)S^2}{a}\right] = 1 - \alpha$$

where $\bar{X}$ and S^2 are as defined in Sec. 7.3.1(b) and a, b, c are determined to have confidence coefficient $(1 - \alpha)$.

[Roussas (1973), p. 348]

(b) Simultaneous confidence region for μ and σ^2, based on a single observation

$$P[X - ck|X| \le \mu \le X + ck|X|, \ \sigma < k|X|] = 1 - \alpha$$

where $c = Z_{[1-(\alpha_1/2)]}$, $k = 1/Z_{(\alpha_2/2)}$ [Rosenblatt (1966), p. 367].

(c) CI for $\frac{\sigma}{\mu}$ [Koopmans et al. (1964), pp. 27-28].

(d) CI for μ

$$P\left[\bar{X} - \frac{d}{\sqrt{n}} H_{[1-(\alpha/2)]} \le \mu \le \bar{X} + \frac{d}{\sqrt{n}} H_{[1-(\alpha/2)]}\right] = 1 - \alpha$$

where $\bar{X} = \sum_1^n (X_i/n)$ and $d = \sum_1^n (|X_i - \bar{X}|/n)$. $H_{[1-(\alpha/2)]}$ is tabulated.

[Herrey (1965), p. 257]

(e) CI for σ, based on quasi-range.

[Leone et al. (1961), pp. 262-263]

7.3.2 LOGNORMAL

$$f(x;\ \theta_1, \theta_2) = \frac{1}{x\sqrt{2\pi\theta_2}} \exp\left\{-\frac{(\log x - \theta_1)^2}{2\theta_2}\right\};\ x > 0,\ \theta_2 > 0,\ -\infty < \theta_1 < \infty$$

(1) Let $Y = \log X$, $\bar{Y} = \sum_1^n (Y_i/n)$ and $v^2 = \sum_1^n [(Y_i - \bar{Y})^2/(n - 1)]$. Then the CI's for the parameters θ_1 and θ_2 can be obtained from the normal distribution after replacing $\bar{X}$ by $\bar{Y}$, S^2 by v^2, μ by θ_1 and σ^2 by θ_2 in Normal Case I.

(2) CI for $\frac{\sigma}{\mu}$

$$P\left[\sqrt{\left\{\exp\left[\underline{\theta}_n^2\ (s)\right] - 1\right\}} \le \frac{\sigma}{\mu} \le \sqrt{\left\{\exp\left[\bar{\theta}_n^2\ (s)\right] - 1\right\}}\right] = 1 - \alpha$$

where $\underline{\theta}_n^2(s) = (n - 1)v^2/(\chi^2_{(\alpha_2;n-1)})$, $\bar{\theta}_n^2(s) = (n - 1)v^2/(\chi^2_{(\alpha_1;n-1)})$.

[Koopmans et al. (1964), p. 30]

7.3.3 INVERSE GAUSSIAN

$$f(x;\ \mu,\ \lambda) = \sqrt{\frac{\lambda}{2\pi x^3}}\ \exp\left[\frac{-\lambda(x-\mu)^2}{2\mu^2 x}\right];\quad x > 0,\ \mu > 0,\ \lambda > 0$$

(1) CI for μ (λ known)

$$P\left[\bar{X}\left\{1 + \sqrt{\frac{\bar{X}}{n\lambda}}\ Z_{[1-(\alpha/2)]}\right\}^{-1} \le \mu \le \bar{X}\left\{\max\left(0,\ 1 - \sqrt{\frac{\bar{X}}{n\lambda}}\ Z_{[1-(\alpha/2)]}\right)\right\}^{-1}\right] = 1 - \alpha$$

(2) CI for μ

$$P\left[\bar{X}\left\{1 - \sqrt{\frac{\bar{X}v}{n}}\ t_{[1-(\alpha/2);n-1]}\right\}^{-1} \le \mu \le \bar{X}\left\{\max\left(0,\ 1 - \sqrt{\frac{\bar{X}v}{n}}\ t_{[1-(\alpha/2);n-1]}\right)\right\}^{-1}\right] = 1 - \alpha$$

where $v = [1/(n-1)] \sum_{i=1}^{n} [(1/X_i) - (1/\bar{X})]$.

[Chhikara (1972), pp. 41-42]

7.3.4 CAUCHY

$$f(x;\ \theta,\ \lambda) = \frac{1}{\Pi\lambda\left[1 + \left(\frac{x-\theta}{\lambda}\right)^2\right]};\quad -\infty < x < \infty,\ -\infty < \theta < \infty,\ \lambda > 0$$

(1) CI for θ (λ known)

$$P\left[\hat{\theta} - a_{1-(\alpha/2)}\frac{\lambda}{\sqrt{n}} \le \theta \le \hat{\theta} - a_{\alpha/2}\frac{\lambda}{\sqrt{n}}\right] = 1 - \alpha$$

(2) CI for θ (λ known)

$$P\left[\hat{\theta} - a'_{1-(\alpha/2)}\frac{\hat{\lambda}}{\sqrt{n}} \le \theta \le \hat{\theta} - a'_{\alpha/2}\frac{\hat{\lambda}}{\sqrt{n}}\right] = 1 - \alpha$$

(3) CI for λ (θ known)

$$P\left[\frac{\hat{\lambda}}{b_{1-(\alpha/2)}} \leq \lambda \leq \frac{\hat{\lambda}}{b_{\alpha/2}}\right] = 1 - \alpha$$

(4) CI for λ (θ unknown)

$$P\left[\frac{\hat{\lambda}}{b'_{1-(\alpha/2)}} \leq \lambda \leq \frac{\hat{\lambda}}{b'_{\alpha/2}}\right] = 1 - \alpha$$

where in (1)-(4) $\hat{\theta}$, $\hat{\lambda}$ are MLE's of θ, λ (taking into account the other parameter is known or unknown), respectively. The 100γ percentage points a_γ, a'_γ, b_γ, b'_γ for selected values of γ are given in Haas et al. (1970), p. 405.

7.3.5 *EXPONENTIAL*

$$f(x;\ \theta) = \frac{1}{\theta} e^{-x/\theta}; \quad x \geq 0,\ \theta > 0$$

(1) CI for mean θ

$$P\left[\frac{2Y}{\chi^2_{(1-\alpha_1, 2n)}} \leq \theta \leq \frac{2Y}{\chi^2_{(\alpha_2, 2n)}}\right] = 1 - \alpha$$

where $Y = \sum_1^n X_i$ [Guenther (1969), p. 23; (1971a), p. 52].

(2) CI for mean θ (using a censored sample)

$$P\left[\frac{2Y}{\chi^2_{(1-\alpha_1; 2r)}} \leq \theta \leq \frac{2Y}{\chi^2_{(\alpha_2; 2r)}}\right] = 1 - \alpha$$

where $Y = \{\sum_1^r X_{(i;n)} + (n - r)X_{(r;n)}\}$.

[Epstein and Sobel (1953), p. 486]

CI for θ, based on quasi-range.

[Leone et al. (1961), pp. 265-266]

7.3.6 *TRUNCATED EXPONENTIAL*

$$f(x;\ \theta) = e^{-(x-\theta)}, \quad x \geq \theta$$

CI for θ

$$P\left[X_{(1;n)} - \frac{\chi^2_{(1-\alpha,2)}}{2n} \leq \theta \leq X_{(1;n)}\right] = 1 - \alpha$$

7.3.7 *GAMMA*

$$f(x;\ \theta,\ m) = \frac{e^{-x/\theta} x^{m-1}}{\theta^m \Gamma(m)}; \quad x \geq 0,\ \theta > 0,\ m > 0$$

(1) CI for θ (m known)

$$P\left[\frac{2Y}{\chi^2_{(1-\alpha_1, 2mn)}} \leq \theta \leq \frac{2Y}{\chi^2_{(\alpha_2, 2mn)}}\right] = 1 - \alpha$$

where $Y = \sum_1^n X_i$ [Guenther (1969), p. 23; (1971), p. 52].

(2) CI for $\frac{\sigma}{\mu}$

$$P\left[\left\{\frac{2nZ}{C_1\chi^2_{[1-(\alpha/2);n-1]}}\right\}^{1/2} \leq \frac{\sigma}{\mu} \leq \left\{\frac{2nZ}{C_2\chi^2_{[(\alpha/2);n-1]}}\right\}^{1/2}\right] \approx 1 - \alpha$$

where $Z = \log \bar{X} - [\sum_1^n (\log X_i/n)]$, $\bar{X} = \sum_1^n (X_i/n)$, and

$$C_1 = \frac{1}{2}\left[1 + \left\{1 + \frac{4(n+1)Z}{3\chi^2_{[1-(\alpha/2);n-1]}}\right\}^{1/2}\right]$$

$$C_2 = \frac{1}{2}\left[1 + \left\{1 + \frac{4(n+1)Z}{3\chi^2_{[(\alpha/2);n-1]}}\right\}^{1/2}\right]$$

[Linhart (1965), pp. 736-737]

7.3.8 *WEIBULL*

(1) $f(x;\ \theta,\ c) = c\left(\frac{x}{\theta}\right)^{c-1} \exp\left\{-\frac{1}{\theta} x^c\right\}; \quad x \geq 0,\ c > 0,\ \theta > 0$

(a) CI for θ^c (c known)

$$P\left[\frac{2Y}{\chi^2_{(1-\alpha_1,2n)}} < \theta^c < \frac{2Y}{\chi^2_{(\alpha_2,2n)}}\right] = 1 - \alpha$$

where $Y = \sum_1^n x_i^c$ [Guenther (1969), p. 24; (1971), p. 53].

(b) CI for θ (c unknown)

$$P\left[\hat{\theta} \exp\left(-\frac{u_{1-(\alpha/2)}}{\sqrt{n}\ \hat{c}}\right) \leq \theta \leq \hat{\theta} \exp\left(-\frac{u_{\alpha/2}}{\sqrt{n}\ \hat{c}}\right)\right] = 1 - \alpha$$

where $\hat{\theta}$ and $\hat{c}$ are the MLE's of θ and c, respectively. The 100γ percentage points u_γ for selected values of γ are tabulated for complete sample in Thoman et al. and for censored sample in Billmann et al.

[Thoman et al. (1969), p. 453]

[Billmann et al. (1972), p. 832]

(c) CI for θ (c unknown)

$$P[\exp(\tilde{u} - \tilde{b}u'_{1-(\alpha/2)}) \leq \theta \leq \exp(\tilde{u} - \tilde{b}u'_{\alpha/2})] = 1 - \alpha$$

where $\tilde{u}$ and $\tilde{b}$ are the best linear invariant estimators of $u = \log\theta$ and $b = 1/c$, respectively. The 100γ percentage points for u'_γ for selected values of γ are tabulated for censored and complete samples in Mann and Fertig (1973), p. 99.

(d) CI for c (θ unknown)

$$P\left[\frac{\hat{c}}{E\left(\frac{\hat{c}}{c}\right) + \frac{1}{\sqrt{n}} Z'_{1-(\alpha/2)}} \leq c \leq \frac{\hat{c}}{E\left(\frac{\hat{c}}{c}\right) + \frac{1}{\sqrt{n}} Z'_{\alpha/2}}\right] = 1 - \alpha$$

where $\hat{c}$ is the MLE of c. The 100γ percentage points Z'_γ for selected values of γ are tabulated for censored and complete samples in Billmann et al. $E(\hat{c}/c)$ is also tabulated [Billman et al. (1972), p. 832].

(e) CI for c (unknown)

$$P\left[\frac{W_{\alpha/2}}{\tilde{b}} \le c \le \frac{W_{1-(\alpha/2)}}{\tilde{b}}\right] = 1 - \alpha$$

where $\tilde{b}$ is the best linear invariant estimator of $b = 1/c$. The 100γ percentage points W_γ for selected values of γ are tabulated for censored and complete samples in Mann and Fertig (1973), p. 99.

7.3.9 POWER FUNCTION

$$f(x;\ \theta) = \theta x^{\theta-1};\ 0 \le x \le 1,\ \theta > 0$$

CI for θ

$$P\left[\frac{\chi^2_{(\alpha_2, 2n)}}{2Y} \le \theta \le \frac{\chi^2_{(1-\alpha_1, 2n)}}{2Y}\right] = 1 - \alpha$$

where $Y = -\sum_1^n \log X_i$ [Guenther (1969), p. 24; (1971), p. 53].

7.3.10 UNIFORM

(1) $f(x;\ \theta) = \frac{1}{\theta},\ 0 \le x < \theta$

(a) CI for θ

$$P\left[X_{(n;n)} \le \theta \le X_{(n;n)} \frac{1}{\alpha^{1/n}}\right] = 1 - \alpha$$

[Kendall and Stuart (1967), p. 132]

[Guenther (1969), p. 24; (1971), p. 53]

(b) $P\left[R \le \theta \le \frac{R}{\psi}\right] = 1 - \alpha$

where $R = X_{(n;n)} - X_{(1;n)}$ and ψ is given by $\psi^{n-1}\{n - (n - 1)\psi\} = \alpha$.

[Kendall and Stuart (1961), p. 131]

(2) $f(x;\ \theta) = \frac{1}{2\theta};\ -\theta < x < \theta,\ \theta > 0$

CI for θ

$$P\left[\frac{Y}{1 - \alpha_1} \le \theta \le \frac{Y}{\alpha_2}\right] = 1 - \alpha$$

where $Y = \max[-X_{(1;n)}, X_{(n;n)}]$ and $\alpha_1 + \alpha_2 = \alpha$.

(3) $f(x; \theta_1, \theta_2) = \dfrac{1}{\theta_2 - \theta_1}$; $\theta_1 < x < \theta_2$, $-\infty < \theta_1 < \infty$, $-\infty < \theta_2 < \infty$

CI for $\theta = \theta_2 - \theta_1$

$$P\left[\frac{Y}{b} \le \theta \le \frac{Y}{a}\right] = 1 - \alpha$$

where a and b are solutions of $na^{n-1} - (n - 1)a^n = \alpha_2$, $nb^{n-1} - (n - 1)b^n = 1 - \alpha_1$, and $Y = X_{(n;n)} - X_{(1;n)}$.

(4) $f(x; \theta_1, \theta_2) = \dfrac{1}{\theta_2}$; $\theta_1 - \dfrac{\theta_2}{2} \le x \le \theta_1 + \dfrac{\theta_2}{2}$, $-\infty < \theta_1 < \infty$, $\theta_2 > 0$

CI for θ_2

$$P\left[\frac{Y}{b} \le \theta_2 \le \frac{Y}{a}\right] = 1 - \alpha$$

where a and b are as defined in (3) and $Y = X_{(n;n)} - X_{(1;n)}$.

7.3.11 PARETO

$$f(x; \theta, \beta) = \frac{\theta\beta^\theta}{x^{\theta+1}}; \quad x \ge \beta > 0, \ \theta > 0$$

(1) CI for $\frac{1}{\theta}$ (β known)

$$P\left[\frac{2Y}{\chi^2_{(1-\alpha_1;2n)}} \le \frac{1}{\theta} \le \frac{2Y}{\chi^2_{(\alpha_2;2n)}}\right] = 1 - \alpha$$

where $Y = \sum_1^n \log(X/\beta)$.

(2) CI for β (θ known)

$$P\left[X_{(1;n)}(\alpha_1)^{1/n\theta} \le \beta \le X_{(1;n)}(1 - \alpha_2)^{1/n\theta}\right] = 1 - \alpha$$

7.3.12 EXTREME-VALUE

$$f(x;\ \theta,\ \beta) = \frac{1}{\beta} \exp\left\{\left(\frac{x - \theta}{\beta}\right) - e^{-(x-\theta)/\beta}\right\};\quad -\infty < x < \infty,$$
$$-\infty < \theta < \infty,\ \beta > 0$$

CI's for θ or β can be obtained from Weibull distribution by making the transformation $X = \log Y$, where Y has the Weibull distribution (see Sec. 7.3.8).

7.3.13 TRUNCATED EXTREME-VALUE

$$f(x;\ \theta) = \frac{1}{\theta} \exp\left\{x - \frac{e^x - 1}{\theta}\right\};\quad x > 0,\ \theta > 0$$

CI for θ

$$P\left[\frac{2Y}{\chi^2_{(1-\alpha_1;2n)}} \le \theta \le \frac{2Y}{\chi^2_{(\alpha_2;2n)}}\right] = 1 - \alpha$$

where $Y = \sum_1^n (e^{X_i} - 1)$.

7.3.14 LAPLACE

$$f(x;\ \theta) = \frac{1}{2\beta} \exp\left\{-\frac{|x - \theta|}{\beta}\right\};\quad -\infty < x < \infty,\ -\infty < \theta < \infty,\ \beta > 0$$

(1) CI for β ($\theta = 0$)

$$P\left[\frac{2Y}{\chi^2_{[1-(\alpha/2);2n]}} \le \beta \le \frac{2Y}{\chi^2_{[(\alpha/2);2n]}}\right] = 1 - \alpha$$

where $Y = \sum_1^n |X_i|$ [Guenther (1969), p. 24; (1971), p. 53].

(2) CI for β (θ unknown)

$$P\left[\frac{2Y}{\chi^2_{[1-(\alpha/2);v]}} \le \beta \le \frac{2Y}{\chi^2_{[(\alpha/2);v]}}\right] \approx 1 - \alpha$$

where $Y = \sum_1^n |X_i - m_0|$, m_0 is the sample median and

$$\frac{v}{2} = E\left(\frac{Y}{\beta}\right) \approx \begin{cases} n - \frac{1}{2} - \frac{3}{4n} & \text{if } n \text{ odd} \\ n - \frac{1}{2} + \frac{1}{4n} & \text{if } n \text{ even} \end{cases}$$

[Bain and Engelhardt (1973), p. 883]

(3) CI for θ (β unknown)

$$P\left[\hat{\theta} - \frac{Z_{[1-(\alpha/2)]}Y}{n\left(n - Z^2_{[1-(\alpha/2)]}\right)^{1/2}} \le \theta \le \hat{\theta} + \frac{Z_{[1-(\alpha/2)]}Y}{n\left(n - Z^2_{[1-(\alpha/2)]}\right)^{1/2}}\right]$$

$$\approx 1 - \alpha$$

where $\hat{\theta} = m_0$ and Y is as defined in (2).

[Bain and Engelhardt (1973), p. 883]

7.3.15 LOGISTIC

$$F(x;\ \theta,\ \beta) = \left[1 + \exp\left\{-\frac{(x - \theta)}{\beta}\right\}\right]^{-1}; \quad -\infty < x < \infty,\ -\infty < \theta < \infty,\ \beta > 0$$

(1) CI for θ (β known)

$$P\left[a - \frac{\beta}{\sqrt{n}} A'_{[1-(\alpha/2);n]} \le \theta \le a + \frac{\beta}{\sqrt{n}} A'_{[1-(\alpha/2);n]}\right] = 1 - \alpha$$

where a is the MLE of θ and $A'_n = \sqrt{n}[(a - \theta)/\beta]$, $P(A'_n \le A'_{(\gamma,n)}) = \gamma$. $A'_{(\gamma,n)}$ are tabulated.

(2) CI for θ (β unknown)

$$P\left[a - \frac{b}{\sqrt{n}} A_{[1-(\alpha/2);n]} \le \theta \le a + \frac{b}{\sqrt{n}} A_{[1-(\alpha/2);n]}\right] = 1 - \alpha$$

where a and b are the MLE's of θ and β, respectively. $A_n = \sqrt{n}[(a - \theta)/b]$ and $P[A_n \leq A_{(\gamma,n)}] = \gamma$. $A_{(\gamma;n)}$ are tabulated.

(3) CI for β (θ unknown)

$$P\left[\frac{b}{B_{[1-(\alpha/2);n]}} \leq \beta \leq \frac{b}{B_{[(\alpha/2);n]}}\right] = 1 - \alpha$$

where b is as defined in (2), $B_n = b/\beta$ and $P(B_n < B_{(\gamma;n)}) = \gamma$. $B_{(\gamma;n)}$ are tabulated.

[For (1)-(3) see Antle et al. (1970), pp. 400-401]

7.3.16 CHI

$$f(x;\ \theta,\ m) = \frac{x^{m-1}e^{-x^2/2\theta}}{\theta^{m/2}2^{[(m/2)-1]}\Gamma\left(\frac{m}{2}\right)};\quad x > 0,\ \theta > 0,\ m > 0$$

CI for θ (m known)

$$P\left[\frac{Y}{\chi^2_{(1-\alpha_1,mn)}} \leq \theta \leq \frac{Y}{\chi^2_{(\alpha_2,mn)}}\right] = 1 - \alpha$$

where $Y = \sum_1^n X_i^2$.

7.3.17 BURR

$$f(x;\ m,\ \theta) = \frac{m\theta x^{m-1}}{(1 + x^m)^{\theta+1}};\quad x > 0,\ \theta > 0,\ m > 0$$

CI for θ (m known)

$$P\left[\frac{\chi^2_{(\alpha_2;2n)}}{2Y} \leq \theta \leq \frac{\chi^2_{(1-\alpha_1;2n)}}{2Y}\right] = 1 - \alpha$$

where $Y = \sum_1^n \log(1 + X_i^m)$.

Chapter 8

PROPERTIES OF DISTRIBUTIONS

Useful properties of several well-known distributions are listed in this chapter. Characterizing properties of most of these distributions are in Chapter 4.

8.1 DISCRETE DISTRIBUTIONS

8.1.1 BINOMIAL

$$f(x;\ m,\ p) = \binom{m}{x} p^x q^{m-x};\ x = 0,\ 1,\ 2,\ \ldots,\ m,\ 0 < p < 1,\ q = 1 - p$$

$$F(x;\ m,\ p) = \begin{cases} \displaystyle\sum_{y=0}^{\min([x],m)} \binom{m}{y} p^y q^{m-y}, & x \geq 0 \\ 0, & x < 0 \end{cases}$$

(1) Properties

(a) If $p = 1/2$, the pf $f(x;\ m,\ p)$ is symmetric about $x = m/2$.

[Kendall and Stuart (1958), p. 122]

For fixed x and m, the cdf $F(x;\ m,\ p)$ is a nonincreasing function of p [Rao (1952), p. 33].

(b) $f(x + 1; m, p) = \frac{(m - x)p}{(x + 1)q} f(x; m, p), \quad x = 0, 1, \ldots, m - 1$

[Freund (1971), p. 84]

$$f(x - 1; m, p) = f(x; m, p)$$

if $x = (m + 1)p$ is an integer.

$f(x; m, p) = f(m - x; m, q)$ [Freund (1971), p. 77]

$$F(x; m, p) = 1 - I_p(x + 1, m - x)$$

where $I_p(a, b)$ is the incomplete beta function ratio.

$$1 - F(x - 1; m, p) = f(x; m, p)qG(m + 1; 1; x + 1; p)$$

where G is the hypergeometric function [Bahadur (1960), p. 43].

(c) If $X_1, X_2, \ldots, X_n$ are independent binomial random variables with pf's $f(x; m_i, p)$ $(i = 1, 2, \ldots, n)$, respectively, then the random variable $Y = \sum_{i=1}^{n} X_i$ also has a binomial distribution with pf $f(y; \sum_{i=1}^{n} m_i, p)$ [Rao (1952), pp. 32-33].

(2) Relationships with Other Distributions

(a) Binomial--Bernoulli. The function $f(y; 1, p)$ is known as Bernoulli pf. If $Y_1, Y_2, \ldots, Y_m$ are iid random variables with Bernoulli pf $f(y; 1, p)$, then the random variable $X = \sum_{i=1}^{m} Y_i$ has a binomial distribution with pf $f(x; m, p)$ [Rao (1952), pp. 32-33].

(b) Binomial--Beta. Let $F_B(x; m, p)$ be a binomial cdf and $F_\beta(y; a, b)$ be a beta cdf (see Sec. 8.2.8). Let a and b be positive integers. Then, for $0 < y < 1$,

$$F_\beta(y; a, b) = 1 - F_B(a - 1; a + b - 1, y)$$

$F_B(x; m, p) = 1 - F_\beta(p; x + 1, m - x)$ [Rao (1952), p. 33]

(c) Binomial--Negative Binomial. Let $f_B(x; m, p)$ be a binomial pf and $f_{NB}(y; s, p)$ be a negative-binomial pf (see Sec. 8.1.3). Then

$$f_{NB}(y; s, p) = \left(\frac{s}{s + y}\right) f_B(s; s + y, p)$$

$$f_B(x; m, p) = \left(\frac{m}{m - x}\right) f_{NB}(x; m - x, 1 - p)$$

[Freund (1971), p. 81]

$$F_{NB}(y;\ s,\ p) = 1 - F_B(s - 1;\ s + y,\ p)$$

[Owen and Gilbert (1959), p. 6]

(d) Binomial--F. Let $F_B(x;\ m,\ p)$ be a binomial cdf and $F_f(y;\ v,\ w)$ be an F cdf (see Sec. 8.2.16). Then

$$F_B(x;\ m,\ p) = F_f\left[\frac{q(x + 1)}{p(m - x)};\ 2(m - x),\ 2(x + 1)\right]$$

[Jowett (1963), p. 56]

(e) Binomial--Poisson. Let $f_B(x;\ m,\ p)$ be a binomial pf and $f_p(y;\ \lambda)$ be a Poisson pf (see Sec. 8.1.2). Then for fixed x, as $m \to \infty$ and $p \to 0$ such that $\lambda = mp$ (λ fixed),

$$f_B(x;\ m,\ p) \to f_p(x;\ \lambda) \quad \text{[Lindgren (1968), pp. 168-169]}$$

$$f_B(x;\ m,\ p) \mathrel{\tilde{\sim}} f_p(x;\ mp)\left[1 + \frac{1}{2m}\{x - (x - mp)^2\}\right]$$

[Burr (1973), p. 299]

(f) Binomial--Normal. Let $f_B(x;\ m,\ p)$ and $F_B(x;\ m,\ p)$ be binomial pf and cdf, respectively. Let $\phi(y)$ and $\Phi(y)$ be standard normal pdf and cdf (see Sec. 8.2.1), respectively. Then for fixed x and p, as $m \to \infty$,

$$F_B(x;\ m,\ p) \to \Phi\left(\frac{x - mp + \frac{1}{2}}{\sqrt{mp(1 - p)}}\right)$$

$$f_B(x;\ m,\ p) \to \Phi\left(\frac{x - mp + \frac{1}{2}}{\sqrt{mp(1 - p)}}\right) - \Phi\left(\frac{x - mp - \frac{1}{2}}{\sqrt{mp(1 - p)}}\right)$$

[Parzen (1960), pp. 244, 246]

[Also see Peizer and Pratt (1968), I and II; Wise (1950); and Molenaar (1970).]

(g) Binomial--Hypergeometric

(i) Let $f_B(x;\ m,\ p)$ be a binomial pf and $f_h(y;\ n,\ N,\ M)$ be a hypergeometric pf (see Sec. 8.1.4). Then for fixed y and n, as $M \to \infty$ and $N \to \infty$ such that $P = M/N$ (p fixed),

$$f_h(y;\ n,\ N,\ M) \to f_B(y;\ n,\ p)$$

[Lindgren (1968), pp. 157-158]

$$f_h(y;\ n,\ N,\ M) = f_B\left(y;\ M,\ \frac{n}{N}\right)\left[1 + \frac{1}{2n}\left\{y - \left(\frac{nM}{N}\right)^2\right\} + O\left(\frac{1}{n^2}\right)\right]$$

[Burr (1973), p. 300]

[Molenaar (1970]

(ii) Let $F_B(x;\ m,\ p)$ be a binomial cdf and $F_h(x;\ n,\ N,\ M)$ be a hypergeometric cdf (see Sec. 8.1.4). Then

$$F_h(x;\ n,\ N,\ M) \approx F_B\left(x;\ n,\ \frac{M}{N}\right)$$

$$F_h(x;\ n,\ N,\ M) \approx F_B\left(x;\ M,\ \frac{n}{N}\right)$$

$$F_h(x;\ n,\ N,\ M) \approx F_B\left(M - x - 1;\ N - n,\ \frac{M}{N}\right)$$

$$F_h(x;\ n,\ N,\ M) \approx F_B\left(n - x - 1;\ N - M,\ \frac{n}{N}\right)$$

Use that approximation $F_B(a;\ b,\ p)$ which has the smallest value of a.

[Lieberman and Owen (1961), p. 17]

(3) Some Other Results

(a) $$\frac{\lambda^x}{x!}\left(1 - \frac{\lambda}{n}\right)^{n-x} \geq \binom{n}{x}p^x q^{n-x} \geq \frac{\lambda^x}{x!}\left(1 - \frac{x}{n}\right)^x\left(1 - \frac{\lambda}{n}\right)^x, \quad \lambda = np$$

[Feller (1960), p. 161]

(b) $$\sum_{i=0}^{x}\binom{n}{i}\left(\frac{\lambda}{n}\right)\left(1 - \frac{\lambda}{n}\right)^{n-i} \underset{(\leq)}{\geq} \sum_{i=0}^{x}\frac{e^{-\lambda}\lambda^i}{i!}, \quad x \leq \lambda - 1 \quad (x \geq \lambda)$$

[Anderson and Samuels (1965), p. 2]

(c) $1 - F(ma - 1;\ m,\ p) \leq \exp(-mg(a))$ if $a \geq p$, $0 < a < 1$

$F(ma;\ m,\ p) \leq \exp(-mg(a))$ if $a \leq p$, $0 < a < 1$

where $g(a) = a \log(a/p) + (1 - a)\log[(1 - a)/q]$.

[Okamoto (1959), p. 29]

(d) $F(\lambda;\ m,\ p) > \frac{1}{2}$, if $p \le \frac{1}{2}$ and $mp = \lambda$ is an integer.

[Kharshikar (1969), p. 495]

(e) For $mp \le x \le (m + 1)p$,

$$f\left(x;\ m,\ \frac{x+1}{m+1}\right) \le f(x;\ m,\ p) \le f\left(x;\ m,\ \frac{x}{m}\right)$$

If $(m + 1)p - 1 < x \le mp$, the above inequality holds with $(x + 1)/(m + 1)$ in the lower bound replaced by $x/(m + 1)$.

[Feller (1960), p. 182]

(f) $$\sum_{i=r}^{n} \binom{n}{i} p^i q^{n-i} = p^r \sum_{i=r}^{n} \binom{i-1}{r-1} q^{i-r}$$

$$\sum_{i=r}^{n} i \binom{n}{i} p^i q^{n-i} = np \sum_{i=r}^{n} \binom{n}{i} p^i q^{n-i} + r\binom{n}{r} p^r q^{n-r+1}$$

[Owen and Gilbert (1959), p. 11]

(g) Let $F(x;\ n,\ p) = \alpha$. Then for fixed x and n

$$p = \frac{x}{x + (n - x + 1)\ F_{\alpha;\,2n-2x+2,\,2x}}$$

where $F_{\alpha;v,w}$ is the 100α upper percentage point of an F-distribution with pdf $f(x;\ v,\ w)$ (see Sec. 8.2.16).

[Owen and Gilbert (1959), p. 10]

8.1.2 POISSON

$$f(x;\ \lambda) = \frac{e^{-\lambda}\lambda^x}{x!};\quad x = 0, 1, 2, \ldots,\ \lambda > 0$$

$$F(x;\ \lambda) = \begin{cases} \sum_{y=0}^{[x]} \dfrac{e^{-\lambda}\lambda^x}{y!}, & x \ge 0 \\ 0, & x < 0 \end{cases}$$

(1) Properties

(a) For fixed x, the cdf $F(x;\ \lambda)$ is a nonincreasing function of λ [Rao (1952), p. 38].

(b) $f(x + 1; \lambda) = \left(\frac{\lambda}{x + 1}\right) f(x; \lambda)$

$$f(x; \lambda) = \frac{\lambda^x}{x!} f(0; \lambda)$$

$$\frac{d}{d\lambda} f(x; \lambda) = f(x - 1; \lambda) - f(x; \lambda)$$

$$xf(x, \lambda) = \lambda f(x - 1, \lambda)$$

$$\sum_{j=0}^{x} jf(x; \lambda) = \lambda F(x - 1; \lambda)$$

[Hadley and Whitin (1961), pp. 408-410]

(c) If $X_1, X_2, \ldots, X_n$ are independent Poisson random variables with pf's $f(x; \lambda_i)$ $(i = 1, 2, \ldots, n)$, respectively, then the random variable $Y = \sum_{i=1}^n X_i$ has also a Poisson distribution with pf $f(y; \sum_1^n \lambda_i)$ [Rao (1952), pp. 36-37].

(2) Relationships with Other Distributions

(a) Poisson--Gamma. Let $F_p(x; \lambda)$ be a Poisson cdf and $F_g(y; \theta, m)$ be a gamma cdf (see Sec. 8.2.6). Let m be a positive integer, then

$$F_g(y; \theta, m) = 1 - F_p(m - 1; y\theta)$$

$$F_p(x; \lambda) = 1 - F_g(\lambda; 1, x + 1)$$ [Rao (1952), p. 38]

(b) Poisson--Exponential. For a renewal counting process $N(t_0)$, if the interarrival times are exponentially distributed random variables, with pdf $f_e(x; \theta)$ (see Sec. 8.2.5), the random variable $N(t_0)$, where t_0 is a constant, has a Poisson distribution with pf $f_p(x; \theta t_0)$ [Parzen (1962), pp. 133-134].

(c) Poisson--Noncentral Chi Square. See Noncentral Chi Square Distribution (Sec. 8.2.17).

(d) Poisson--Noncentral F. See Noncentral F Distribution (Sec. 8.2.19).

(e) Poisson--Binomial. See Binomial Distribution (Sec. 8.1.1).

(f) Poisson--Normal. Let $f_p(x; \lambda)$ and $F_p(x; \lambda)$ be a Poisson pf and a cdf, respectively. Let $\Phi(y)$ be the standard normal cdf (see Sec. 8.2.1). Then for fixed x and as $\lambda \to \infty$,

$$F_p(x; \lambda) \to \Phi\left(\frac{x - \lambda + \frac{1}{2}}{\sqrt{\lambda}}\right)$$

$$f_p(x; \lambda) \to \Phi\left(\frac{x - \lambda + \frac{1}{2}}{\sqrt{\lambda}}\right) - \Phi\left(\frac{x - \lambda - \frac{1}{2}}{\sqrt{\lambda}}\right) \quad \text{[Parzen (1960), p. 248]}$$

[Also, see Peizer and Pratt (1968), I and II; Molenaar (1970).]

(3) Some Other Results

(a) $F(x; \lambda) \geq F(x - 1; \lambda - 1), \; x \leq \lambda - 1$

$F(x; \lambda) \leq F(x - 1; \lambda - 1), \; x \geq \lambda$

[Anderson and Samuels (1965), p. 3]

(b) See Binomial (Sec. 8.1.1(3)b).

(c) $F(x; \lambda) \leq \Phi[(x + 1 - \lambda)/\sqrt{\lambda}]$ for all x, where Φ is the standard normal cdf (see Sec. 8.2.1). $F(x; \lambda) \geq F_g(x; 1, \lambda + 1)$ for all x, where F_g is the gamma cdf (see Sec. 8.2.6).

[Bohman (1963), pp. 47-50]

(d) $F(\lambda; \lambda) > \frac{1}{2}$ if λ is an integer [Teicher (1955), p. 149].

(e) $$\sum_{x=c_1-1}^{c_2-1} f(x; \lambda) \geq \sum_{x=c_1}^{c_2} f(x; \lambda), \; \lambda \leq m(c_1, c_2)$$

$$\sum_{x=c_1-1}^{c_2-1} f(x; \lambda) \leq \sum_{x=c_1}^{c_2} f(x; \lambda), \; \lambda \geq m(c_1, c_2)$$

where $m(c_1, c_2) = [c_1(c_1 + 1) \cdots c_2]^{1/(c_2-c_1+1)}$.

[Crow and Gardner (1959), p. 442]

8.1.3 NEGATIVE BINOMIAL

$$f(x;\ s,\ p) = \binom{s + x - 1}{x} p^s q^x;\quad x = 0, 1, 2, \ldots,\ 0 < p < 1,\quad s > 0,\ q = 1 - p$$

$$F(x;\ s,\ p) = \begin{cases} \sum_{y=0}^{[x]} \binom{s + y - 1}{y} p^s q^y, & x \geq 0 \\ 0, & x < 0 \end{cases}$$

(1) Properties

(a) For fixed x and s, the cdf $F(x;\ s,\ p)$ is a nondecreasing function of p [Peizer and Pratt (1968), p. 1449].

(b) $f(x + 1;\ s,\ p) = [(s + x)/(x + 1)q]f(x;\ s,\ p)$.

[Freund (1971), p. 81]

Also, $F(x;\ s,\ p) = I_p(s,\ x + 1)$, where $I_p(a,\ b)$ is the incomplete beta function ratio [Peizer and Pratt (1968), p. 1449].

(c) If $X_1, X_2, \ldots, X_n$ are independent negative binomial random variables with pf's $f(x;\ s_i,\ p)$ $(i = 1, 2, \ldots, n)$, respectively, then the random variable $Y = \sum_{i=1}^n X_i$ also has a negative binomial distribution with pf $f(x;\ \sum_1^n s_i,\ p)$.

(d) The negative binomial distribution is known as a geometric distribution when s = 1. In this case, $f(x;\ 1,\ p) = pq^x$ for $x = 0, 1, 2, \ldots$. If s = 1, $P[X \geq i + j | X \geq i] = P(X \geq j)$ $(i, j = 0, 1, 2, \ldots)$. This is the no memory property [Mood et al. (1974), pp. 100-101].

(2) Relationships with Other Distributions

(a) Negative Binomial--Binomial. See Binomial Distribution (Sec. 8.1.1).

(b) Geometric--Exponential. Let $F_{NB}(x;\ 1,\ p)$ be a geometric cdf and $F_e(y;\ \theta)$ be an exponential cdf (see Sec. 8.2.5). Then

$$F_{NB}(x;\ 1,\ p) = F_e\{[x + 1],\ -\log(1 - p)\}$$

where $[x + 1]$ is the greatest integer $\leq (x + 1)$.

[Prochaska (1973), p. 27]

(c) Negative Binomial--Beta. See (1)b of this section.

(d) Negative Binomial--Poisson. Let $f_{NB}(x; s, p)$ denote a negative binomial pf and $f_p(y; \lambda)$ denote a Poisson pf (see Sec. 8.1.2). Then for fixed x, as $p \to 1$ and $s \to \infty$ such that $\lambda = s(1 - p)$ (λ is fixed), $f_{NB}(x; s, p) \to f_p(x; \lambda)$ [Feller (1960), p. 162].

$f_{NB}(x; s, p) \to f_p(x; \lambda)$ [Feller (1960), p. 162]

(3) Some Other Results

(a) $F(\lambda; s, p) > \frac{1}{2}$ if $p \leq \frac{1}{2}$ and $\lambda = \frac{sp}{1 - p}$ is an integer.

[Kharshikar (1969), p. 495]

(b) Let $F_{NB}(x; s, p)$ be a negative binomial cdf and $F_g(y; \theta, m)$ be a gamma cdf (see Sec. 8.2.6). Then

$$F(x; s, p) \approx F_g\left[x + 0.5 + \frac{s(1 - p)}{(2 - p)}; \frac{2p}{2 - p}, \frac{4s(1 - p)}{(2 - p)^2}\right]$$

$$- F_g\left[h; \frac{2p}{2 - p}, \frac{4s(1 - p)}{(2 - p)^2}\right]$$

where $h = \max\{0, [s(1 - p)/(2 - p)] - 0.5\}$.

[Best and Gipps (1974), p. 621]

(c) Normal Approximation to Negative Binomial. See Peizer and Pratt (1968), I and II.

8.1.4 HYPERGEOMETRIC

$$f(x; n, N, M) = \frac{\binom{M}{x}\binom{N - M}{n - x}}{\binom{N}{n}}, \quad \max(0, n - N + M) \leq x \leq \min(n, M)$$

$$F(x; n, N, M) = \begin{cases} \displaystyle\sum_{y=\max(0,n-N+M)}^{\min([x],\min(n,M))} \frac{\binom{M}{y}\binom{N - M}{n - y}}{\binom{N}{n}}, & x \geq 0 \\ 0, & x < 0 \end{cases}$$

(1) Properties

(a) $$f(x + 1, n, N, M) = \frac{(n - x)(M - x)}{(x + 1)(N - M - n + x + 1)} f(x; n, N, M)$$

$$f(x; n, N, M + 1) = \frac{(M + 1)(N - M - n + x)}{(N - M)(M + 1 - x)} f(x; n, N, M)$$

$$f(x;\ n+1,\ N,\ M) = \frac{(N - M - n + x)(n + 1)}{(n + 1 - x)(N - n)}\, f(x;\ n,\ N,\ M)$$

$$f(x;\ n,\ M,\ N+1) = \frac{(N + 1 - n)(N + 1 - M)}{(N + 1 - n - M + x)(N + 1)}\, f(x;\ n,\ N,\ M)$$

[Johnson and Kotz (1969), pp. 145-146]

(b)
$$\begin{aligned} f(x;\ n,\ N,\ M) &= f(n - x;\ n,\ N,\ N - M) \\ &= f(M - x;\ N - n,\ N,\ M) \\ &= f(N - n - M + x;\ N - n,\ N,\ N - M) \end{aligned}$$

$$\begin{aligned} F(x;\ n,\ N,\ M) &= F(N - n - M + x;\ N - n,\ N,\ N - M) \\ &= 1 - F(n - x - 1;\ n,\ N,\ N - M) \\ &= 1 - F(M - x - 1;\ N - n,\ N,\ M) \end{aligned}$$

[Lieberman and Owen (1961), p. 4]

(2) Relationships with Other Distributions

(a) Hypergeometric--Binomial. See Binomial Distribution (Sec. 8 1.1).

(b) Hypergeometric--Negative Hypergeometric. Let $H(x;\ n,\ N,\ M)$ be a hypergeometric cdf and $F_{Nh}(x;\ n,\ N,\ M)$ be defined by

$$F_{Nh}(x;\ n,\ N,\ M) = \sum_{i=0}^{[x]} \frac{\binom{n + i - 1}{n - 1}\binom{N - n - i}{N - n - M}}{\binom{N}{M}}\ ;\ 0 \le x \le M,\quad N \ge n + M$$

Then
$$\begin{aligned} F_{Nh}(x;\ n,\ N,\ M) &= 1 - F_h(n - 1;\ x + n,\ N,\ N - M) \\ &= F_h(x;\ x + n,\ N,\ M) \end{aligned}$$

where $F_n(x;\ n,\ N,\ M) = 1$ if $n - x - 1 < 0$ or $k - x - 1 < 0$.

[Lieberman and Owen (1961), p. 7]

(c) Hypergeometric--Poisson. Let $f_h(x;\ n,\ N,\ M)$ be a hypergeometric pf and let $f_p(y;\ \lambda)$ be a Poisson pf (see Sec. 8.1.2). Then for fixed x, as $(M/N) \to 0$ and $n \to \infty$ such that $\lambda = n(M/N)$ (λ fixed), $f_h(x;\ n,\ N,\ M) \to f_p(x;\ \lambda)$ [Feller (1960, p. 162].

$$f_h(x;\ n,\ N,\ M) = f_p\left(x;\ \frac{Mn}{N}\right)\left[1 + \left(\frac{1}{2M} + \frac{1}{2n}\right)\left\{x - \left(x - \frac{Mn}{N}\right)^2\right\} + 0\left(\frac{1}{k^2} + \frac{1}{n^2}\right)\right]$$

[Burr (1973), p. 300]

(d) Hypergeometric--Normal. Let $f_h(x; n, N, M)$ be a hypergeometric pf and $\phi(y)$ be the standard normal pdf (see Sec. 8.2.1). Then as $(n/N) \to t$, $(M/N) \to p$ and $h\{x - np\} \to y$, where $(1/h) = \{Npqt(1 - t)\}^{1/2}$, $f_h(x; n, N, M) \to h\phi(y)$ [Feller (1960), p. 180]. [Also see Nicholson (1956), Molenaar (1970), Lieberman and Owen (1961).]

(e) $1 - F(n - 1; x + n, N, N - M) = F(x; n + x, N, M)$

This result is useful in establishing the relationship between the hypergeometric distribution and negative hypergeometric distribution.

[Lieberman and Owen (1961), p. 7]

(3) Some Other Results

$$\binom{n}{x}\left(\frac{M - x}{N}\right)^x\left(\frac{(N - M) - (n - x)}{N}\right)^{n-x}\left(1 + \frac{6n^2 - 6n - 1}{12N}\right)$$

$$< f(x; n, N, M) < \binom{n}{x}\left(\frac{M}{N}\right)^x\left(1 - \frac{M}{N}\right)^{n-x}\left(1 + \frac{6n^2 + 6n - 1}{12N}\right)^{-N}$$

[Johnson and Kotz (1969), p. 148]

8.1.5 LOGARITHMIC SERIES

$$f(x; \theta) = \frac{\alpha\theta^x}{x}; \quad x = 1, 2, \ldots, \quad 0 < \theta < 1, \quad \alpha = \frac{1}{-\log(1 - \theta)}$$

$$F(x; \theta) = \begin{cases} \sum_{y=1}^{[x]} f(y; \theta), & x \geq 1 \\ 0, & x < 1 \end{cases}$$

(1) Properties

(a) $f(x; \theta)$ is a decreasing function of x on the positive integers.

(b) $f(x + 1; \theta) = \left(\frac{x}{x + 1}\right)\theta f(x; \theta)$

[Johnson and Kotz (1969), p. 169]

8.2 CONTINUOUS DISTRIBUTIONS

8.2.1 NORMAL

$$f(x\ \mu, \sigma^2) = \frac{1}{\sqrt{2\pi}\sigma} \exp\left\{-\frac{(x-\mu)^2}{2\sigma^2}\right\}; \quad -\infty < x < \infty,\ -\infty < \mu < \infty,\ \sigma > 0$$

$$F(x; \mu, \sigma^2) = \int_{-\infty}^{x} f(y; \mu, \sigma^2)\, dy$$

Standard Normal: $\phi(x) = \frac{1}{\sqrt{2\pi}} \exp\left\{-\frac{x^2}{2}\right\}, \quad -\infty < x < \infty$

$$\Phi(x) = \int_{-\infty}^{x} \phi(y)\, dy$$

(1) Properties

(a) The pdf $f(x; \mu, \sigma)$ is symmetric about $x = \mu$. The pdf $\phi(x)$ is symmetric about $x = 0$.

(b) $\phi(-x) = \phi(x), \quad \Phi(-x) = 1 - \Phi(x)$

$$F(x; \mu, \sigma) = \Phi\left(\frac{x-\mu}{\sigma}\right), \quad F(x; 0, 1) = \Phi(x)$$

(c) If $X_1, X_2, \ldots, X_n$ are independent normal random variables with pdf's $f(x; \mu_i, \sigma_i^2)$ $(i = 1, 2, \ldots, n)$, respectively, then the random variable $Y = \sum_{i=1}^{n} C_i X_i$ has also a normal distribution with pdf $f(y; \sum_{i=1}^{n} C_i\mu_i, \sum_{i=1}^{n} C_i^2\sigma_i^2)$ where C_i are some constants.

(d) If $X_1, X_2, \ldots, X_n$ are iid normal random variables with pdf $f(x; \mu, \sigma^2)$, μ and σ^2 known, then the random variable $Y = \sum_{i=1}^{n} [(X_i - \mu)^2/\sigma^2]$ has a chi square distribution with n degrees of freedom (see Sec. 8.2.14). If $X_1, X_2, \ldots, X_n$ are iid standard normal random variables, then the random variable $Y = \sum_{i=1}^{n} (X_i - \bar{X})^2$, where $\bar{X} = \sum_{i=1}^{n} (X_i/n)$, has a chi square distribution with $(n - 1)$ degrees of freedom (see Sec. 8.2.14) [Mood et al. (1974), p. 243].

(2) Relationships with Other Distributions

(a) Normal--Lognormal. Let $F_N(x;\ \mu,\ \sigma)$ be a normal cdf and $F_{LN}(y;\ \theta_1,\ \theta_2)$ be a lognormal cdf (see Sec. 8.2.2). If X is a normal random variable, then $Y = e^X$ has a lognormal distribution. More specifically,

$$F_N(x;\ \mu,\ \sigma^2) = F_{LN}(e^x;\ \mu,\ \sigma)$$

$$F_{LN}(y;\ \theta_1,\ \theta_2) = F_N(\log y;\ \theta_1,\ \theta_2^2) \quad \text{[Mood et al. (1974), p. 117]}$$

(b) Normal--Chi square. Let $F_{CH}(y;\ v)$ be a chi square cdf with v degrees of freedom (see Sec. 8.2.14). If X is the standard normal random variable then $Y = X^2$ has a chi square distribution with degree of freedom 1.

$$F_{CH}(y;\ 1) = 2\Phi(\sqrt{y}) - 1, \quad y > 0$$

$$\Phi(x) = \frac{1 + F_{CH}(x^2;\ 1)}{2}, \quad x > 0$$

(c) Normal--Cauchy. Let $f_{CA}(x;\ \theta,\ \lambda)$ be a Cauchy pdf (see Sec. 8.2.4). If X_1 and X_2 are independent standard normal random variables, then the random variable $Y = X_1/|X_2|$ has a Cauchy distribution with pdf $f_{CA}(y;\ 0,\ 1)$ [Fcllcr (1966), p. 51].

(d) Normal--F. Let $F_f(y;\ v,\ w)$ be an F pdf (see Sec. 8.2.16). If X_1 and X_2 are independent standard normal random variables, then the random variable $Y = (X_1/X_2)^2$ has an F distribution with pdf $f_f(y,\ 1,\ 1)$ [Mood et al. (1974), p. 246].

(3) Some Other Results

(a) For $x > 0$,

$$\left\{\frac{1}{x} - \frac{1}{x^3}\right\}\phi(x) < 1 - \Phi(x) < \frac{1}{x}\,\phi(x) \quad \text{[Feller (1960), p. 166]}$$

(b) For $x \geq 0$,

$$[2\Phi(x) - 1]\phi(x) \geq \Phi(x)[1 - \Phi(x)] \geq \frac{\pi}{2}\phi^2(x)$$

[Tate (1953), p. 134]

8.2.2 LOGNORMAL

$$f(x; \theta_1, \theta_2) = \frac{1}{\theta_2 x\sqrt{2\pi}} \exp\left\{-\frac{1}{2\theta_2^2}(\log x - \theta_1)^2\right\}; \quad x > 0$$

$$-\infty < \theta_1 < \infty, \; \theta_2 > 0$$

$$F(x; \theta_1, \theta_2) = \begin{cases} \int_0^x f(y; \theta_1, \theta_2)\, dy, & x > 0 \\ 0, & \text{otherwise} \end{cases}$$

(1) Properties

(a) If X is a lognormal random variable with pdf $f(x; \theta_1, \theta_2)$, then the random variable $Y = e^a X^b$ (a and b are constants) also has a lognormal distribution with pdf $f(y; a + b\theta_1, b\theta_2)$.

(b) If X_1 and X_2 are independent lognormal random variables with pdf $f(x; \theta_1, \theta_2)$ and $f(x; \alpha_1, \alpha_2)$, respectively, then the random variable $Y = X_1X_2$ also has a lognormal distribution with pdf $(y; \theta_1 + \alpha_1, \theta_2 + \alpha_2)$. The random variable $Y = X_1/X_2$ also has a lognormal distribution with pdf $f(y; \theta_1 - \alpha_1, \theta_2 + \alpha_2)$.

(c) If X_i (i = 1, 2, ..., n) are independent and identically distributed (iid) lognormal random variables with pdf $f(x; \theta_1, \theta_2)$, then their geometric mean $Y = (\Pi_{i=1}^n X_i)^{1/n}$ also has a lognormal distribution with pdf $f(y; \theta_1, \theta_2/n)$. The random variable $Y = (\Pi_{i=1}^n X_i)^{1/n}$ is also asymptotically distributed with pdf $f(y; \theta_1, \theta_2/n)$.

[For (a)-(c), see Aitchison and Brown (1957), pp. 11-14]

(2) Relationships with Other Distributions: Lognormal--Normal. See Normal Distribution (Sec. 8.2.1).

8.2.3 INVERSE GAUSSIAN

$$f(x;\ \mu,\ \lambda) = \sqrt{\frac{\lambda}{2\pi x^3}}\ \exp\left\{-\frac{\lambda(x-\mu)^2}{2\mu^2 x}\right\};\quad x > 0,\ \lambda > 0,\ \mu > 0$$

$$F(x;\ \mu,\ \lambda) = \begin{cases} \int_0^x f(y;\ \mu,\ \lambda)\ dy, & x > 0 \\ 0, & \text{otherwise} \end{cases}$$

(1) Properties

$$F(x;\ \mu,\ \lambda) = \Phi\left[\left(\sqrt{\frac{\lambda}{x}}\right)\left(\frac{x}{\mu} - 1\right)\right] + e^{2\lambda/\mu}\ \Phi\left[-\left(\sqrt{\frac{\lambda}{x}}\right)\left(1 + \frac{x}{\mu}\right)\right]$$

$$= \begin{cases} \frac{1}{2}\ G(a) + \frac{1}{2}\ \exp\left(\frac{2\lambda}{\mu}\right) G\left(a + \frac{4\lambda}{\mu}\right), & 0 \le x \le \mu \\ 1 - \frac{1}{2}\ G(a) + \frac{1}{2}\ \exp\left(\frac{2\lambda}{\mu}\right) G\left(a + \frac{4\lambda}{\mu}\right), & \mu \le x \end{cases}$$

where $a = \lambda(x - \mu)^2/\mu^2 x$, $G(a) = 1 - F_{CH}(a;\ 1)$, Φ is the standard normal cdf (see Sec. 8.2.1), and $F_{CH}(x;\ v)$ is a chi square cdf with v degrees of freedom (see Sec. 8.2.14).

[Chikkara and Folks (1974), p. 251]

[Shuster (1968), p. 1514]

(2) Relationships with Other Distributions: Inverse Gaussian--Chi Square. If X is an inverse Gaussian random variable with pdf $f(x;\ \mu,\ \lambda)$, then the random variable $Y = \lambda(X - \mu)^2/\mu^2 X$ has a chi square distribution with 1 degree of freedom (see Sec. 8.2.14).

[Shuster (1968), p. 1514]

(3) Some Other Results

$$6M_1 x^{-5/2} e^{-x/2} < 1 - F(x;\ t,\ t^2) < 2Mx^{-3/2} e^{-x/2}$$

where $M = (te^t/\sqrt{2\pi})$, $M_1 = (te^t/\sqrt{2\pi})e^{-t^2/2x}$ [Wasan (1968), p. 70].

8.2.4 CAUCHY

$$f(x;\ \theta,\ \lambda) = \frac{1}{\pi\lambda\left[1 + \left(\frac{x - \theta}{\lambda}\right)^2\right]};\ -\infty < x < \infty,\ -\infty < \theta < \infty,\ \lambda > 0$$

$$F(x;\ \theta,\ \lambda) = \frac{1}{2} + \frac{1}{\pi}\tan^{-1}\left(\frac{x - \theta}{\lambda}\right)$$

(1) Properties

(a) For fixed θ and λ, the pdf $f(x;\ \theta,\ \lambda)$ is symmetric about $x = \theta$.

(b) If X has a Cauchy distribution with pdf $f(x;\ \theta,\ \lambda)$, then the sample mean $Y = \bar{X}$ also has the same distribution with pdf $f(y;\ \theta,\ \lambda)$. Also, the random variable $Y = 1/X$ has a Cauchy distribution with pdf $f[y;\ \theta/(\theta^2 + \lambda^2),\ \lambda/(\theta^2 + \lambda^2)]$.

[Johnson and Kotz (1970a), p. 160]

(2) Relationships with Other Distributions

(a) Cauchy--t Distribution. Let $f_{CA}(x;\ \theta,\ \lambda)$ be a Cauchy pdf and $f_t(y;\ v)$ be the pdf of a t-distribution (see Sec. 8.2.15). Then $f_{CA}(x;\ 0,\ 1) = f_t(x;\ 1)$.

(b) Cauchy--Normal. See Normal Distributions (Sec. 8.2.1).

8.2.5 EXPONENTIAL

$$f(x;\ \theta) = \theta e^{-\theta x};\ x > 0,\ \theta > 0$$

$$F(x;\ \theta) = \begin{cases} 1 - e^{-\theta x}, & x > 0 \\ 0, & x \le 0 \end{cases}$$

(1) Properties

(a) For fixed θ, the pdf $f(x;\ \theta)$ is a decreasing function of x for $x > 0$.

(b) The exponential distribution has no memory, i.e. $P(x > a + b \mid X > a) = P(X > b);\ a > 0,\ b > 0$ [Mood et al. (1974), p. 114].

(c) $f(x;\ \theta) = \theta[1 - F(x;\ \theta)]$

(d) If $X_1, X_2, \ldots, X_n$ are iid exponential random variables with pdf $f_e(x; \theta)$, then the random variables $Y = \sum_{i=1}^{n} X_i$ does not have an exponential distribution but has a gamma distribution with pdf $f_g(y; \theta, n)$ (see Sec. 8.2.6) [Mood et al. (1974), p. 193].

(e) If the random variable X has an exponential distribution with pdf $f(x; \theta)$, then the smallest order statistic $Y = X_{(1;n)}$ also has an exponential distribution with pdf $f(y; n\theta)$.

[David (1970), p. 17]

(f) Let $X_{(r;n)}$ $(r = 1, 2, \ldots, n)$ be the rth order statistic in a sample of size n from an exponential pdf $f(x; 1)$, then the random variable $Y_r = (n - r + 1)(X_{(r;n)} - X_{(r-1;n)})$ $(r = 1, 2, \ldots, n)$ also has the same distribution with pdf $f(y; 1)$ [David (1970), p. 17].

(2) Relationship with Other Distributions

(a) Exponential--Gamma. Let $f_e(x; \theta)$ be an exponential pdf and $f_g(y; \theta, m)$ be a gamma pdf (see Sec. 8.2.6). Then $f_e(x; \theta) = f_g(x; \theta, 1)$.

(b) Exponential--Weibull. See Weibull Distribution (Sec. 8.2.7).

(c) Exponential--Uniform. Let $F_e(x; \theta)$ be an exponential cdf and $F_u(y; (\theta/2), (\theta/2))$ be a uniform cdf (see Sec. 8.2.9). If Y has the uniform distribution then the random variable $X = -(1/\theta)\log(Y/\theta)$ has an exponential distribution. More specifically,

$$F_u\left(y; \frac{\theta}{2}, \frac{\theta}{2}\right) = 1 - F_e\left[-\frac{1}{\theta}\log\left(\frac{y}{\theta}\right); \theta\right]$$

$$F_e(x; \theta) = F_u\left[\theta\left(1 - e^{-\theta x}\right); \frac{\theta}{2}, \frac{\theta}{2}\right]$$

(d) Truncated Exponential--Pareto. Let $F_{Te}(x; \theta, a) = 1 - e^{-(x-a)\theta}$, $x \geq a \geq 0$, be a truncated exponential cdf and $F_{Pa}(y; a, k)$ be a Pareto cdf (see Sec. 8.2.10). If X has the truncated exponential distribution then the random variable $Y = ke^{X-a}$ has a Pareto distribution. More specifically,

$$F_{Pa}(y;\ a,\ k) = F_{Te}(\log y;\ a,\ \log k)$$

$$F_{Te}(x;\ \theta,\ a) = F_{Pa}(e^x;\ \theta,\ e^a)$$

(e) Exponential--Geometric. See Negative Binomial Distribution (Sec. 8.1.3).

(f) Exponential--Poisson. See Poisson Distribution (Sec. 8.1.2).

(g) Exponential--Extreme Value. See Weibull Distribution (Sec. 8.2.7(2)b).

8.2.6 GAMMA

$$f(x;\ \theta,\ m) = \frac{e^{-x\theta} x^{m-1} \theta^m}{\Gamma(m)}\ ;\ x > 0,\ \theta > 0,\ m > 0$$

$$F(x;\ \theta,\ m) = \begin{cases} \int_0^x f(y,\ \theta,\ m)\ dy, & x > 0 \\ 0, & x \leq 0 \end{cases}$$

(1) Properties

(a) For $m \leq 1$ and fixed θ, the pdf $f(x;\ \theta,\ m)$ is decreasing in x and unbounded ($m < 1$) near the origin.

(b) $F(x; 1, m) - F(x; 1, m+1) = f(x; 1, m)$ [Rao (1952), p. 41]

(c) If $X_1, X_2, \ldots, X_n$ are independent gamma random variables with pdf $f(x;\ \theta,\ m_1)$ ($i = 1, 2, \ldots, n$), respectively, then the random variable $Y = \sum_{i=1}^n X_i$ also has a gamma distribution with pdf $f(y,\ \theta,\ \sum_{i=1}^n m_i)$ [Rao (1952), p. 41].

(2) Relationships with Other Distributions

(a) Gamma--Poisson. See Poisson Distribution (Sec. 8.1.2).

(b) Gamma--Chi Square. Let $f_g(x;\ \theta,\ m)$ be a gamma pdf and $f_{CH}(y;\ v)$ be a chi square pdf (see Sec. 8.2.14). Then $f_g(x;\ (1/2),\ 2m) = f_{CH}(x;\ m)$.

(c) Gamma--Beta. If X_1 and X_2 are independent gamma random variables with pdf's $f_g(x; 1, m_1)$ and $f_g(x; 1, m_2)$, respectively, then the random variable $y = X_1/(X_1 + X_2)$ has a beta distribution with pdf $f_\beta(y; m_1, m_2)$ (see Sec. 8.2.8).

[Hogg and Craig (1970), p. 134]

(3) Some Other Results

(a) See Incomplete Gamma Functions (Sec. 10.2).

(b) $F(x; 1, \frac{1}{2}) = 2\Phi(\sqrt{2x}) - 1$ where Φ is the standard normal cdf (see Sec. 8.2.1).

8.2.7 WEIBULL

$$f(x; \theta, c) = c\theta x^{c-1} \exp(-\theta x^c);\ x > 0,\ \theta > 0,\ c > 0$$

$$F(x; \theta, c) = \begin{cases} 1 - \exp(-\theta x^c), & x \geq 0 \\ 0, & x < 0 \end{cases}$$

(1) Properties

(a) For $c \leq 1$ and fixed θ, the pdf $f(x; \theta, c)$ is a decreasing function of x for $x > 0$ and unbounded ($c < 1$) near the origin.

(b) For $c = 1$, the Weibull distribution is known as an exponential distribution, and for $c = 2$, it is known as a Rayleigh distribution.

(c) If the random variable X has a Weibull distribution with pdf $f(x; \theta, c)$, then the smallest order statistic $y = X_{(1;n)}$ also has a Weibull distribution with pdf $f(y; n\theta, c)$.

(2) Relationships with Other Distributions

(a) Weibull--Exponential. Let $F_w(x; \theta, c)$ be a Weibull cdf and $F_e(x; \theta)$ be an exponential cdf (see Sec. 8.2.5). If X is a Weibull random variable then the random variable $Y = X^c$ has an exponential distribution. More specifically,

$$F_w(x;\ \theta,\ c) = F_e(x^c;\ \theta)$$

$$F_e(y;\ \theta) = F_w(y^{1/c};\ \theta,\ c)$$

(b) Weibull--Extreme-Value. Let $F_w(x;\ \theta,\ c)$ be a Weibull cdf and $F_{EV}(y;\ \alpha,\ \beta)$ be an extreme-value cdf (see Sec. 8.2.11). If X is a Weibull random variable then the random variable $Y = -\log(X^c\theta)$ has an extreme-value distribution with $\alpha = 0$, $\beta = 1$. More specifically,

$$F_{EV}(y;\ \alpha,\ \beta) = 1 - F_w\left\{\left[\frac{1}{\theta}\exp\left(-\frac{y-\alpha}{\beta}\right)\right]^{1/c};\ \theta,\ c\right\}$$

$$F_w(x;\ \theta,\ c) = 1 - F_{EV}[-\beta\log(x^c\theta);\ 0,\ \beta]$$

8.2.8 BETA

$$f(x;\ a,\ b) = \frac{x^{a-1}(1-x)^{b-1}}{B(a,\ b)};\ 0 < x < 1,\ a > 0,\ b > 0$$

$$F(x;\ a,\ b) = \begin{cases} 0, & x \le 0 \\ \int_0^x f(y;\ a,\ b)\,dy = I_x(a,\ b), & 0 < x < 1 \\ 1, & x \ge 1 \end{cases}$$

where $I_x(a,\ b)$ is an incomplete beta function ratio.

(1) Properties

(a) If $a = b$, the pdf $f(x;\ a,\ b)$ is symmetric about $x = 1/2$.

(b) $F(x;\ a,\ b) = 1 - F(1 - x;\ b,\ a)$

(c) If $a = 1/2$, $b = 1/2$, the beta distribution is known as an arcsine distribution [Feller (1966), p. 49].

(d) If $b = 1$, the beta distribution is known as the power function distribution. If $b = 1$, $a = 1$, the beta distribution is the uniform distribution (see Sec. 8.2.9).

(e) Let $X_1, X_2, \ldots, X_n$ be n independent beta random variables with pdf $f(x;\ a_i,\ b_i)$ $(i = 1, 2, \ldots, n)$. If $a_{i+1} = a_i + b_i$

$(i = 1, 2, \ldots, n - 1)$, then the random variable $Y = \Pi_1^n X_i$ also has a beta distribution with pdf $f(y; a_1, \sum_1^n b_i)$; $a_i > 0$, $b_i > 0$.

[Jambunathan (1954), p. 402]

(2) Relationships with Other Distributions

(a) Beta--Binomial. See Binomial Distribution (Sec. 8.1.1).

(b) Beta--Gamma. See Gamma Distribution (Sec. 8.2.6).

(c) Beta--Uniform. See Uniform Distribution (Sec. 8.2.9).

(d) Beta--F Distribution. Let $F_\beta(x; a, b)$ be a beta cdf and $F_f(y; v, w)$ be an F cdf (see Sec. 8.2.16). Then if X is a beta random variable, the random variable $Y = (w/v)[(1/X) - 1]$ has an F distribution. More specifically,

$$F_f(y; v, w) = 1 - F_\beta\left(\frac{w}{w + vy}; \frac{w}{2}, \frac{v}{2}\right)$$

[Abramowitz and Stegun (1970), p. 945]

If the random variable Y has an F distribution (see Sec. 8.2.16), the random variable $X = vY/(w + vY)$ has a beta distribution. More specifically,

$$F_f\left(\frac{wx}{v(1 - x)}; v, w\right) = F_\beta\left(x; \frac{v}{2}, \frac{v}{2}\right)$$ [Mood et al. (1974), p. 267]

(e) Beta--Chi Square. Let X_1 and X_2 be independent chi square random variables with degrees of freedom v_1 and v_2, respectively. Then the random variable $Y = X_1/(X_1 + X_2)$ has a beta distribution with pdf $f[y; (v_1/2), (v_2/2)]$ [Johnson and Kotz (1970b), p. 38].

(3) Some Other Results

(a) See Incomplete Beta Function (10.4).

(b) Let x_α be the $100(\alpha)$ lower percentage point of a beta distribution with pdf $f(x; a, b)$, and let $F_{\alpha;v,w}$ be the $100(\alpha)$ upper percentage point of an F-distribution with pdf $f_f(x; v, w)$ (see Sec.

8.2.16). Then

$$X_\alpha = \frac{a}{a + bF_{\alpha;2b,2a}}$$ [Owen and Gilbert (1959), p. 10]

8.2.9 UNIFORM

$$f(x;\ h,\ a) = \frac{1}{2h};\ a - h < x < a + h,\ h > 0$$

$$F(x;\ h,\ a) = \begin{cases} 0, & x \leq a - h \\ \dfrac{x - a + h}{2h}, & a - h < x < a + h \\ 1, & x > a + h \end{cases}$$

(1) Properties

(a) For fixed a and h, the pdf f(x; h, a) is symmetric about x = a.

(b) For the distributions of the sample mean $\bar{X}$ and geometric mean from a uniform distribution refer to Kendall and Stuart (1958), pp. 258, 262.

(c) Probability Integral Transform. Let X be any continuous random variable with cdf F(x). Then the random variable Y = F(X) has a uniform distribution with pdf f[y; (1/2), (1/2)].

[Mood et al. (1974), p. 202]

(2) Relationships with Other Distributions

(a) Uniform--Exponential. See Exponential Distribution (Sec. 8.2.5).

(b) Uniform--Beta. If X is a uniform random variable with pdf $f_u[x;\ (1/2),\ (1/2)]$ then the rth order statistic $Y = X_{(r;n)}$ has a beta distribution with pdf $f_\beta(y;\ r,\ n - r + 1)$ (see Sec. 8.2.8).

[Mood et al. (1974), p. 254]

8.2.10 PARETO

$$f(x;\ a,\ k) = ak^a x^{-a-1};\ x \geq k,\ a > 0$$

$$F(x;\ a,\ k) = 1 - \left(\frac{k}{x}\right)^a,\ x \geq k$$

(1) Property. For fixed a and k, the pdf f(x; a, k) is a nonincreasing function of x.

(2) Relationships with Other Distributions

(a) Pareto--Exponential. See Exponential Distribution (Sec. 8.2.5).

(b) Pareto--Chi Square. If $X_1, X_2, \ldots, X_n$ are iid Pareto random variables with pdf f(x; a, k), then the random variable $Y = 2a \log[\prod_1^n (X_i/k^n)]$ has a chi square distribution with 2n degrees of freedom (see Sec. 8.2.14) [Malik (1970), p. 20].

8.2.11 EXTREME-VALUE

$$f(x;\ \alpha,\ \beta) = \frac{1}{\beta} \exp\left\{-e^{-(x-\alpha)/\beta} - \left(\frac{x - \alpha}{\beta}\right)\right\};\quad -\infty < x < \infty,\ -\infty < \alpha < \infty,\ \beta > 0$$

$$F(x;\ \alpha,\ \beta) = \exp\{-e^{-(x-\alpha)/\beta}\}$$

(1) Properties

(a) For fixed α and β, the pdf $f(x;\ \alpha,\ \beta)$ has a mode at $x = \alpha$.

(b) If X is an extreme-value random variable with pdf $f(x;\ \alpha,\ \beta)$, then the random variable $Y = -X$ has an extreme-value distribution of different form with the cdf $1 - F(-y;\ \alpha,\ \beta)$.

(c) If X is an extreme-value random variable with pdf $f(x;\ \alpha,\ \beta)$, then the largest order statistic $Y = X_{(n;n)}$ also has an extreme-value distribution with pdf $f[y;\ \alpha,\ (\beta/n)]$.

(2) Relationships with Other Distributions: Extreme-Value--Weibull. See Weibull Distribution (Sec. 8.2.7).

8.2.12 LAPLACE

$$f(x;\ \alpha,\ \beta) = \frac{1}{2\beta} \exp\left\{-\frac{|x - \alpha|}{\beta}\right\};\quad -\infty < x < \infty,\ -\infty < \alpha < \infty,\ \beta > 0$$

$$F(x;\ \alpha,\ \beta) = \begin{cases} \frac{1}{2}\exp\left(\frac{x-\alpha}{\beta}\right), & x \le \alpha \\ 1 - \frac{1}{2}\exp\left(\frac{-x+\alpha}{\beta}\right), & x > \alpha \end{cases}$$

A property of this distribution is that for fixed α and β, the pdf $f(x;\ \alpha,\ \beta)$ is symmetric about $x = \alpha$.

8.2.13 LOGISTIC

$$f(x;\ \alpha,\ \beta) = \frac{1}{\beta}\frac{\exp\left\{-\left(\frac{x-\alpha}{\beta}\right)\right\}}{\left[1+\exp\left\{-\left(\frac{x-\alpha}{\beta}\right)\right\}\right]^2};\quad -\infty < x < \infty,\ -\infty < \alpha < \infty,\ \beta > 0$$

$$F(x;\ \alpha,\ \beta) = \left[1+\exp\left\{-\left(\frac{x-\alpha}{\beta}\right)\right\}\right]^{-1}$$

Properties for this distribution are as follows.

(1) For fixed α and β, the pdf $f(x;\ \alpha,\ \beta)$ is symmetric about $x = \alpha$.

(2) $x = \log\left[\frac{F(x)}{1 - F(x)}\right]$ if $\alpha = 0,\ \beta = 1$

$f(x) = F(x)[1 - F(x)]$ if $\alpha = 0,\ \beta = 1$

[Johnson and Kotz (1970b), p. 5]

8.2.14 CHI SQUARE

$$f(x;\ v) = \frac{e^{-x/2}(x)^{(v-2)/2}}{2^{v/2}\Gamma\left(\frac{v}{2}\right)};\quad x > 0,\ v = 1, 2, \ldots$$

$$F(x;\ v) = \begin{cases} \int_0^x f(y;\ v)\,dy, & x > 0 \\ 0, & x \le 0 \end{cases}$$

(1) Properties

(a) If $v \le 2$, the pdf $f(x;\ v)$ is a decreasing function of x and unbounded ($v < 2$) near the origin.

(b) $F(x;\ v) - F(x;\ v + 2) = \left(\frac{1}{2}x\right)^{v/2} \frac{\exp\left(-\frac{x}{2}\right)}{\Gamma\left(\frac{v}{2} + 1\right)}$

[Peizer and Pratt (1968), p. 1450]

$$F(x;\ 2v) = 1 - 2 \sum_{j=1}^{v} f(x;\ 2j) \quad \text{[Puri (1973), p. 63]}$$

$$\sum_{v=1}^{\infty} f(x;\ 2v) = \frac{1}{2} \quad \text{[Puri (1973), p. 63]}$$

$$xf(x;\ v) = vf(x;\ v + 2)$$

(c) If $X_1, X_2, \ldots, X_n$ are independent chi square random variables with pdf's $f(x;\ v_i)$ $(i = 1, 2, \ldots, n)$, respectively, then the random variable $Y = \sum_{i=1}^{n} X_i$ also has a chi squared distribution with pdf $f(y;\ \sum_1^n v_i)$ [Rao (1952), p. 41].

(2) Relationships with Other Distributions

(a) Chi Square--Gamma. See Gamma Distribution (Sec. 8.2.6).

(b) Chi Square--Normal. See Normal Distribution (Sec. 8.2.1).

(c) Chi Square--F. If X_1 is a chi square random variable with pdf $f(x;\ v)$, and X_2 is another chi square random variable (independent of X_1) with pdf $f(x;\ w)$, then the random variable $Y = wX_1/vX_2$ has an F distribution with pdf $F_f(y;\ v,\ w)$ (see Sec. 8.2.16).

(d) Chi Square--t. If X_1 is a chi square random variable with pdf $f(x;\ 1)$, and X_2 is another chi square random variable (independent of X_1) with pdf $f(x;\ w)$, then the random variable $Y = U\sqrt{wX_1/X_2}$ has a t distribution with pdf $f_t(y;\ w)$ (see Sec. 8.2.15), where U is a random variable independent of X_1 and X_2 with $P[U = 1] = 1/2$, $P[U = -1] = 1/2$. Also, if X_1 and X_2 are iid chi square random variables with pdf $f(x;\ v)$, then the random variable $Y = (1/2)[\sqrt{v}(X_2 - X_1)/\sqrt{X_1X_2}]$ has a t distribution with pdf $f_t(y;\ v)$ (see Sec. 8.2.15).

[Johnson and Kotz (1970b), p. 95]

(e) Chi Square--Beta. See Beta Distribution (Sec. 8.2.8).

(3) Some Other Results

(a) $$F(x;\ 2v+1) = 2\Phi(\sqrt{x}) - 1 - 2\sum_{j=1}^{v} f(x;\ 2j+1)$$

$$\sum_{v=1}^{\infty} f(x;\ 2v+1) = \Phi(\sqrt{x}) - \frac{1}{2}, \quad x > 0$$

where Φ is the standard normal cdf (see Sec. 8.2.1).

[Puri (1973), p. 63]

(b) $$F(x;\ v) \approx \Phi\left[\left\{\left(\frac{x}{v}\right)^{1/3} - 1 + \frac{2}{9v}\right\}\sqrt{\frac{9v}{2}}\,\right]$$

where Φ is the standard normal cdf (see Sec. 8.2.1).

[Johnson and Kotz (1970a), p. 176]

(c) Let $X^2_{\alpha,v}$ and Z_α denote the 100(α) lower percentage point of the chi square distribution and standard normal distribution, respectively. Then

$$X^2_{\alpha;v} \approx \frac{1}{2}\left(Z_\alpha + \sqrt{2v-1}\right)^2$$

$$X^2_{\alpha,v} \approx v\left[1 - \frac{2}{9v} + Z_\alpha\sqrt{\frac{2}{9v}}\right]^3$$ [Johnson and Kotz (1970a), p. 176]

(d) Let $X^2_{\alpha;v}$ and $F_{\alpha;v,\infty}$ denote the 100(α) lower percentage point of the chi square and an F distribution (see Sec. 8.2.16), respectively. Then $X^2_{\alpha;v} = vF_{\alpha;v,\infty}$ [Scheffé (1959), p. 27].

8.2.15 t

$$f(x;\ v) = \frac{\left(1 + \frac{x^2}{v}\right)^{-(v+1)/2}}{\sqrt{v}\ B\left(\frac{1}{2}, \frac{v}{2}\right)}; \quad -\infty < x < \infty,\ v = 1, 2, \ldots$$

For odd values of v,

$$F(x;\ v) = \frac{1}{2} + \frac{(\arctan A)}{\pi} + \frac{AB}{\pi}\Big[b_0 + b_1 B + b_2 B^2 + \cdots$$
$$+ b_{(v-3)/2} B^{(v-3)/2}\Big]$$

where $b_0 = 1$ and $b_r = [2r/(2r + 1)]b_{r-1}$. For even values of v,

$$F(x;\ v) = \frac{1}{2} + \frac{A\sqrt{B}}{2}\Big[c_0 + c_1 B + c_2 B^2 + \cdots + c_{(v-2)/2} B^{(v-2)/2}\Big]$$

where $c_0 = 1$, $c_r = [(2r - 1)/2r]c_{r-1}$, $A = x/\sqrt{v}$, and $B = v/(v + x^2)$.

[Owen (1968), p. 465]

(1) Property. The pdf f(x; v) is symmetric about x = 0.

(2) Relationships with Other Distributions

(a) t--Normal. Let $f_t(x;\ v)$ be a t pdf and $\phi(x)$ be the standard normal pdf (see Sec. 8.2.1). Then for fixed x and as $v \to \infty$,

$f_t(x;\ v) \to \phi(x)$ [Johnson and Kotz (1970b), p. 10]

(b) t--Chi Square. See Chi Square Distribution (Sec. 8.2.14).

(c) t--F. Let $F_t(x;\ v)$ be a t cdf and $F_f(x;\ m_1,\ m_2)$ be an F cdf (see Sec. 8.2.16). If the random variable X has a t distribution with degrees of freedom v, then the random variable $Y = X^2$ has an F distribution with degrees of freedom 1 and v. More specifically,

$$F_f(y;\ 1,\ v) = 2F_t(\sqrt{y};\ v) - 1$$

If the random variable X has a t distribution with pdf f(x; n - 2), and a random variable Y is defined by $X = (1 - Y)\sqrt{(n - 2)}/2\sqrt{Y}$, then the random variable Y has an F distribution with pdf $f_f(y;\ n - 2,\ n - 2)$ (see Sec. 8.2.16) [Guenther (1971b), p. 19].

(3) Some Other Results

(a) Let $t_{\alpha;v}$ and $F_{\alpha;v,w}$ denote the upper $100(\alpha)$ percentage points of the t distribution with pdf $f_t(x;\ v)$ and an F distribution with pdf $f_F(x;\ m_1,\ m_2)$ (see Sec. 8.2.16), respectively. Then

$$(t_{\alpha/2;v})^2 = F_{\alpha;1,v}$$

$$t_{\alpha;v} = \frac{\sqrt{v}}{2}\left(\sqrt{F_{\alpha;v,v}} - \frac{1}{\sqrt{F_{\alpha;v,v}}}\right)$$

$$F_{\alpha;v,v} = 1 + \frac{2\left(t_{\alpha;v}\right)^2}{v} + \frac{2t_{\alpha;v}}{\sqrt{v}}\sqrt{1 + \frac{\left(t_{\alpha;v}\right)^2}{v}}$$

[Cacoullos (1965), p. 529]

$$F_{\alpha;v,w} \approx \left[\frac{v}{x^2_{\alpha;v}} + \frac{v}{w}\left(\frac{\frac{v}{2} - 1}{x^2_{\alpha;v}} - \frac{1}{2}\right)\right]^{-1}$$

[Johnson and Kotz (1970b), p. 84]

(b) Normal Approximation to t Distribution. See Peizer and Pratt (1968), I and II.

8.2.16 F

$$f(x;\ v,\ w) = \frac{\left(\frac{v}{w}\right)^{v/2} x^{(v-2)/2}}{B\left(\frac{v}{2}, \frac{w}{2}\right)}\left(1 + \frac{v}{w}x\right)^{-(v+w)/2} \quad ;\ x > 0,\ v = 1, 2, \ldots,\ w = 1, 2, 3, \ldots$$

$$F(x;\ v,\ w) = \int_0^x f(y;\ v,\ w)\, dy$$

(1) Properties

(a) For fixed w and v = 2 the pdf $f(x;\ v,\ w)$ is a decreasing function of x for $x > 0$.

(b) $F(x;\ v,\ w) = 1 - I_a\left(\frac{w}{2}, \frac{v}{2}\right)$

where $a = w/(w + vx)$ [Abramowitz and Stegun (1970), p. 946].

(c) If the random variable X has an F distribution with pdf $f(x;\ v,\ w)$, then the random variable $y = 1/X$ also has an F distribution with pdf $f(y;\ w,\ v)$ [Mood et al. (1974), p. 248].

(2) Relationships with Other Distributions

(a) F--Chi Square. See Chi Square Distribution (Sec. 8.2.14).

(b) F--t. See t Distribution (Sec. 8.2.15).

(c) F--Beta. See Beta Distribution (Sec. 8.2.8).

(3) Some Other Results

(a) Let $F_{\alpha;v,w}$ denote the $100(\alpha)$ lower percentage point of the F distribution with pdf $f(v, w)$. Then

$$F_{1-\alpha;v,w} = \frac{1}{F_{\alpha;w,v}}$$

(b) See Sec. 8.2.15(3)a.

(c) $F(x; v, w) \approx \Phi(y)$

where Φ is the standard normal cdf (see Sec. 8.2.1) and

$$y = \frac{x - \dfrac{w}{w-2}}{\dfrac{w}{w-2}\sqrt{\dfrac{2(v+w-2)}{v(w-4)}}}$$ [Abramowitz and Stegun (1970), p. 947]

(d) See Sec. 8.2.8(3)b.

8.2.17 NONCENTRAL CHI SQUARE

$$f(x; v, \lambda) = \sum_{j=0}^{\infty} \frac{e^{-\lambda/2}\left(\frac{\lambda}{2}\right)^j}{j!} \frac{x^{(v/2)+j-1}e^{-x/2}}{2^{(v/2)+j}\Gamma\left(\frac{v}{2}+j\right)}; \quad x > 0, \lambda > 0, \quad v = 1, 2, 3, \ldots$$

$$F(x; v, \lambda) = \begin{cases} \int_0^x f(y; v, \lambda)\, dy, & x > 0 \\ 0, & x < 0 \end{cases}$$

(λ is the noncentrality parameter.)

(1) Properties

(a) For fixed v, λ, the cdf $F(x; v, \lambda)$ is nondecreasing in x. For fixed λ and x, the cdf $F(x; v, \lambda)$ is nonincreasing in v. For fixed v and x, the cdf $F(x; v, \lambda)$ is nonincreasing in λ.

[Johnson and Kotz (1970b), p. 135]

(b) If $X_1, X_2, \ldots, X_n$ are independent noncentral chi square random variables with pdf's $f(x; v_i, \lambda_i)$ $(i = 1, 2, \ldots, n)$, respectively, then the random variable $Y = \sum_{i=1}^{n} X_i$ also has a noncentral chi square distribution with pdf $f(y; \sum_{i=1}^{n} v_i, \sum_{i=1}^{n} \lambda_i)$.

[Graybill (1961), p. 77]

(c) If $\lambda = 0$, the noncentral chi square distribution becomes the chi square distribution (see Sec. 8.2.14).

(d) $$f(x; v, \lambda) = e^{-\lambda/2} \sum_{j=0}^{\infty} \frac{\lambda}{2^r (r!)} f(x; v + 2j, 0)$$

$$2 \frac{d}{d\lambda} f(x; v, \lambda) = f(x; v + 2, \lambda) - f(x; v, \lambda)$$

$$2 \frac{d}{d\lambda} F(x; v, \lambda) = F(x; v + 2, \lambda) - F(x; v, \lambda) = -2f(x; v + 2, \gamma)$$

[Alam and Rizvi (1967), p. 21]

(2) Relationships with Other Distributions

(a) Noncentral Chi Square--Normal. If X is a noncentral chi square random variable with pdf $f(x; v, \lambda)$, then for fixed λ and as $v \to \infty$ (or for v fixed and as $\lambda \to \infty$), the random variable $Y = [X - (v + \lambda)]/[2(v + 2\lambda)]^{1/2}$ approaches the standard normal distribution (see Sec. 8.2.1) [Johnson and Kotz (1970b), p. 135].

If $Y_1, Y_2, \ldots, Y_v$ are v independent standard normal random variables (see Sec. 8.2.1), and $a_1, a_2, \ldots, a_v$ are constants with $\sum_1^v a_i^2 = \lambda$, then the random variable $X = \sum_{i=1}^{v} (Y_i + a_i)^2$ has a noncentral chi square distribution with pdf $f(x; v, \lambda)$.

$$F(x; 1, \lambda) = \Phi(a) - \Phi(b)$$

$$F(x; 2k + 1, \lambda) = F(x; 1, \lambda) + \sum_{i=1}^{k} \sum_{j=1}^{i} \binom{i - 1}{j - 1} 2^j F^{(j)}(x; 1, \lambda), \quad \lambda > 0,\ k = 1, 2, \ldots$$

where $a = \sqrt{\lambda} + \sqrt{x}$, $b = \sqrt{\lambda} - \sqrt{x}$, $F^{(j)}(x; 1, \lambda)$ is the jth derivative of $F(x; 1, \lambda)$ wrt λ, and $\Phi(\cdot)$ is the standard normal cdf (see Sec. 8.2.1) [Han (1975), p. 213].

(b) Noncentral Chi Square--Noncentral Beta. Let $(Y_i - a_i)$ $(i = 1, 2, \ldots, n_1)$ and Z_i $(i = 1, 2, \ldots, n_2)$ be iid normal random variables (see Sec. 8.2.1) with mean zero and variance σ^2. Let $Y = \sum_{i=1}^{n_1} Y_i^2$ and $Z = \sum_1^{n_2} Z_i^2$. Then the random variable $X = Y/(Y + Z)$ has a noncentral beta distribution (see Sec. 8.2.21) with pdf $f_{N\beta}[x; (n_1/2), (n_2/2), 2\lambda]$, $\lambda = (1/2\sigma^2)\sum_{i=1}^{n_1} a_i^2$.

[Seber (1963), p. 542]

(c) Noncentral Chi Square--Noncentral F. See Noncentral F Distribution (Sec. 8.2.19).

(d) Noncentral Chi Square--Poisson. Let Y and Z be two independent Poisson random variables with pf's $f[y; (x/2)]$ and $f[z; (\lambda/2)]$, respectively (see Sec. 8.1.2). Then $F(x; v, \lambda) = P[(Y - Z) \geq (v/2)]$, v even [Johnson (1959), p. 353].

(3) Some Other Results

(a) $$F(x; v, \lambda) \approx F\left(\frac{x}{1 + b}; \frac{a}{1 + b}, 0\right)$$

$$F(x; v, \lambda) \approx \Phi\left[\frac{\left(\frac{x}{a}\right)^{1/3} - \left\{1 - \frac{2}{9}\left(\frac{1 + b}{a}\right)\right\}}{\sqrt{\frac{2}{9}\left(\frac{1 + b}{a}\right)}}\right]$$

$$F(x; v, \lambda) \approx \Phi\left[\left(\frac{2x}{1 + b}\right)^{1/2} - \left(\frac{2a}{1 + b} - 1\right)^{1/2}\right]$$

where $a = v + \lambda$, $b = \lambda/(v + \lambda)$ and $\Phi(\cdot)$ is the standard normal cdf (see Sec. 8.2.1) [Abramowitz and Stegun (1970), p. 942].

(b) Let χ'_p, χ_p and Z_p be the 100(p) lower percentage points of noncentral chi square, (central) chi square (see Sec. 8.2.14), and standard normal cdf (see Sec. 8.2.1), respectively. Then

$$\chi'_p \approx (1 + b)\chi_p$$

$$\chi'_p \approx \frac{1 + b}{2}\left[Z_p + \sqrt{\frac{2a}{1 + b} - 1}\right]^2$$

$$\chi'_p \approx a\left[Z_p\sqrt{\frac{2}{9}\left(\frac{1+b}{a}\right)} + 1 - \frac{2}{9}\left(\frac{1+b}{a}\right)\right]^3$$

where $a = v + \lambda$, $b = \lambda/(v + \lambda)$.

[Abramowitz and Stegun (1970), p. 942]

8.2.18 NONCENTRAL t

$$f(x;\ v,\ \delta) = \frac{(v)^{v/2}}{\sqrt{\pi}\,\Gamma\left(\frac{v}{2}\right)} \frac{e^{-\delta^2/2}}{(v + x^2)^{(v+1)/2}} \sum_{i=0}^{\infty} \Gamma\left(\frac{v + i + 1}{2}\right)\frac{\delta^i}{i!} \times \left(\frac{2x^2}{v + x^2}\right)^{i/2},\quad -\infty < x < \infty$$

(δ is the noncentrality parameter.) [Rao (1973), p. 171]

$$F(x;\ v,\ \delta) = \frac{\sqrt{2\pi}}{\sqrt{\left(\frac{v}{2}\right)}\ 2^{(v-2)/2}} \int_0^{\infty} \Phi\left(\frac{xy}{\sqrt{v}} - \delta\right) y^{v-1}\ \phi(y)\ dy$$

where $\Phi(Z)$ and $\phi(Z)$ are the standard normal cdf and pdf (see Sec. 8.2.1), respectively [Owen (1968), p. 464].

(1) Properties

(a) If $\delta = 0$, the noncentral t distribution becomes t distribution.

(b) $$F(x;\ v,\ \delta) - F(-x;\ v,\ \delta) = \sum_{j=0}^{\infty} \frac{e^{-\delta^2/2}\left(\frac{\delta^2}{2}\right)^j}{j!} I_y\left(j + \frac{1}{2},\ \frac{v}{2}\right)$$

where $I_y(a, b)$ is the incomplete beta function ratio and $y = x^2/(v + x^2)$ [Amos (1964), p. 455].

(c) $F(x;\ v,\ \delta) = 1 - F(-x;\ v,\ -\delta)$

$F(0;\ v,\ \delta) = \Phi(-\delta)$

$$F(1;\ 1,\ \delta) = 1 - \left[\Phi\left(\frac{\delta}{\sqrt{2}}\right)\right]^2$$

where Φ is the standard normal cdf (see Sec. 8.2.1).

[Owen (1968), p. 465]

(2) Relationships with Other Distributions: Noncentral t--Normal--Chi Square. Let Y be a normal random variable with pdf $f(y; \mu, \sigma^2)$ (see Sec. 8.2.1) and Z/σ^2 be a chi square random variable with pdf $f(z; v)$ (see Sec. 8.2.14). Let Y and Z be independent. Then the random variable $X = Y\sqrt{v}/\sqrt{Z}$ has a noncentral t distribution with noncentrality parameter $\delta = \mu/\sigma$.

(3) Some Other Results

$$F(x; v, \delta) \approx \Phi(y)$$

where $\Phi(\cdot)$ is the standard normal cdf (see Sec. 8.2.1) and

$$y = \frac{x\left(1 - \frac{1}{4v}\right) - \delta}{\left(1 + \frac{x^2}{2v}\right)^{1/2}}$$ [Abramowitz and Stegun (1970), p. 949]

8.2.19 NONCENTRAL F

$$f(x; r_1, r_2, \lambda)$$

$$= \sum_{i=0}^{\infty} \frac{\Gamma\left(\frac{2i + r_1 + r_2}{2}\right)\left(\frac{r_1}{r_2}\right)^{(2i+r_1)/2} x^{(2i+r_1-2)/2} e^{-\lambda/2}\left(\frac{\lambda}{2}\right)^i}{\Gamma\left(\frac{r_2}{2}\right)\Gamma\left(\frac{2i + r_1}{2}\right)(i!)\left(1 + \frac{r_1}{r_2} x\right)^{(2i+r_1+r_2)/2}};$$

$$x > 0, \lambda > 0, r_1, r_2 = 1, 2, \ldots$$

$$F(x; r_1, r_2, \lambda) = \int_0^x f(y; r_1, r_2, \lambda)\, dy, \quad x > 0$$

[Graybill (1961), p. 79]

The following form of the noncentral pdf is also useful.

$$f_1(x; r_1, r_2, \lambda)$$

$$= \sum_{i=0}^{\infty} \frac{e^{-\lambda/2}\left(\frac{\lambda}{2}\right)^i (r_1 + 2i)^{(r_1+2i)/2} (r_2)^{(r_2/2)} x^{(r_1+2i-2)/2}}{i!B\left(\frac{r_1 + 2i}{2}, \frac{r_2}{2}\right)\left[r_2 + (r_1 + 2i)x\right]^{(r_1+2i+r_2)/2}};$$

$$x > 0, \lambda > 0, r_1, r_2 = 1, 2, \ldots$$

$$F_1(x;\ r_1,\ r_2,\ \lambda) = \int_0^x f_1(y;\ r_1,\ r_2,\ \lambda)\ dy,\ x \geq 0$$

(1) Properties

(a) If $\lambda = 0$, the noncentral F distribution becomes the F distribution.

$$\text{(b)}\quad F_1(x;\ r_1,\ r_2,\ \lambda) = \sum_{j=0}^{\infty} \frac{e^{-\lambda/2}\left(\frac{\lambda}{2}\right)^j}{j!} F(x;\ r_1 + 2j,\ r_2,\ 0)$$

$$F_1(x;\ r_1,\ r_2,\ \lambda) = \sum_{j=0}^{\infty} \frac{e^{-\lambda/2}\left(\frac{\lambda}{2}\right)^j}{j!} I_y\left(\frac{r_1}{2} + j,\ \frac{r_2}{2}\right)$$

where $I_y(a, b)$ is the incomplete beta function ratio and $y = r_1x/(r_1x + r_2)$ [Abramowitz and Stegun (1970), p. 947].

$$\text{(c)}\quad 2\frac{\partial}{\partial\lambda} f(x;\ r,\ r,\ \lambda) = f(x;\ r + 2,\ r,\ \lambda) - f(x;\ r,\ r,\ \lambda)$$

$$2\frac{\partial}{\partial\lambda} F(x;\ r,\ r,\ \lambda) = F(x;\ r + 2,\ r,\ \lambda) - F(x;\ r,\ r,\ \lambda)$$
$$= -\frac{2}{r - 2} f(x;\ r + 2,\ r - 2;\ \lambda),\ r > 2$$

[Alam and Rizvi (1967), p. 22]

(2) Relationships with Other Distributions

(a) Noncentral F--Noncentral Chi Square. If the random variable Y has a noncentral chi square distribution with pdf $f(y;\ r_1,\ \lambda)$ (see Sec. 8.2.17) and the random variable Z has a (central) chi square distribution with pdf $f(z;\ r_2)$, and if Y and Z are independent, then the random variable $X = (Y/r_1)(r_2/Z)$ has a noncentral F distribution with pdf $f(x;\ r_1,\ r_2,\ \lambda)$ [Graybill (1961), pp. 77-78].

(b) Noncentral F--Noncentral Beta. If the random variable X has a noncentral F distribution with pdf $f(x;\ r_1,\ r_2,\ \lambda)$, then the random variable $Y = r_1X/(r_2 + r_1X)$ has a noncentral beta distribution with pdf $f(y; r_1, r_2, \lambda)$ (see Sec. 8.2.20) [Graybill (1961), p. 79].

(c) Noncentral F--Poisson. Let Y and Z be two independent Poisson random variables with pdf's $f[y; (1/2)(r_1/r_2)x]$ and $f[z; (\lambda/2)]$, respectively (see Sec. 8.1.2). Then, if r_1 is even,

$$F\left(\frac{x}{r_1}; r_1, r_2, \lambda\right) = P\left(Y - Z \geq \frac{r_1}{2}\right) \quad \text{[Johnson (1959), p. 357]}$$

(3) Some Other Results. Let $F_{1Nf}(x; r_1, r_2, \lambda)$, $F_{Nc}(x; v, \lambda)$, and $\Phi(x)$ be noncentral F, noncentral chi square (see Sec. 8.2.17), and standard normal cdf (see Sec. 8.2.1), respectively.

(a) $\lim\limits_{r_2 \to \infty} F_{1Nf}(x; r_1, r_2, \lambda) = F_{Nc}(r_1x; r_1, \lambda)$

(b) $F_{1Nf}(x; r_1, r_2, \lambda) \approx F_{1Nf}\left(\frac{r_1}{r_1 + \lambda}\, x; \frac{(r_1 + \lambda)^2}{r_1 + 2\lambda}, r_2, 0\right)$

(c) $F_{1Nf}(x; r_1, r_2, \lambda) \approx \Phi(y)$ (r_1, r_2 large)

where

$$y = \frac{x - \dfrac{r_2(r_1 + \lambda)}{r_1(r_2 - 2)}}{\dfrac{r_2}{r_1}\left[\dfrac{2}{(r_2 - 2)(r_2 - 4)}\left\{\dfrac{(r_1 + \lambda)^2}{(r_2 - 2)} + r_1 + 2\lambda\right\}\right]^{1/2}}$$

[For (a)-(c) see Abramowitz and Stegun (1970), p. 948.]

8.2.20 NONCENTRAL BETA

$$f(x;\ a,\ b,\ \lambda) = \sum_{i=0}^{\infty} \frac{\Gamma\left(\frac{2i + a + b}{2}\right)}{\Gamma\left(\frac{b}{2}\right)\Gamma\left(\frac{2i + a}{2}\right)} \frac{e^{-\lambda/2}}{i!} \left(\frac{\lambda}{2}\right)^{i} (x)^{(2i+a-2)/2}$$

$$\times\ (1 - x)^{(b-2)/2};\quad 0 \le x \le 1,\ a > 0,\ b > 0,\ \lambda > 0$$

(λ is the noncentrality parameter.)

$$F(x;\ a,\ b,\ \lambda) = \int_0^x f(y;\ a,\ b,\ \lambda)\ dy \quad \text{[Graybill (1961), p. 79]}$$

(1) Properties

(a) If $\lambda = 0$, the noncentral beta distribution becomes the beta distribution.

(b) $F(x;\ a,\ b,\ 2\lambda) = \sum_{j=0}^{\infty} \frac{e^{-\lambda}\lambda^{j}}{j!} I_x\left(\frac{a}{2} + j,\ \frac{b}{2}\right)$

where $I_x(c,\ d)$ is the incomplete beta function ratio.

(2) Relationships with Other Distributions

(a) Noncentral Beta--Noncentral F. See Noncentral F Distribution (Sec. 8.2.19).

(b) Noncentral Beta--Noncentral Chi Square. See Noncentral Chi Square Distribution (Sec. 8.2.17).

Chapter 9

BASIC LIMIT THEOREMS

In this chapter some useful basic results on the limiting behavior of a sequence of random variables are listed.

9.1 TYPES OF CONVERGENCE

Consider the random variables as functions X(s), where s is an element of the sample space S.

9.1.1 DEFINITIONS

(1) Convergence in Probability. A sequence of random variables $\{X_n(s)\}$, n = 1, 2, ...; s $\in$ S, is said to converge in probability to another random variable X(s) as $n \to \infty$, and is written $X_n \overset{p}{\to} X$, if for every $\varepsilon > 0$, $\lim_{n\to\infty} P[|X_n(s) - X(s)| > \varepsilon] = 0$.

[Roussas (1973), p. 132]

(2) Convergence with Probability 1. A sequence of random variables $\{X_n(s)\}$, n = 1, 2, ..., s $\in$ S, is said to converge with probability

1 or almost surely (a.s.) to another random variable X as $n \to \infty$, and is written $X_n \xrightarrow{a.s.} X$, if $P[\lim_{n\to\infty} X_n(s) = X(s)] = 1$. This convergence is known as strong convergence [Roussas (1973), p. 132].

(3) Convergence in rth Mean. A sequence of random variables $\{X_n(s)\}$, $n = 1, 2, \ldots, s \in S$, is said to converge in the rth mean or converges in L^r $(r > 0)$ to another random variable X(s) as $n \to \infty$, and is written $X_n \xrightarrow{r} X$, if $\lim_{n\to\infty} E|X_n - X|^r = 0$. If $r = 2$, this convergence is called convergence in quadratic mean [Chung (1968), p. 64].

(4) Convergence in Distribution. A sequence of random variables $\{X_n(s)\}$, $n = 1, 2, \ldots, s \in S$, is said to converge in distribution to another random variable X(s) as $n \to \infty$, and is written $X_n \xrightarrow{d} X$, if $F_n(x) \to F(x)$ as $n \to \infty$ for all x for which F is continuous. Here $F_n(x)$ is the cdf of the random variable $X_n(s)$ and F(x) is the cdf of the random variable X(s) [Roussas (1973), p. 132].

9.1.2 COMMENTS

(1) $X_n \xrightarrow{a.s.} X$ implies $X_n \xrightarrow{p} X$. The converse is not true. [See, e.g., Roussas (1973), p. 136.]

(2) $X_n \xrightarrow{r} X$ implies $X_n \xrightarrow{p} X$ [Chung (1968), p. 64].

(3) $X_n \xrightarrow{r} X$ does not imply $X_n \xrightarrow{a.s.} X$; $X_n \xrightarrow{p} X$ does not imply $X_n \xrightarrow{r} X$. [See, e.g., Chung (1968), p. 65, Example 1.]

(4) $X_{(n)} \xrightarrow{a.s.} X$ does not imply $X_n \xrightarrow{r} X$. [See, e.g., Chung (1968), p. 66.]

(5) $X_n \xrightarrow{p} X$ implies $X_n \xrightarrow{d} X$. The converse is true if X(s) is a degenerate random variable. [See, e.g., Roussas (1973), p. 137.]

(6) A diagram useful in remembering the various modes of convergences is given below, where => denotes implications.

a.s. conv. => conv. in prob. => conv. in dist.

$\Uparrow$

(7) If F_n have pdf's f_n, then $X_n \xrightarrow{d} X$ does not imply the convergence of $f_n(x)$ to a pdf. [See, e.g., Roussas (1973), p. 133.]

(8) If $X_n \xrightarrow{p} X$, $Y_n \xrightarrow{p} Y$ then

$$X_n + Y_n \xrightarrow{p} X + Y,$$

$$X_n Y_n \xrightarrow{p} XY,$$

$$aX_n + bY_n \xrightarrow{p} aX + bY, \quad (a, b, \text{ constants}),$$

$$\frac{X_n}{Y_n} \xrightarrow{p} \frac{X}{Y}, \text{ provided } P(Y_n \neq 0) = P(Y \neq 0) = 1 \text{ (for all } n).$$

[Roussas (1973), p. 152]

(9) If $X_n \xrightarrow{d} X$ and $Y_n \xrightarrow{p} c \neq 0$, then

$$X_n + Y_n \xrightarrow{d} X + c,$$

$$X_n Y_n \xrightarrow{d} cX,$$

$$\frac{X_n}{Y_n} \xrightarrow{d} \frac{X}{c}, \text{ provided } P(Y_n \neq 0) = 1 \text{ (for all } n)$$

[Roussas (1973), p. 152]

9.1.3 SOME OTHER RESULTS

(1) $X_n \xrightarrow{p} 0$ iff

$$E\left(\frac{|X_n|}{1 + |X_n|}\right) \to 0 \quad \text{[Chung (1968), p. 64]}$$

(2) If a sequence of random variables $\{X_n\}$ converges in probability to a random variable X, it is always possible to pick out a subsequence $\{X_{n_k}\}$ (k = 1, 2, ...), which converges almost surely to X, and moreover it is possible to do this in such a way that

$$\sum_{k=1}^{\infty} \Pr(|X_{n_k} - X| > 2^{-k}) < \infty \quad \text{[Moran (1968), p. 347]}$$

(3) If $X_n \xrightarrow{r} X$, then $E|X_n|^r \to E|X|^r$ [Moran (1968), p. 349].

(4) If $X_n \xrightarrow{r} x$, then $X_n \xrightarrow{s} X$, for any s satisfying $0 < s < r$.
[Moran (1968), p. 350]

(5) If $\{X_n\}$ is a sequence of random variables such that $|X_n| < Y$ for each n, where Y is another random variable such that $E|Y|^r = k < \infty$ $(r > 0)$, then $X_n \xrightarrow{p} X$ implies $X_n \xrightarrow{r} X$ and $E|X|^r < \infty$.
[Moran (1968), p. 352]

9.2 LAWS OF LARGE NUMBERS

There are two types of laws of large numbers, the weak law of large numbers in which the convergence involved is convergence in probability and the strong law of large numbers in which the convergence involved is convergence almost surely.

9.2.1 WEAK LAW OF LARGE NUMBERS

(1) Let $X_1, X_2, \ldots, X_n$ be independent random variables which have a common mean μ and a common (finite) variance σ^2, and let $\bar{X}_n = \sum_1^n (X_i/n)$. Then $\bar{X}_n \xrightarrow{p} \mu$ [Woodroofe (1975), p. 244].

(2) Khintchine's Theorem. Let $X_1, X_2, \ldots, X_n$ be iid random variables with a (finite) mean μ. Then $\bar{X}_n \xrightarrow{p} \mu$ [Woodroofe (1975), p. 245].

(3) Markov's Theorem. If the sequence of random variables $X_1, X_2, \ldots, X_n$ is such that $(1/n^2)\operatorname{var}(\sum_1^n X_i) \to 0$ for $n \to \infty$, then for any $\varepsilon > 0$, $\bar{X}_n \xrightarrow{p} \mu$ where $\mu = \lim_{n\to\infty} E[(1/n)\sum_{i=1}^n X_i]$.

[Gnedenko (1962), p. 232]

(4) Let $X_1, X_2, \ldots, X_n$ be jointly distributed random variables with common mean μ and bounded variances $\sigma_1^2, \sigma_2^2, \ldots, \sigma_n^2$, say $\sigma_i^2 \leq b$ $(i = 1, 2, \ldots, n)$, where b is independent of n. If $\lim \operatorname{cov}(X_i, X_j) = 0$, where the limit is taken as $|i - j| \to \infty$, then $\bar{X}_n \xrightarrow{p} \mu$ as $n \to \infty$ [Woodroofe (1975), p. 247].

(5) Let $X_1, X_2, \ldots, X_n$ be uncorrelated random variables with common mean μ and variances $\sigma_1^2, \ldots, \sigma_n^2$, respectively. If there are constants $\alpha > 0$ and $\beta < 1$ such that $\sigma_k^2 \leq \alpha k^\beta$ $(k = 1, 2, 3, \ldots, n)$, then $\bar{X}_n \xrightarrow{p} \mu$ [Woodroofe (1975), p. 248].

(6) A Necessary and Sufficient Condition. The sequence of random variables $\{X_k\}$ satisfies the weak law of large numbers iff

$$\lim_{n\to\infty} E\left[\frac{\left\{\sum_{k=1}^n [X_k - E(X_k)]\right\}^2}{n^2 + \left\{\sum_{k=1}^n [X_k - E(X_k)]\right\}^2}\right] = 0$$

[Harris (1966), p. 237]

9.2.2 STRONG LAW OF LARGE NUMBERS

(1) Let X_1, X_2, ... be independent random variables with means μ_1, μ_2, ... and finite variances σ_1^2, σ_2^2, ... If $\sum_{k=1}^{\infty}(\sigma_k^2/k^2) < \infty$, then $\bar{X}_n \overset{a.s.}{\to} \bar{\mu}_n$, where $\bar{X}_n = \sum_1^n (X_i/n)$, $\bar{\mu}_n = \sum_1^n(\mu_i/n)$. The condition $\sum_{k=1}^{\infty}(\sigma_k^2/k^2) < \infty$ is known as Kolmogorov's condition.

[Woodroofe (1975), p. 317]

(2) Let X_1, X_2 ... be iid random variables with a (finite) mean μ, then $\bar{X}_n \overset{a.s.}{\to} \mu$. The converse is also true, that is, if $\bar{X}_n \overset{a.s.}{\to}$ to some finite constant μ, then $E(X_i)$ is finite and equal to μ.

[Roussas (1973), p. 145]

(3) Necessary and Sufficient Condition. The existence of the expectation is a necessary and sufficient condition for the strong law of large numbers to hold for a sequence of identically distributed and mutually independent random variables [Gnedenko (1962), p. 245].

9.3 THE CENTRAL LIMIT THEOREM

9.3.1 INDEPENDENT RANDOM VARIABLES CASE

This theorem provides a simple, effective approximation to probabilities determined by sums of independent random variables and explains the great importance of the normal distribution in probability theory. There are several versions of this theorem.

(1) The Lindberg-Levy Theorem. Let X_1, X_2, ..., X_n be iid random variables with mean μ and finite variance σ^2. Let $S_n = \sum_i^n X_i$. Then

$$\lim_{n\to\infty} P\left[\frac{S_n - n\mu}{\sigma\sqrt{n}} \le a\right] = \Phi(a)$$

for all a, $-\infty < a < \infty$, where Φ denotes the standard normal cdf.

[Woodroofe (1975), p. 251]

(2) Berry-Essen Theorem. If, in addition to the hypotheses of the Lindberg-Levy Theorem, $\gamma = E|X_i^3|$ is finite, then

$$\left| P\left[\frac{S_n - n\mu}{\sigma\sqrt{n}} \le a\right] - \Phi(a)\right| \le \frac{5\gamma}{\sqrt{n}\,\sigma^3}$$

for all a, $-\infty < a < \infty$ and $n = 1, 2, \ldots$ [Woodroofe (1975), p. 251].

(3) The Lindberg-Feller Theorem. Let $X_1, X_2, \ldots, X_n$ be independent random variables with distribution functions $F_1, F_2, \ldots, F_n$, means $\mu_1, \mu_2, \ldots, \mu_n$, and finite variances $\sigma_1^2, \sigma_2^2, \ldots, \sigma_n^2$. Let $v_n = \sum_1^n \mu_i$, $B_n^2 = \sum_1^n \sigma_i^2$. If

$$\lim_{n\to\infty} \frac{1}{B_n^2} \sum_{k=1}^{n} \int_{|x| \ge \varepsilon B_n} (x - v_k)^2 \, dF_k(x) = 0 \quad \text{for all } \varepsilon > 0$$

then for any a, $-\infty < a < \infty$,

$$\lim_{n\to\infty} P\left[\frac{S_n - v_n}{B_n} \le a\right] = \Phi(a)$$

where Φ denotes the standard normal cdf [Woodroofe (1975), p. 255].

(4) Liapounov's Theorem. If for a sequence of mutually independent random variables $X_1, X_2, \ldots$, a positive number δ can be found such that as $n \to \infty$

$$B_n^{-(2+\delta)} \sum_{k=1}^{n} E|X_k - \mu_k|^{2+\delta} \to 0$$

Then as $n \to \infty$

$$\lim_{n\to\infty} P\left[\frac{S_n - v_n}{B_n} \le a\right] = \Phi(a)$$

where μ_k, v_n, B_n and Φ are as defined in the Lindberg-Feller Theorem.

[Gnedenko (1962), p. 294]

9.3.2 DEPENDENT RANDOM VARIABLES CASE

References to central limit theorems for sums $S_n = X_1 + X_2 + \cdots + X_n$, where X_i are not independent random variables, are given in Moran (1968), p. 403. Also, see Serfling (1968), pp. 1158-1175.

9.3.3 SOME OTHER RESULTS

(1) The DeMoivre-Laplace Theorem. Let $\{X_n\}$ be a sequence of random variables distributed as the binomial distribution, given by $P(X_n = x) = \binom{n}{x}p^x q^{n-x}$; $x = 0, 1, 2, \ldots, n$, $0 < p < 1$, $q = 1 - p$. Let $\{F_n(y)\}$ be a sequence of distribution functions of the random variables $Y_n = (X_n - np)/\sqrt{npq}$. Then for every y, $\lim_{n\to\infty} F_n(y) = \Phi(y)$ where Φ is the standard normal cdf [Fisz (1963), p. 192].

(2) The Gnedenko Theorem. Suppose that iid random variables X_i $(i = 1, 2, \ldots)$ of the discrete type can take on with positive probability only integer values, and let $E(X_i) = \mu$ and $\mathrm{var}(X_i) = \sigma^2 > 0$. Then $\lim_{n\to\infty} [\sigma\sqrt{n}P_n(x) - \phi(z)] = 0$ where $P_n(x) = P(\sum_1^n X_i = x)$ and $z = (x - \mu n)/\sigma\sqrt{n}$ and ϕ is the standard normal pdf.

[Fisz (1963), p. 211]

(3) Let $\{X_n\}$, $n = 1, 2, \ldots$, be a sequence of random variables with finite mean μ and variance σ^2. Let $g(x)$ be a function which has a first derivative $g'(x)$ in some neighborhood of the point $x = \mu$ such that $g'(\mu) \neq 0$. Then the random variable $g(\bar{x})$, where $\bar{X} = \sum_1^n (X_i/n)$, has an asymptotic normal distribution with mean $g(\mu)$ and variance $(\sigma^2/n)[g'(\mu)]^2$ for large n [Wilks (1962), p. 259].

9.4 SOME OTHER LIMIT THEOREMS

(1) Let $X_1, X_2, \ldots, X_n$ be iid random variables with cdf F. Let $Y_n = X_{(n;n)}$ be the largest order statistic in a sample of size n from F. Let $\{a_n\}$, $\{b_n\}$ be sequences of constants. If $(Y_n - a_n)/b_n$ has a limiting distribution, then that limiting distribution must be one of the following three types.

$$G_1(y;\gamma) = \exp(-y^{-\gamma});\ y > 0,\ \gamma > 0$$

$$G_2(y;\gamma) = \begin{cases} \exp(-|y|^{\gamma});\ y < 0,\ \gamma > 0 \\ 1;\ y > 0,\ \gamma > 0 \end{cases}$$

$$G_3(y;\gamma) = \exp(-e^{-y}),\ -\infty < y < \infty$$

(a) The limiting distribution is G_1 iff

$$\lim_{x\to\infty} \frac{1 - F(x)}{1 - F(\tau x)} = \tau^{\gamma} \text{ for every } \tau > 0$$

(b) The limiting distribution is G_2 iff there exists an x_0 such that $F(x_0) = 1$ and $F(x_0 - \varepsilon) < 1$ for every $\varepsilon > 0$ and

$$\lim_{0<x\to 0} \frac{1 - F(x_0 - \tau x)}{1 - F(x_0 - x)} = \tau^{\gamma} \text{ for every } \tau > 0$$

(c) The limiting distribution is G_3 iff

$$\lim_{n\to\infty} n[1 - F(\beta_n X + \alpha_n)] = e^{-x} \text{ for each } x$$

where $\alpha_n = \inf\{z\colon\ [(n - 1)/n] \le F(z)\}$ and $\beta_n = \inf\{z\colon\ 1 - (ne)^{-1} \le F(\alpha_n + z)\}$ [Mood et al. (1974), pp. 261-262].

(2) Let $X_1, X_2, \ldots, X_n$ be iid random variables with a continuous cdf F. Let $X_{(i;n)}$ be the ith order statistic in a sample of size n from F. Then for fixed k, $nF(X_{(k;n)})$, $n = k, k + 1, \ldots$, is a sequence of random variables converging in distribution to a gamma distribution $G(y; 1, k)$, where $G(y; 1, k) = \int_0^y (e^{-x}x^{k-1}/\Gamma(k))\,dx$.

[Wilks (1962), p. 269]

(3) Let $X_1, X_2, \ldots, X_n$ be iid random variables with cdf F. Let $X_{(i;n)}$ be the ith order statistic in a sample of size n from a continuous cdf F. Let np_n be an integer such that $p_n = p + O(1/n)$, where $0 < p < 1$, then for large n, the random variable $F(X_{(np_n;n)})$

is asymptotically distributed according to a normal distribution with mean p and variance $p(1 - p)/n$ [Wilks (1962), p. 271].

(4) If in addition to the assumption given in (3), suppose a unique pth quantile ζ_p exists, then as $n \to \infty$, $X_{(np_n;n)} \xrightarrow{p} \xi_p$.

[Wilks (1962), p. 272]

(5) If in addition to the assumption given in (3), suppose F(x) has a derivative f(x) in some neighborhood of $x = \xi_p$ such that $f(\xi_p) > 0$, then, for large n, the random variable $X_{(np_n;n)}$ is asymptotically distributed as normal with mean ξ_p and variance $p(1 - p)/nf^2(\xi_p)$.

[Wilks (1962), p. 273]

(6) Continuity Theorem. See Sec. 1.3.3(6).

Chapter 10

MISCELLANEOUS RESULTS

10.1 GAMMA FUNCTIONS

10.1.1 DEFINITION

These functions, denoted by $\Gamma(a)$, are defined by

$$\Gamma(a) = \int_0^\infty e^{-t} t^{a-1}\, dt, \quad a > 0$$

10.1.2 PROPERTIES

(1) $\Gamma(a) = (a - 1)\Gamma(a - 1), \quad a - 1 > 0$

(2) $\Gamma(a) = (a - 1)!$ (if a is a positive integer)

(3) $\Gamma(a)\,\Gamma(1 - a) = \dfrac{\pi}{\sin(\pi a)}, \quad 0 < a < 1$

(4) $\Gamma(0) = \infty, \ \Gamma\left(\frac{1}{2}\right) = \sqrt{\pi}, \ \Gamma\left(a + \frac{1}{2}\right) = \dfrac{1\cdot 3\cdot 5 \cdots (2a - 1)}{2^a}\sqrt{\pi},$

$$a = 1, 2, 3, \ldots$$

$$\Gamma\left(-a + \frac{1}{2}\right) = \frac{(-1)^a 2^a \sqrt{\pi}}{1\cdot 3\cdot 5 \cdots (2a - 1)}, \quad a = 1, 2, 3, \ldots$$

(5) $\Gamma(na) = (2\pi)^{(1-n)/2} (n)^{na-(1/2)} \prod_{k=0}^{n-1} \Gamma\left(a + \frac{k}{n}\right)$

(a) Legender's Duplication Formula

$$\Gamma(2a) = \frac{(2)^{2a-1}}{\sqrt{\pi}} \Gamma(a)\Gamma\left(a + \frac{1}{2}\right)$$

(b) $\Gamma(3a) = \frac{1}{2\pi} (3)^{3a-(1/2)} \Gamma(a)\Gamma\left(a + \frac{1}{3}\right)\Gamma\left(a + \frac{2}{3}\right)$

[For (1)-(5), see Abramowitz and Stegun (1970), pp. 255-256]

(6) $\Gamma(a) = \lim_{k\to\infty} \frac{1\cdot 2\cdot 3 \cdots k}{a(a + 1) \cdots (a + k)} k^a, \; a \neq 0, -1, -2, \ldots$

[Jordan (1965), p. 54]

10.2 INCOMPLETE GAMMA FUNCTIONS

10.2.1 DEFINITION

These functions, denoted by $\gamma(a, x)$, are defined by

$$\gamma(a, x) = \int_0^x e^{-t} t^{a-1}\, dt; \; a > 0, \; x > 0$$

Also, $P(a, x) = \gamma(a, x)/\Gamma(a)$ is generally known as the incomplete gamma function ratio or the gamma cdf. Let

$$\Gamma(a, x) = \Gamma(a) - \gamma(a, x) = \int_x^\infty e^{-t} t^{a-1}\, dt$$

10.2.2 PROPERTIES

(1) $P(a + 1, x) = 1 - \sum_{k=0}^{a} \frac{e^{-x} x^k}{k!}$, if $a = 0, 1, 2, \ldots$

(2) $P(a + 1, x) = P(a, x) - \frac{x^a e^{-x}}{\Gamma(a + 1)}$

$$\gamma(a + 1, x) = a\, \gamma(a, x) - x^a e^{-x}$$

$$\gamma^*(a - 1, x) = x\,\gamma^*(a, x) + \frac{e^{-x}}{\Gamma(a)}$$

where $\gamma^*(a, x) = P(a, x)/x^a$ [Abramowitz and Stegun (1970), p. 262].

(3) $(a + 1)P(a + 2, x) = (a + 1 + x)P(a + 1, x) - xP(a, x)$

for $a > 0$ [Khamis (1965), p. 927].

(4) $\Gamma\left(\frac{1}{2}, x\right) = 2\sqrt{\pi}\,[1 - \Phi(\sqrt{2x})]$

where Φ is the normal cdf [Gupta and Waknis (1965), p. 144].

(5) $a^{1-x} \le \dfrac{\Gamma(a + 1)}{\Gamma(a + x)} \le (a + x)^{1-x}$; $a > 0$, $0 \le x \le 1$

[Shanbhag (1967), p. 45]

10.3 BETA FUNCTIONS

10.3.1 DEFINITION

These functions, denoted by $B(a, b)$, are defined by

$$B(a, b) = \int_0^1 y^{a-1}(1 - y)^{b-1}\,dy;\quad a > 0,\ b > 0$$

10.3.2 PROPERTIES

(1) $B(a, b) = B(b, a)$

(2) $B(a, b) = \dfrac{\Gamma(a)\Gamma(b)}{\Gamma(a + b)}$

where $\Gamma(c)$ is a gamma function (see Sec. 10.1).

(3) $B(a, b) = \dfrac{1}{a\binom{a + b - 1}{a}}$

(4) $B(a + 1, b) = \left(\dfrac{a}{a + b}\right)B(a, b)$

(5) $B(a, b) = \frac{1}{a} \prod_{i=1}^{\infty} \frac{i(a + b + i - 1)}{(a + i)(b + i - 1)}$ (if a and b are integers)

[For (1)-(5) see Jordan (1965), pp. 80-82]

10.4 INCOMPLETE BETA FUNCTIONS

10.4.1 DEFINITION

These functions, denoted by $B_x(a, b)$, are defined by

$$B_x(a, b) = \int_0^x y^{a-1}(1 - y)^{b-1}\, dy;\ a > 0,\ b > 0,\ 0 < x < 1$$

Also, $I_x(a, b) = B_x(a, b)/B(a, b)$ is generally known as the incomplete beta function ratio or the beta cdf.

10.4.2 PROPERTIES

(1) $I_x(a, b) = 1 - I_{1-x}(b, a)$

(2) $I_x(a, 1) = x^a,\ I_x(1, b) = 1 - (1 - x)^b$

(3) $I_x(a, n - a + 1) = \sum_{j=a}^{n} \binom{n}{j} x^j (1 - x)^{n-j}$ (if a is an integer)

(4) $I_x(a, b) = \Gamma(a + b) \sum_{i=0}^{b} \frac{x^{a+i}(1 - x)^{b-1-i}}{(a + i + 1)\ (b - i)} + I_x(a + m, b - m)$

(if a and b are integers). [For (1)-(4) see Jordan (1965), pp. 84-86.

(5) $(a + b)I_x(a, b) = aI_x(a + 1, b) + bI_x(a, b + 1)$

$$(a + b + n - 1)^{(n)} I_x(a, b) = \sum_{r=0}^{n} \binom{n}{r} (a + n - r - 1)^{(n-r)}$$

$$\times\ (b + r - 1)^{(r)} I_x(a + n - r, b + r)$$

where $(c)^{(n)} = c(c - 1)(c - 2) \ldots (c - n + 1)$.

[Bancroft (1945), pp. 98-99]

(6) $xI_x(a, b) - I_x(a + 1, b) + (1 - x)I_x(a + 1, b - 1) = 0$

$$(a + b - ax)I_x(a, b) - bI_x(a, b + 1) - a(1 - x)I_x(a + 1, b - 1) = 0$$

[Bancroft (1949), pp. 451-455]

(7) $$I_x(a, b) = \frac{\Gamma(a + b)}{\Gamma(a + 1)\Gamma(b)} x^a(1 - x)^{b-1} + I_x(a + 1, b - 1)$$
$$= \frac{\Gamma(a + b)}{\Gamma(a + 1)\Gamma(b)} x^a(1 - x)^b + I_x(a + 1, b)$$

[Jordan (1965), p. 84]

(8) $I_x(a, b) > I_x(a, a) > I_x(b, a)$ if $b > a$

$I_x(b, a) + I_{1-x}(b, a) < 1$ if $b > a$ [Jordan (1965), p. 85]

(9) $$B_x(a, b) = \frac{x^a}{a} F(a, 1 - b; a + 1; x), \ b > 0,$$

where F is the hypergeometric function [Bancroft (1949), p. 452].

10.5 CONVEX (CONCAVE) FUNCTIONS

10.5.1 DEFINITIONS

A real-valued function ϕ, defined on some nondegenerate interval (a, b), $-\infty \leq a < b \leq \infty$, is convex if $\phi[\alpha x + (1 - \alpha)y] \leq \alpha\phi(x) + (1 - \alpha)\phi(y)$ for $0 \leq \alpha \leq 1$, $a \leq x, y \leq b$.

If the inequality holds in the opposite direction the function ϕ is called concave. If the function ϕ is twice differentiable, a necessary and sufficient condition for a function ϕ to be convex is $d^2\phi(x)/dx^2 \geq 0$ for all $x \in (a, b)$, and ϕ is concave iff $d^2\phi(x)/dx^2 \leq 0$ for all $x \in (a, b)$.

10.5.2 PROPERTIES

(1) If $\phi(x)$ is convex, then $-\phi(x)$ is concave.

(2) A function ϕ is convex if for every interior point x_0 of (a, b), there exists a straight line L having $L(x_0) = \phi(x_0)$ and lying wholly

on or below the graph of ϕ. The line L is the line of support of ϕ at $x = x_0$.

(3) Let $0 \leq x_1 \leq x_2 \leq \cdots \leq x_n$, and let $\bar{A}_i = \sum_i^n a_j$. Let ϕ be convex and $\phi(0) = 0$. Consider

$$\text{(a)} \quad \phi\left(\sum_1^n a_j x_j\right) \leq \sum_1^n a_j \phi(x_j)$$

$$\text{(b)} \quad \phi\left(\sum_1^n a_j x_j\right) \geq \sum_1^n a_j \phi(x_j)$$

Note that (a) holds iff $0 \leq \bar{A}_i \leq 1$, $1 \leq i \leq n$, and (b) holds iff there exists j, $0 \leq j \leq n$, such that $\bar{A}_i \geq 1$, $1 \leq i \leq j$, $\bar{A}_i \leq 0$, $j + 1 \leq i \leq n$ [Barlow et al. (1969), p. 39].

10.6 TRANSFORMATION OF STATISTICS

Let $\{T_n\}$, n = 1, 2, 3, ..., be a sequence of statistics such that $\sqrt{n}(T_n - \theta)$ is asymptotically distributed as $N(0, \sigma^2(\theta))$, and $N(0, \sigma^2(\theta))$ indicates the random variable is normally distributed with mean 0 and variance $\sigma^2(\theta)$. Let g be a function of a single variable admitting the first derivative g' and $g'(\theta) \neq 0$, then $\sqrt{n}[g(T_n) - g(\theta)]$ is asymptotically distributed as $N(0, \{g'(\theta)\sigma(\theta)\}^2)$. Choose g such that $g'(\theta)\sigma(\theta) = c$ (independent of θ). Then $g = \int [c/\sigma(\theta)]\, d\theta$.

[Rao (1973), p. 426]

The purpose of such transformations is to stabilize the variance of the transformed random variable.

10.6.1 SQUARE ROOT TRANSFORMATION OF A POISSON RANDOM VARIABLE

Let X be a random variable with Poisson distribution having parameter λ. Then the transformed random variable $\sqrt{X}$ has the asymptotic normal distribution with mean $\sqrt{\lambda}$ and variance 1/4 when λ is large. The transformation $\sqrt{X + (3/8)}$ is more stable than $\sqrt{X}$.

[Rao (1973), p. 426]

10.6.2 SIN^{-1} TRANSFORMATION OF THE SQUARE ROOT OF A BINOMIAL RANDOM VARIABLE

Let X be a random variable with binomial distribution having parameters p and n. Then the transformed random variable $\sin^{-1}\sqrt{X/n}$ has the asymptotic normal distribution with variance (1/4n). If n is of moderate size the transformation $\sin^{-1}\sqrt{[X + (3/8)]/[n + (3/4)]}$ should be used [Rao (1973), pp. 427-428].

10.6.3 $TANH^{-1}$ TRANSFORMATION OF THE CORRELATION COEFFICIENT

Let ρ, r be the population and sample correlation coefficient, respectively. Then the random variable $\tanh^{-1}(r) - \tanh^{-1}(\rho)$ has an approximate normal distribution with mean $\rho/2(n - 1)$ and variance $= [1/(n - 1)] + [(4 - \rho^2)/2(n - 1)^2] \approx 1/(n - 3)$.

[Rao (1973), pp. 431-433]

10.6.4 ADDITIONAL TRANSFORMATIONS

For $\cosh^{-1}$ and other transformations of a noncentral F random variable, see Laubscher (1960), pp. 1108-1111. Also, for $\sinh^{-1}$ transformation of a noncentral t random variable, see Laubscher (1960), p. 1106. For log transformation on a chi square random variable, see Rao (1952), p. 214. For some additional transformations (including above), see Hoyle (1973), where a comprehensive review has been given.

10.7 STIRLING NUMBERS

10.7.1 DEFINITIONS

The coefficients $U_{m,n}$ defined by

$$x(x - 1) \cdots (x - n + 1) = \sum_{m=0}^{n} U_{m,n} x^m$$

are known as the Stirling numbers of the first kind. Similarly, the coefficients $v_{m,n}$ defined by

$$x^n = \sum_{m=0}^{n} v_{m,n} x(x - 1) \cdots (x - m + 1)$$

are known as the Stirling numbers of the second kind. For $n > 0$, $U_{m,n} = 0$ (if $m > n$ or $m < 1$), $v_{m,n} = 0$ (if $m > n$ or $m < 1$), and $U_{00} = v_{00} = 1$ [Harris (1966), p. 26].

10.7.2 PROPERTIES

(1) $U_{m,n+1} = U_{m-1,n} - nU_{m,n}, \quad n \geq m \geq 1$

$$\binom{m}{r} U_{m,n} = \sum_{k=m-r}^{n-r} \binom{n}{k} U_{r,n-k} U_{m-r,k}, \quad n \geq m \geq r$$

$$v_{m,n+1} = mv_{m,n} + v_{m-1,n}, \quad n \geq m \geq 1$$

$$\binom{m}{r} v_{m,n} = \sum_{k=m-r}^{n-r} \binom{n}{k} v_{r,n-k} v_{m-r,k}, \quad n \geq m \geq r$$

(2) $\sum_{m=1}^{n} U_{m,n} = 0, \quad \sum_{m=0}^{n} (-1)^{n-m} m! v_{m,n} = 1$

(3) Also, $v_{m,n}$ is the number of ways of partitioning a set of n elements into m nonempty subsets.

[For (1)-(3) see Abramowitz and Stegun (1970), pp. 824-825]

10.8 BERNOULLI NUMBERS

The Bernoulli number of order j, B_j, is defined as the coefficient of $t^j/j!$ in the expansion of $t/(e^t - 1)$, i.e.

$$\frac{t}{e^t - 1} = \sum_{j=0}^{\infty} B_j \frac{t^j}{j!}$$

$$B_0 = 1, \quad B_1 = -\frac{1}{2}, \quad B_2 = \frac{1}{6}, \quad B_4 = -\frac{1}{30}$$

$B_{2k+1} = 0$ for every integer $k > 0$

[Kendall and Stuart (1958), p. 80]

10.9 HYPERGEOMETRIC FUNCTIONS

10.9.1 DEFINITIONS

The hypergeometric function with arguments α, β, γ and x is

$$F(\alpha, \beta; \gamma; x) = 1 + \frac{\alpha\beta}{\gamma}\frac{x}{1!} + \frac{\alpha(\alpha + 1)\beta(\beta + 1)}{\gamma(\gamma + 1)}\frac{x^2}{2!} + \cdots, \quad \gamma > 0$$

The series converges for $|x| < 1$. The confluent hypergeometric function with arguments α, γ, and x is

$$M(\alpha; \gamma; x) = 1 + \frac{\alpha}{\gamma}\frac{x}{1!} + \frac{\alpha(\alpha + 1)}{\gamma(\gamma + 1)}\frac{x^2}{2!} + \cdots, \quad \gamma > 0$$

It also converges for $|x| < 1$ [Johnson and Kotz (1969), p. 8].

[Abramowitz and Stegun (1970), p. 504, 556]

10.9.2 PROPERTIES

(1) $$F(\alpha, \beta; \gamma; x) = (1 - x)^{\gamma-\alpha-\beta} F(\gamma - \alpha, \gamma - \beta; \gamma; x)$$
$$= (1 - x)^{-\alpha} F\left(\alpha, \gamma - \beta; \gamma; \frac{x}{x - 1}\right)$$

$M(\alpha; \gamma; x) = e^x M(\gamma - \alpha; \gamma; -x)$ [Johnson and Kotz (1969), p. 9]

(2) $F(a, b; c; 1) = \frac{\Gamma(c)\Gamma(c - a - b)}{\Gamma(c - a)\Gamma(c - b)}$; $c \neq 0, -1, -2, \ldots,$

$c - a - b > 0$

$$F(a, b; b; x) = \frac{1}{(1 - x)^a}$$

$$F\left(\frac{1}{2}, 1; \frac{3}{2}; x^2\right) = \frac{\log\left(\frac{1 + x}{1 - x}\right)}{2x}$$

[Abramowitz and Stegun (1970), p. 556]

(3) $F(a, 1 - b; a + 1; x) = \frac{a}{x^a} B_x(a, b)$ where $B_x(a, b)$ is the incomplete beta function [Abramowitz and Stegun (1970), p. 945].

10.10 THE NOTATIONS *O* and *o*

The Notation *O*. Let f(x) and g(x) be two functions and assume that g(x) is positive for sufficiently large x. Then f(x) is said to be, at most, of the order of g(x) as x tends to infinity and is written

$$f(x) = O[g(x)] \text{ as } x \to \infty$$

if there exists a value x_0 and a constant $A > 0$ such that $|f(x)| < Ag(x)$ for $x \geq x_0$. Thus $f(x) = O[g(x)]$ means that the quotient $|f(x)|/g(x)$ is bounded for sufficiently large x.

The Symbol *o*. Let f(x) and g(x) be both positive and defined for sufficiently large x. Then f(x) is said to be of smaller order than g(x) as x tends to infinity and is written

$$f(x) = o[g(x)] \text{ as } x \to \infty$$

if $\lim_{x\to\infty} [f(x)/g(x)] = 0$ [Lukacs (1970), p. 327].

10.11 K-STATISTICS

The K-statistic K_p of order p is a symmetric and homogeneous polynomial statistic of order p such that $E(K_p) = \kappa_p$ for any distribution which has moments up to order p. Here κ_p denotes the pth cumulant of the distribution. These statistics are unique and are not defined for $p > n$, where n denotes a random sample size from the same population [David and Barton (1962), pp. 323-324].

10.12 SOME USEFUL COMBINATORIALS

The binomial coefficients $\binom{n}{k}$ are defined only when n and k are positive integers. But this definition can be extended. Let

$$\binom{n}{k} = \frac{n(n - 1) \cdots (n - k + 1)}{k!}$$

Then $\binom{n}{k}$ defines the binomial coefficients for all n and all positive integers k with the following convention: $\binom{n}{0} = 1$, $0! = 1$, $\binom{n}{k} = 0$ if $k < 0$ or $k > n$.

(1) $$\binom{n}{k - 1} + \binom{n}{k} = \binom{n + 1}{k}$$

(2) $$(1 + t)^a = \sum_{j=0}^{z} \binom{a}{j} t^j$$

where the upper limit z of the sum is a, if a is a positive integer, and infinity, otherwise. A consequence of this result is $\binom{n}{0} + \binom{n}{1} + \cdots + \binom{n}{n} = 2^n$ [Feller (1960), pp. 48-51].

(3) For integers $n \geq 2$,

$$\binom{n}{0} - \binom{n}{1} + \binom{n}{2} - + \cdots = 0$$

$$\binom{n}{1} + 2\binom{n}{2} + 3\binom{n}{3} + \cdots = n2^{n-1}$$

$$\binom{n}{1} - 2\binom{n}{2} + 3\binom{n}{3} - + \cdots = 0$$

$$2 \cdot 1\binom{n}{2} + 3 \cdot 2\binom{n}{3} + 4 \cdot 3\binom{n}{4} + \cdots = n(n-1)2^{n-2}$$

[Feller (1960), p. 61]

(4) $\sum_j \binom{n}{j}\binom{n-j}{k-j} t^j = \binom{n}{k}(1+t)^k$; n, k positive integers

[Feller (1960), p. 61]

(5) $\binom{-a}{k} = (-1)^k \binom{a+k-1}{k}$, $a > 0$

$\sum_{j=0}^{n} (-1)^j \binom{a}{j} = (-1)^n \binom{a-1}{n}$, any a and positive integer n

[Feller (1960), p. 61]

(6) $\sum_{j=0}^{r} \binom{j+k-1}{k-1} = \binom{r+k}{k}$; r, k positive integers

$\sum_{j=0}^{n} \binom{a}{j}\binom{b}{n-j} = \binom{a+b}{n}$; a, b, n positive integers

$\sum_{j=0}^{n} \binom{n}{j}^2 = \binom{2n}{n}$, n positive integer

$\sum_{j=1}^{a} (-1)^{a-j} \binom{a}{j}\binom{b+j}{b+1} = \binom{b}{a-1}$; $0 < a < b$, a, b positive integer

$\sum_j (-1)^j \binom{a}{j}\binom{n-j}{k} = \binom{n-a}{n-k}$; n, j, k positive integers

[Feller (1960), p. 62]

(7) $\sum_{j=0}^{c} \binom{m}{j}\binom{n}{j} = \binom{m+n}{m}$; $c = \min(m, n)$, m, n positive integers

$$\sum_{j=0}^{d} \binom{m}{j}\binom{n}{j+1} = \binom{m+n}{m+1}; \quad d = \min(m, n-1),\ m, n \text{ positive integers}$$

[Gibbons (1971), pp. 55-56]

(8) $$\binom{n}{m}\binom{m}{p} = \binom{n}{p}\binom{n-p}{m-p} = \binom{n}{m-p}\binom{n-m+p}{p}$$

$$\binom{n}{m}\binom{n-m}{p} = \binom{n}{p}\binom{n-p}{m} = \binom{n}{m+p}\binom{m+p}{m}$$ [Riordon (1968), p. 3]

(9) $$\sum_{k=m}^{n} \binom{n}{k}\binom{k}{m} = 2^{n-m}\binom{n}{m}; \quad n, m \text{ positive integers}$$

[Riordon (1968), p. 32]

(10) $$\sum_{k=0}^{m} \binom{2m+1}{2k}\binom{n+k}{2m} = \binom{2n+1}{2m}$$

$$\sum_{k=0}^{m} \binom{2m+1}{2k+1}\binom{n+k}{2m} = \binom{2n}{2m}$$ [Riordon (1968), p. 36]

(11) $$\binom{2n}{n} \approx \frac{2^{2n}}{\sqrt{\pi n}}$$ [Feller (1960), p. 63]

(12) $$\sum_{j=0}^{x} \binom{a}{b-j}\binom{c}{j} = \sum_{j=0}^{a-b+x} \binom{c+j}{x}\binom{a-1-j}{b-x-1}$$

for a, b, c, x positive integers, $0 \le x \le \min(c, b-1)$, and $0 \le b \le a$ [Lieberman and Owen (1961), p. 24].

(13) $$\sum_{j=0}^{x} \binom{a}{b-j}\binom{c}{j} = \sum_{j=0}^{x} \binom{c-x-1+j}{c-x-1}\binom{a+x-j}{a+x-b}$$

where $0 \le b \le a$, $0 \le x \le \min(c-1, b)$, and a, b, c, x are positive integers [Lieberman and Owen (1961), p. 25].

(14) $$\sum_{i=r}^{n} \binom{n}{i} p^i (1-p)^{n-i} = p^r \sum_{i=0}^{n-r} \binom{r+i-1}{r-1}(1-p)^i$$

$$= p^r \sum_{i=r}^{n} \binom{i-1}{r-1}(1-p)^{i-r}; \quad 0 \le p \le 1,\ n, r \text{ positive integers}$$

$$\sum_{i=0}^{k} (-1)^i \binom{x + n}{k - i}\binom{x - k + i}{i} = \binom{n - 1 + k}{k}; \; k = 0, 1, \ldots, x,$$

n, r positive integers

[Lieberman and Owen (1961), p. 25]

(15) $$\sum_{i=0}^{n} \binom{n}{i}(a + i)^i (b - i)^{n-i-1} = \frac{(a + b)^n}{(b - n)}$$

for all real a, b, and integers $n \geq 0$.

$$\sum_{i=0}^{n} \binom{n}{i}(a + i)^i (b - i)^{n-1} = n! \sum_{i=0}^{n} \frac{(a + b)^i}{i!}$$

for all real a, b, and integers $n \geq 0$.

[Lieberman and Owen (1961), p. 25]

(16) Stirling's Formula

$$n! \approx \sqrt{2\pi}\left(n + \frac{1}{2}\right)^{n+(1/2)} e^{-n};$$

$$\sqrt{2\pi}\left(n + \frac{1}{2}\right)^{n+(1/2)} \exp\left\{- \frac{(n + 1)}{2} - \frac{1}{24}\left(n + \frac{1}{2}\right)\right\}$$

$$< n! < \sqrt{2\pi}\left(n + \frac{1}{2}\right)^{n+(1/2)} \exp\left\{- \frac{n + 1}{2}\right\}$$ [Feller (1960), p. 64]

10.13 SOME USEFUL SERIES

A good collection of summation of series is given by Jolley (1961).

10.13.1 TAYLOR'S SERIES

Let f be a function that is continuous together with its first (n + 1) derivatives on an interval containing a and x. Then

$$f(x) = f(a) + f'(a)(x - a) + \frac{f''(a)}{2!}(x - a)^2 + \cdots$$

$$+ \frac{f^{(n)}(a)(x - a)^n}{n!} + R_n(x, a)$$

where

$$R_n(x, a) = \int_a^x \frac{(x - t)^n}{n!} f^{(n+1)}(t)\, dt$$

is the remainder after (n + 1) terms.

The different forms of the remainder are as follows.

(1) Lagrange's Form

$$R_n(x, a) = \frac{f^{(n+1)}(c)(x - a)^{n+1}}{(n + 1)!}$$

for some c such that $a < c < x$.

(2) Cauchy's Form

$$R_n(x, a) = \frac{f^{(n+1)}(c)(x - c)^n (x - a)}{n!}$$

for some c such that $a < c < x$.

If $\lim_{n\to\infty} R_n(x, a) = 0$, the infinite series obtained is called the Taylor's Series for f(x) about x = a. If a = 0, the series is also called a Maclaurin Series [Thomas (1968), pp. 636-640].

10.13.2 BINOMIAL SERIES

$$(a + x)^n = a^n + \binom{n}{1} a^{n-1} x + \binom{n}{2} a^{n-2} x^2 + \binom{n}{3} a^{n-3} x^3 + \cdots$$

If n is a positive integer, the series is finite with the last term $\binom{n}{n} x^n$ [Thomas (1968), p. 737].

$$\frac{1}{1 + x} = 1 - x + x^2 - x^3 + \cdots, \quad -1 < x < 1$$

$$\frac{1}{(1 + x)^2} = 1 - 2x + 3x^2 - 4x^3 + \cdots, \quad -1 < x < 1$$

10.13.3 EXPONENTIAL AND LOGARITHMIC SERIES

$$e^x = 1 + x + \frac{x^2}{2!} + \frac{x^3}{3!} + \cdots, \quad -\infty < x < \infty$$

$$\log(1 + x) = x - \frac{x^2}{2} + \frac{x^3}{3} - \frac{x^4}{4} + \cdots, \quad -1 < x < 1$$

$$\log(x) = 2\left\{\left(\frac{x - 1}{x + 1}\right) + \frac{1}{3}\left(\frac{x - 1}{x + 1}\right)^3 + \frac{1}{5}\left(\frac{x - 1}{x + 1}\right)^7 + \cdots\right\}, \quad x > 0$$

$$\log(x) = \left(\frac{x - 1}{x}\right) + \frac{1}{2}\left(\frac{x - 1}{x}\right)^2 + \frac{1}{3}\left(\frac{x - 1}{x}\right)^3 + \cdots, \quad x \geq \frac{1}{2}$$

10.13.4 GEOMETRIC AND ARITHMETIC SERIES

$$\frac{a(1 - r^n)}{1 - r} = a + ar + ar^2 + \cdots + ar^{n-1}, \quad r \neq 1$$

$$\frac{a}{1 - r} = a + ar + ar^2 + \cdots, \quad |r| < 1$$

$$\frac{n}{2}\{2a + (n - 1)\,d\} = a + (a + d) + (a + 2d) + \cdots + \{a + (n - 1)\,d\}$$

$$\frac{1}{(1 \pm x)^n} = 1 \mp nx + \frac{n(n + 1)}{2!}\,x^2 \mp \frac{n(n + 1)(n + 2)x^3}{3!} + \cdots, \quad x^2 < 1$$

10.13.5 POWERS OF NATURAL NUMBERS

$$\frac{n(n + 1)}{2} = 1 + 2 + 3 + \cdots + n$$

$$\frac{n(n + 1)(2n + 1)}{6} = 1^2 + 2^2 + 3^2 + \cdots + n^2$$

$$\left\{\frac{n(n + 1)}{2}\right\}^2 = 1^3 + 2^3 + 3^3 + \cdots + n^3$$

10.13.6 INVERSE NATURAL NUMBERS

$$\frac{\pi}{2\sqrt{2}} = 1 + \frac{1}{3} - \frac{1}{5} - \frac{1}{7} + \frac{1}{9} + \frac{1}{11} - \cdots$$

$$\frac{\pi}{4} = 1 - \frac{1}{3} + \frac{1}{5} - \frac{1}{7} + \frac{1}{9} - \cdots$$

10.13.7 POWER SERIES

$$\frac{\pi^2}{6} = 1 + \frac{1}{2^2} + \frac{1}{3^2} + \frac{1}{4^2} + \cdots$$

$$\frac{\pi^2}{12} = 1 - \frac{1}{2^2} + \frac{1}{3^2} - \frac{1}{4^2} + \cdots$$

$$\frac{\pi^2}{8} = 1 + \frac{1}{3^2} + \frac{1}{5^2} + \frac{1}{7^2} + \cdots$$

10.13.8 TRIGONOMETRICAL SERIES

$$\sin x = x - \frac{x^3}{3!} + \frac{x^5}{5!} - \frac{x^7}{7!} + \cdots$$

$$\cos x = 1 - \frac{x^2}{2!} + \frac{x^4}{4!} - \frac{x^6}{6!} + \cdots$$

$$\tan x = x + \frac{x^3}{3} + \frac{2x^5}{15} + \frac{17x^7}{315} + \cdots , \quad |x| < \frac{\pi}{2}$$

$$\sin^{-1} x = x + \frac{1}{2}\frac{x^3}{3} + \frac{1\cdot 3}{2\cdot 4}\frac{x^5}{5} + \frac{1\cdot 3\cdot 5}{2\cdot 4\cdot 6}\frac{x^7}{7} + \cdots , \quad |x| < 1$$

$$\cos^{-1} x = \frac{\pi}{2} - \sin^{-1} x, \quad |x| < 1$$

$$\tan^{-1} x = x - \frac{x^3}{3} + \frac{x^5}{5} - \frac{x^7}{7} + \cdots , \quad |x| < 1$$

10.14 SOME WELL-KNOWN INEQUALITIES

10.14.1 HARMONIC MEAN-GEOMETRIC MEAN-ARITHMETIC MEAN INEQUALITY

Let $a = (a_1, a_2, \ldots, a_n)$ be any finite sequence of positive numbers. Let the harmonic mean $H_n(a)$ of the numbers $a_1, a_2, \ldots, a_n$ be defined as $H_n(a) = n/\sum_{i=1}^{n}(1/a_i)$, their geometric mean $G_n(a)$ be defined as $(\prod_{i=1}^{n} a_i)^{1/n}$ and their arithmetic mean $A_n(a)$ be defined as $\sum_{i=1}^{n}(a_i/n)$. Then

$$\min(a_1, a_2, \ldots, a_n) \le H_n(a) \le G_n(a) \le A_n(a) \le \max(a_1, a_2, \ldots, a_n)$$

with equality iff $a_1 = a_2 = \cdots = a_n$ [Mitrinović (1970), p. 27].

10.14.2 CAUCHY-SCHWARTZ'S INEQUALITY (Also, see Sec. 2.1.1)

Let $a = (a_1, a_2, \ldots, a_n)$ and $b = (b_1, b_2, \ldots, b_n)$ be two sequences of real numbers. Then

$$\left(\sum_{i=1}^{n} a_i^2\right)\left(\sum_{i=1}^{n} b_i^2\right) \ge \left(\sum_{i=1}^{n} a_i b_i\right)^2$$

Equality holds iff the sequences a and b are linearly dependent.

[Mitrinović (1970), p. 41]

10.14.3 ABEL'S INEQUALITY

Let $a_1, a_2, \ldots, a_n$ and $b_1, b_2, \ldots, b_n$ $(b_1 \ge b_2 \ge \cdots \ge b_n \ge 0)$ be two sequences of real numbers, and let $S_k = \sum_{i=1}^{k} a_i$ $(k = 1, 2, \ldots, n)$. If $m = \min_{1 \le k \le n} S_k$ and $M = \max_{1 \le k \le n} S_k$, then

$$mb_1 \le a_1b_1 + a_2b_2 + \cdots + a_nb_n \le Mb_1$$ [Mitrinović (1970), p. 32]

10.14.4 BERNOULLI'S INEQUALITY AND ITS GENERALIZATIONS

(1) If $x > -1$ and if n is a positive integer, then

$$(1 + x)^n \geq 1 + nx$$

(2) If $-2 \leq x \leq -1$ and if n is a positive integer, then

$$(1 + x)^n \geq 1 + x \geq 1 + nx$$

(3) If $n = 2, 3, \ldots$ and $-1 < x < 1/(n - 1)$, then

$$(1 + x)^n \leq 1 + \frac{nx}{1 + (1 - n)x}$$

with equality holding iff $x = 0$.

(4) If each of real numbers x_i $(i = 1, 2, \ldots, n)$ is greater than -1 and either all are positive or all are negative, then

$$(1 + x_1)(1 + x_2) \cdots (1 + x_n) > 1 + x_1 + x_2 + \cdots + x_n$$

[Mitrinović (1970), pp. 34-35]

10.14.5 CHEBYCHEV'S INEQUALITY

If $a = (a_1, a_2, \ldots, a_n)$ and $b = (b_1, b_2, \ldots, b_n)$ are two real sequences such that

$$a_1 \leq a_2 \leq \cdots \leq a_n \text{ and } b_1 \leq b_2 \leq \cdots \leq b_n$$

or

$$a_1 \geq a_2 \geq \cdots \geq a_n \text{ and } b_1 \geq b_2 \geq \cdots \geq b_n$$

then

$$\left(\frac{1}{n} \sum_{i=1}^{n} a_i\right)\left(\frac{1}{n} \sum_{i=1}^{n} b_i\right) \leq \frac{1}{n} \sum_{i=1}^{n} a_i b_i$$

Equality holds iff $a_1 = a_2 = \cdots = a_n$, or $b_1 = b_2 = \cdots = b_n$.

[Mitrinović (1970), pp. 36-37]

10.14.6 HÖLDER'S INEQUALITY (Also, see Sec. 2.1.1)

(1) If $a_k \geq 0$, $b_k \geq 0$ for $k = 1, 2, \ldots, n$, and $(1/p) + (1/q) = 1$ with $p > 1$, then

$$\left(\sum_{k=1}^{n} a_k^p\right)^{1/p}\left(\sum_{k=1}^{n} b_k^q\right)^{1/q} \geq \sum_{k=1}^{n} a_k b_k$$

with equality holding iff $\alpha a_k^p = \beta b_k^q$ for $k = 1, 2, \ldots, n$, where α and β are real nonnegative constants with $\alpha^2 + \beta^2 > 0$.

(2) If $a_k > 0$ and $b_k > 0$ for $k = 1, 2, \ldots, n$, and $(1/p) + (1/q) = 1$ with $p < 0$ or $q < 0$, then

$$\left(\sum_{k=1}^{n} a_k^p\right)^{1/p}\left(\sum_{k=1}^{n} b_k^q\right)^{1/q} \leq \sum_{k=1}^{n} a_k b_k$$

with equality iff $\alpha a_k^p = \beta b_k^p$ for $k = 1, 2, \ldots, n$, where α and β are real nonnegative constants with $\alpha^2 + \beta^2 > 0$.

[Mitrinović (1970), pp. 50-51]

10.14.7 MINKOWSKI'S INEQUALITY (Also, see Sec. 2.1.1)

(1) If $a_k \geq 0$ and $b_k \geq 0$, for $k = 1, 2, \ldots, n$, and $p > 1$, then

$$\left[\sum_{k=1}^{n} (a_k + b_k)^p\right]^{1/p} \leq \left(\sum_{k=1}^{n} a_k^p\right)^{1/p} + \left(\sum_{k=1}^{n} b_k^p\right)^{1/p}$$

with equality holding iff the sequences $a = (a_1, a_2, \ldots, a_n)$ and $b = (b_1, b_2, \ldots, b_n)$ are proportional.

If $a_k > 0$ and $b_k > 0$, for $k = 1, 2, \ldots, n$, and $p < 0$, then the inequality holds with the direction reversed.

(2) If $a_k \geq 0$ and $b_k \geq 0$, for $k = 1, 2, \ldots, n$, and $p > 1$, then

$$\left(\sum_{k=1}^{n} a_k^{1/p}\right)^p + \left(\sum_{k=1}^{n} b_k^{1/p}\right)^p \leq \left[\sum_{k=1}^{n} (a_k + b_k)^{1/p}\right]^p$$

For $0 < p < 1$, the direction of the inequalities in (1) and (2) is reversed. [For (1) and (2), see Mitrinović (1970), pp. 55-56.]

(3) For $x_i, y_i \geq 0$,

$$\left[\prod_{i=1}^{n} (x_i + y_i)\right]^{1/n} \geq \left(\prod_{i=1}^{n} x_i\right)^{1/n} + \left(\prod_{i=1}^{n} y_i\right)^{1/n}$$

[Beckenbach and Bellman (1961), p. 26]

10.14.8 CONVEX FUNCTION INEQUALITY (Also, see Sec. 10.5)

(1) If $a_1 > a_2 > \cdots > a_{2m-1} > 0$ and ϕ is a convex function in $[0, a_1]$, then

$$\sum_{k=1}^{2m-1} (-1)^{k-1} \phi(a_k) \geq \phi\left(\sum_{k=1}^{2m-1} (-1)^{k-1} a_k\right)$$

(2) If $a_1 \geq a_2 \geq \cdots \geq a_n \geq 0$ and ϕ is a convex function in $[0, a]$ with $\phi(0) \leq 0$, then

$$\sum_{k=1}^{n} (-1)^{k-1} \phi(a_k) \geq \phi\left(\sum_{k=1}^{n} (-1)^{k-1} a_k\right)$$ [Mitrinović (1970), p. 112]

10.14.9 SAMUELSON'S INEQUALITY

For any n numbers $x_1, x_2, \ldots, x_n$,

$$\max|x_i - \bar{x}| \leq \left[(n - 1)\sum_{i=1}^{n} \frac{(x_i - \bar{x})^2}{n}\right]^{1/2}$$ [Dwass (1975), p. 108]

10.14.10 INEQUALITIES ON MILL'S RATIO

The function R defined by

$$R(x) = e^{x^2/2}\int_x^\infty e^{-t^2/2}\,dt$$

is known as Mill's ratio.

(1) For all x > 0

$$\frac{1}{2}\left(\sqrt{4 + x^2} - x\right) < R(x) \leq \frac{1}{x}$$

(2) $$\frac{2}{\sqrt{x^2 + 4} + x} < R(x) < \frac{2}{\sqrt{x^2 + \frac{8}{\pi}} + x}$$

(3) For x > 0,

$$\frac{\pi}{\sqrt{x^2 + 2\pi} + (\pi - 1)x} < R(x) < \frac{\pi}{\sqrt{(\pi - 2)^2 x^2 + 2\pi} + 2x}$$

[For (1)-(3), see Mitrinović (1970), pp. 177-179]

BIBLIOGRAPHY

Abramowitz, M., and Stegun, I. A. (1970). *Handbook of Mathematical Functions*. National Bureau of Standards, Washington, D.C.
[See Sections 1.5.7(3); 8.2.8(2)(d); 8.2.16(1)(b), (3)(c); 8.2.17(3)(a), (b); 8.2.18(3); 8.2.19(1)(b), (2)(d), (3); 10.12(1)-(5); 10.2.2(2); 10.7.2(1)-(3); 10.9.1; 10.9.2(2), (3).]

Ahsanullah, M., and Kabir, A. B. M. L. (1973). A characterization of Pareto distribution. *Canad. J. Statist. 1,* 101-112.
[See Section 5.3.9(1).]

Ahsanullah, M., and Kabir, A. B. M. L. (1974). A characterization of Pareto distribution. *Commun. Statist. 3,* 953-957.
[See Section 5.3.9(5).]

Ahsanullah, M., and Rahman, M. (1972). A characterization of the exponential distribution. *J. Appl. Prob. 9,* 457-461.
[See Section 5.3.4(10).]

Aitchison, J., and Brown, J. A. C. (1957). *The Lognormal Distribution*. Cambridge University Press, London.
[See Sections 8.2.2(1)(a)-(c).]

Alam, K., and Rizvi, M. H. (1967). On non-central chisquared and non-central F distributions. *Amer. Statist. 21* (4), 21-22.
[See Sections 8.2.17(1)(d); 8.2.19(1)(c).]

Amos, D. E. (1964). Representations of the central and non-central t distributions. *Biometrika 51,* 451-458.
[See Section 8.2.18(1)(b).]

Anderson, T. W., and Samuels, S. M. (1965). Some inequalities among binomial and Poisson probabilities. *Proc. 5th Berkeley Symp. Math. Statist. Prob. 1.* University of California Press, Los Angeles and Berkeley, 1-12.
[See Sections 8.1.1(3)(b); 8.1.2(3)(a).]

Antle, C., Klimko, L., and Harkness, W. (1970). Confidence interval for the parameters of the logistic distribution. *Biometrika 57,* 397-402.
[See Sections 7.3.15(1)-(3).]

Arnold, B. C. (1972). Some examples of minimum variance unbiased estimates. *Amer. Statist. 26* (4), 34-36.
[See Section 6.6.1(5).]

Bahadur, R. R. (1960). Some approximation to binomial distribution function. *Ann. Math. Statist. 31,* 43-54.
[See Section 8.1.1(1)(b).]

Bain, L. J. (1969). Moments of non-central t and non-central F-distribution. *Amer. Statist. 23* (4), 33-34.
[See Sections 1.5.1(2)(b); 1.5.19-20.]

Bain, L. J., and Englehardt, M. (1973). Interval estimation for the two parameters double exponential distribution. *Technometrics 15,* 875-887.
[See Sections 7.3.14(2), (3).]

Bancroft, T. A. (1945). Note on an identity in the incomplete beta function. *Ann. Math. Statist. 16,* 98-99.
[See Section 10.4.2(5).]

Bancroft, T. A. (1949). Some recurrence formulae in the incomplete beta function ratio. *Ann. Math. Statist. 20,* 451-455.
[See Sections 10.4.2(6), (9).]

Barlow, R. E., Marshall, A. W., and Proschan, F. (1963). Properties of probability distributions with monotone hazard rate. *Ann. Math. Statist. 34,* 375-389.
[See Sections 4.5.2(2); 4.7.2(3).]

Barlow, R. E., Marshall, A. W., and Proschan, F. (1969). Some inequalities for starshaped and convex functions. *Pacific J. Math. 29,* 19-42.
[See Section 10.5.2(3).]

Barlow, R. E., and Proschan, F. (1965). *Mathematical Theory of Reliability.* John Wiley and Sons, Inc., New York.
[See Sections 4.7.1; 4.7.2(2), (4), (5); 4.7.3(1)-(3), (7); 4.8.1; 4.8.2(1)-(4); 4.12.1(4); 4.12.2(4); 4.13.1(4); 4.13.2(4); 4.13.5(4); 4.13.6(4); 4.13.12(4).]

Barlow, R. E., and Proschan, F. (1966). Inequalities for linear combinations of order statistics from restricted families. *Ann. Math. Statist. 37,* 1574-1592.
[See Sections 4.5.3(3); 4.7.2(1); 4.7.3(5).]

Barlow, R. E., and Proschan, F. (1975). *Statistical Theory of Reliability and Life Testing.* Holt, Rinehart and Winston, Inc., New York.
[See Sections 4.8.2(1)-(4).]

Barnett, V. D. (1966). Order statistics estimators of the location of the Cauchy distribution. *J. Amer. Statist. Assoc. 61,* 1205-1218. (Correction: *63,* 383-385).
[See Sections 3.5.2(1), (2).]

Beckenbach, E. F., and Bellman, R. (1961). *Inequalities.* Springer-Verlag, Berlin.
[See Section 10.14.7.]

Bennett, G. (1965). Upper bounds on the moments and probability inequalities for the sum of independent, bounded random variables. *Biometrika 52,* 559-569.
[See Section 2.1.2(11).]

Best, D. J., and Gipps, P. G. (1974). An improved gamma approximation to the negative binomial. *Technometrics 16,* 621-624.
[See Section 8.1.3(3)(b).]

Billmann, B. R., Antle, C. E., and Bain, L. J. (1972). Statistical inference from censored Weibull samples. *Technometrics 14,* 831-840.
[See Sections 7.3.8(1)(b), (d).]

Birnbaum, Z. W., Esary, J. D., and Marshall, A. W. (1966). A stochastic characterization of wear-out for components and systems. *Ann. Math. Statist. 37,* 816-825.
[See Section 4.7.3(4).]

Blyth, C. R., and Roberts, D. M. (1972). On inequalities of Cramér-Rao type and admissibility proofs. *Proc. 6th Berkeley Symp. Math. Statist. Prob. 1,* University of California Press, Los Angeles and Berkeley, 17-30.
[See Section 2.1.2(6).]

Bohman, H. (1963). Two inequalities for Poisson distributions. *Skand. Aktuarietidskr. 46,* 47-52.
[See Section 8.1.2(3)(c).]

Breitler, M. D., and Krishnaiah, P. R. (1968). Tables for the moments of gamma order statistics. *Sankhyā B 30,* 59-72.
[See Sections 3.5.4(1), (2).]

Buehler, R. J. (1957). Confidence intervals for the product of two binomial parameters. *J. Amer. Statist. Assoc. 52,* 482-493.
[See Section 7.2.1(5).]

Burr, I. W. (1973). Some approximate relations between terms of the hypergeometric, binomial and Poisson distributions. *Commun. Statist. 1,* 297-301.
[See Sections 8.1.1(2)(e), (g); 8.1.4(2)(c).]

Cacoulos, T. (1965). A relation between t and F distributions. *J. Amer. Statist. Assoc. 60,* 528-531. (Correction: *60,* 1249).
[See Section 8.2.15(3)(a).]

Carlson, P. G. (1958). A recurrence formula for the mean range for odd sample sizes. *Skand. Aktuarietidskr. 41,* 55-56.
[See Sections 3.2.4(7), 3.2.7(6).]

Chhikara, R. S. (1972). "Statistical Inference Related to the Inverse Gaussian Distribution." Unpublished Ph.D. dissertation, Oklahoma State University, Stillwater, Okla.
[See Sections 7.3.3(1), (2).]

Chhikara, R. S., and Folks, J. L. (1974). Estimation of the inverse Gaussian distribution function. *J. Amer. Statist. Assoc. 69,* 250-254.
[See Sections 6.7.3(4); 8.2.3(1).]

Chung, K. L. (1968). *A Course in Probability Theory.* Harcourt, Brace and World, Inc., New York.
[See Sections 2.1.2(8); 9.1.1(3); 9.1.2(2)-(4); 9.1.3(1).]

Churchill, E. (1946). Information given by odd moments. *Ann. Math. Statist. 17,* 244-246.
[See Sections 1.1.2b(5); 1.1.5(7).]

Clemans, K. G. (1959). Confidence limits in the case of the geometric distribution. *Biometrika 46,* 260-264.
[See Section 7.2.3.]

Cross, M. J. (1974). Tables of finite-mean nonsymmetric stable distributions as computed from their convergent and asymptotic series. *J. Statist. Comp. Simul. 3,* 1-27.
[See Section 4.9.1.]

Crow, E. L. (1956). Confidence intervals for a proportion. *Biometrika 43,* 423-435. (Correction: *45,* 291).
[See Section 7.2.1(1).]

Crow, E. L., and Gardner, R. S. (1959). Confidence interval for the expectation of a Poisson variable. *Biometrika 46,* 441-453.
[See Sections 7.2.2(1); 8.1.2(3)(e).]

Dallas, A. C. (1974). A characterization of the geometric distribution. *J. Appl. Prob. 11,* 609-611.
[See Section 5.2.3(9).]

David, F. N., and Barton, D. E. (1962). *Combinatorial Chance*. Hafner Pub. Co., Inc., New York.
[See Section 10.11.]

David, H. A. (1970). *Order Statistics*. John Wiley and Sons, Inc., New York.
[See Sections 3.2; 3.2.1(1), (2); 3.2.2(1); 3.2.3(5)(a); 3.2.4(1), (2), (4)(a), (6), (7)(b); 3.2.6(4); 3.2.7(3), (5); 3.2.9(1)-(3), (5); 3.3(1)-(3); 3.5.1(1); 8.2.5(1)(e), (f).]

David, H. A., and Mishriky, R. S. (1968). Order statistics for discrete populations and for grouped sample. *J. Amer. Statist. Assoc. 63,* 1390-1398.
[See Section 3.2.7(2).]

Dubey, S. D. (1966). Characterization theorems for several distributions and their applications. *J. Industrial Math. 16,* Part 1.
[See Sections 5.3.6(1); 5.3.7(2); 5.3.10.]

Dwass, M. (1975). The extreme deviations inequality. *Amer. Statist. 29,* 108.
[See Section 10.14.9.]

Efron, B. (1965). Increasing properties of Pólya frequency functions. *Ann. Math. Statist. 36,* 272-279.
[See Sections 4.5.2(1); 4.5.3(2).]

Epstein, B., and Sobel, M. (1953). Life testing. *J. Amer. Statist. Assoc. 48,* 486-502.
[See Section 7.3.5(2).]

Fama, E. F., and Roll, R. (1968). Some properties of symmetric stable distributions. *J. Amer. Statist. Assoc. 63,* 817-836.
[See Section 4.9.3(4).]

Feldman, D., and Fox, M. (1968). Estimation of the parameter in the binomial distribution. *J. Amer. Statist. Assoc. 63,* 150-158.
[See Section 6.7.1(3).]

Feller, W. (1957). *An Introduction to Probability Theory and Its Applications, 1.* John Wiley and Sons, Inc., New York.
[See Sections 8.1.1(3)(a), (e); 8.1.3(2)(d); 8.1.4(2)(c), (d); 8.2.1(3)(a); 10.12(1)-(6), (11), (16).]

Feller, W. (1966). *An Introduction to Probability Theory and Its Applications, 2.* John Wiley and Sons, Inc., New York.
[See Sections 4.9.1; 4.9.2(2), (5), (10); 4.9.3(1), (3), (5), (6); 4.10.1; 4.10.2(4); 4.11.3(2), (3); 4.13.1(5), 4.13.4(4); 8.2.1(2)(c); 8.2.8(1)(c).]

Ferguson, T. S. (1964). A characterization of exponential distribution. *Ann. Math. Statist. 35,* 1199-1207.
[See Section 5.3.4(7).]

Ferguson, T. S. (1965). A characterization of the geometric distribution. *Amer. Math. Monthly 72,* 256-260.
[See Sections 5.2.3(3); 5.3.1(4).]

Ferguson, T. S. (1967a). *Mathematical Statistics.* Academic Press, Inc., New York.
[See Sections 4.5.2(3); 4.12.1(2); 4.12.2(2); 4.12.3(2); 4.12.4(2); 4.13.4(3)(a); 4.13.14(2); 5.1(9); 5.3.4(8); 6.4.2(5).]

Ferguson, T. S. (1967b). On characterizing distributions by properties of order statistics. *Sankhyā A 29,* 265-278.
[See Section 5.3.4(8).]

Fisz, M. (1958). Characterization of some probability distributions. *Skand. Aktuarietidskr. 41,* 65-67.
[See Section 5.3.8(1).]

Fisz, M. (1962). Infinitely divisible distributions: recent results and applications. *Ann. Math. Statist. 33,* 68-84.
[See Sections 4.10.1; 4.10.2(5); 4.10.3(2), (3).]

Fisz, M. (1963). *Probability Theory and Mathematical Statistics.* John Wiley and Sons, Inc., New York.
[See Sections 1.3.2(6); 2.2.1(1), (12)(b)-(e); 9.3.3(1), (2).]

Freund, J. E. (1971). *Mathematical Statistics.* Prentice-Hall, Inc., Englewood Cliffs, N. J.
[See Sections 8.1.1(1)(b), (2)(c); 8.1.3(1)(b).]

Galambos, J. (1972). Characterization of certain populations by independence of order statistics. *J. Appl. Prob. 9,* 224-230.
[See Sections 5.3.4(5); 5.3.8(2).]

Geisser, S. (1956). A note on the normal distribution. *Ann. Math. Statist. 27,* 858-859.
[See Section 5.3.1(8).]

Geisser, S. (1973). Normal characterization via the squares of random variables. *Sankhyā A 35,* 492-494.
[See Section 5.3.1(18).]

Ghosh, J. K., and Singh, R. (1966). Unbiased estimation of location and scale parameters. *Ann. Math. Statist. 37,* 1671-1675.
[See Section 6.7.4(1).]

Gibbons, J. D. (1971). *Nonparametric Statistical Inference*. McGraw-Hill Book Co., New York.
[See Section 10.12(7).]

Gnendenko, B. V. (1962). *The Theory of Probability*. Chelsea Pub. Co., New York.
[See Sections 1.3.2(1); 2.2.1(14); 9.2.1(3); 9.2.2(3); 9.3.1(4).]

Gnendenko, B. V., and Kolmogorov, A. N. (1954). *Limit Distributions for Sums of Independent Random Variables*. Addison-Wesley Pub. Co., Cambridge, Mass.
[See Sections 4.10.2(2), (3); 4.11.2(2).]

Goodman, L. A. (1965). On simultaneous confidence intervals for multinomial proportions. *Technometrics 6,* 247-254.
[See Section 7.2.4.]

Godwin, H. J. (1964). *Inequalities on Distribution Functions*. Hafner Pub. Co., Inc., New York.
[See Section 1.1.5(5).]

Govindarajulu, Z. (1963). On moments of order statistics and quasi-ranges from normal populations. *Ann. Math. Statist. 34,* 633-651.
[See Sections 3.2.4(4)(b), (5); 3.2.5(3); 3.2.7(4); 3.3(4).]

Govindarajulu, Z. (1966a). Best linear estimates under symmetric censoring of the parameters of a double exponential population. *J. Amer. Statist. Assoc. 61,* 248-258.
[See Sections 3.5.10(1), (2).]

Govindarajulu, Z. (1966b). Characterization of the exponential and power distributions. *Skand. Aktuarietidskr. 49,* 132-136.
[See Sections 5.3.4(4); 5.3.8(3).]

Govindarajulu, Z. (1968). Best linear unbiased estimation of location and scale parameters of Weibull distributions using ordered observations. *Reports of Statistical Application Research, Union of Japanese Scientists and Engineers 15,* 1-14.
[See Sections 3.5(1), (2).]

Govindarajulu, Z., and Eisenstat, S. (1965). Best estimates of location and scale parameter of a chi (1 d.f.) distribution, using ordered observations. *Reports of Statistical Application Research, Union of Japanese Scientists and Engineers 12* (4), 1-16.
[See Sections 3.5.12(1), (2).]

Gray, H. L., Watkins, T. A., and Schucany, W. R. (1973). On the jackknife statistic and its relation to UMVU estimators in the normal case. *Commun. Statist. 2,* 285-320.
[See Section 6.7.1(4)(f).]

Graybill, F. A. (1961). *Introduction to Linear Statistical Models, 1.* McGraw-Hill Book Co., New York.
[See Sections 8.2.17(1)(b); 8.2.19; 8.2.19(2)(a), (b); 8.2.20.]

Graybill, F. A., and Morrison, R. D. (1960). Sample size for a specified width confidence interval on the variance of a normal distribution. *Biometrics 16,* 636-641.
[See Section 7.3.1(1)(d).]

Greenwood, J. A., and Sandomire, M. M. (1950). Sample size required for estimating the standard deviation as a percent of its true value. *J. Amer. Statist. Assoc. 45,* 257-260.
[See Section 7.3.1(d).]

Guenther, W. C. (1969). Shortest confidence intervals. *Amer. Statist. 23* (1), 22-25.
[See Sections 7.3.1(1)(b), (d); 7.3.5(1); 7.3.7(1); 7.3.8(1)(a); 7.3.9; 7.3.10(1)(a); 7.3.14(1).]

Guenther, W. C. (1971a). Unbiased confidence intervals. *Amer. Statist. 25* (1), 51-53.
[See Sections 7.1.3(2); 7.3.1(1)(a), (b), (d); 7.3.5(1); 7.3.7(1); 7.3.8(1)(a); 7.3.9; 7.3.10(1)(a); 7.3.14(1).]

Guenther, W. C. (1971b). A note on the minimum variance unbiased estimate of the fraction of a normal distribution below a specification limit. *Amer. Statist. 25* (2), 18-20.
[See Section 8.2.15(2)(c).]

Gumbel, E. J. (1958). *Statistics of Extremes.* Columbia University Press, New York.
[See Section 3.2.1(3).]

Gupta, R. C. (1974). Characterization of distributions by a property of discrete order-statistics. *Commun. Statist. 3,* 287-289.
[See Section 3.2.3(5)(b).]

Gupta, S. S. (1960). Order statistics from the gamma distribution. *Technometrics 2,* 243-262.
[See Sections 3.5.4(1), (2).]

Gupta, S. S., and Shah, B. K. (1965). Exact moments and percentage points of the order statistics and the distribution of the range from the logistic distribution. *Ann. Math. Statist. 36,* 907-920.
[See Sections 3.5.11(1), (2).]

Gupta, S. S., and Waknis, M. N. (1965). A system of inequalities for the incomplete gamma functions and the normal integral. *Ann. Math. Statist. 36,* 139-149.
[See Section 10.2.2(4).]

Gurland, J. (1967). An inequality satisfied by the expectation of the reciprocal of a random variable. *Amer. Statist. 21* (2), 24-25.
[See Section 2.1.1(6)(b).]

Gurland, J. (1968). Inequalities of expectations of random variables derived by monotonicity or convexity. *Amer. Statist. 22* (2), 26-27.
[See Section 2.1.1(6)(a).]

Guttman, I. (1958). A note on a series solution of a problem in estimation. *Biometrika 45,* 565-567.
[See Section 6.6.3(3).]

Guttman, L. (1948). An equality for kurtosis. *Ann. Math. Statist. 19,* 277-279.
[See Section 1.1.5(6).]

Hadley, G., and Whitin, T. M. (1961). Useful properties of the Poisson distribution. *Operat. Res. 9,* 408-410.
[See Section 8.1.2(1)(b).]

Haight, F. A. (1967). *Handbook of the Poisson Distribution.* John Wiley and Sons, Inc., New York.
[See Sections 1.4.2(1)(e), (2)(c).]

Haines, A. L., and Singpurwalla, N. D. (1974). Some contributions to the stochastic characterization of wear. *Reliability and Biometry, Statistical Analysis of Life Length* (Eds., F. Proschan and R. Serfling). Published by Society for Industrial and Applied Mathematics, 47-80.
[See Section 4.8.1.]

Hamdan, M. A. (1972). On a characterization by conditional expectations. *Technometrics 14,* 497-499.
[See Section 5.1(1).]

Han, C. P. (1975). Some relationships between noncentral chi-squared and normal distributions. *Biometrika 62,* 213-214.
[See Section 8.2.17(2)(a).]

Harris, B. (1966). *Theory of Probability.* Addison-Wesley Pub. Co., Reading, Mass.
[See Sections 1.1.3(3); 1.1.5(2), (3); 4.12.1(5); 9.2.1(6); 10.7.1.]

Harter, H. L. (1961). Expected values of normal order statistics. *Biometrika 48,* 151-165. (Correction: *48,* 476.)
[See Sections 3.5.1(1), (2).]

Harter, H. L. (1969). *Order Statistics and Their Use in Testing and Estimation, 1 and 2*. Aerospace Research Laboratories, Office of Aerospace Research, United States Air Force.
[See Sections 3.5; 3.5.1(1); 3.5.4(2); 3.5.5(2).]

Haas, G., Bain, L., and Antle, C. (1970). Inferences for the Cauchy distribution based on maximum likelihood estimators. *Biometrika 57,* 403-408.
[See Section 7.3.4(4).]

Herrey, Erna M. J. (1965). Confidence intervals based on the mean absolute deviation of a normal case. *J. Amer. Statist. Assoc. 60,* 257-269.
[See Section 7.3.1(4)(d).]

Heyde, C. C. (1963). On a property of the lognormal distribution. *J. R. Statist. Soc. B 25,* 392-393.
[See Section 1.1.5(8)(a).]

Hodges, J. L., Jr., and Lehmann, E. L. (1967). Moments of chi and power of t. *Proc. 5th Berkeley Symp. Math. Statist. Prob., 1.* University of California Press, Los Angeles and Berkeley, 187-201.
[See Section 1.5.14(2)(b).]

Hogg, R. V., and Craig, A. T. (1970). *Introduction to Mathematical Statistics*. The MacMillan Co, New York.
[See Sections 1.2.2(1)(b); 2.2.1(12)(a), (15); 4.2.1(1)(a), (b), (2)(a), (b); 4.2.2(3); 6.5.3(2)(d); 6.7.1(4)(a); 8.2.6(2)(c).]

Holt, D. R., and Crow, E. L. (1973). Tables and graphs of stable probability density functions. *J. Res. Nat. Bur. Stand. 77* (B), 143-197.
[See Sections 4.9.1; 4.9.2(1), (3), (4), (6)-(9); 4.9.3(7).]

Hoyle, M. H. (1973). Transformations--an introduction and a bibliography. *Int. Statist. Rev. 41,* 203-223.
[See Section 10.6.4.]

Huang, J. S. (1974). Characterizations of the exponential distribution by order statistics. *J. Appl. Prob. 11,* 605-608.
[See Section 5.3.4(9).]

Huzurbazar, V. S. (1955). Confidence intervals for the parameter of a distribution admitting a sufficient statistic when the range depends on the parameter. *J. R. Statist. Soc. B 17,* 86-96.
[See Section 7.1.5(4).]

Ifram, A. F. (1970). On the characteristic functions of the F and t distributions. *Sankhyā A 32,* 350-352.
[See Sections 1.5.16(3)(b); 1.5.17(3)(b).]

Isii, K. (1957). Some investigations of the relation between distribution functions and their moments. *Ann. Inst. Statist. Math., Tokyo 9,* 1-11.
[See Section 1.1.6(2).]

Jambunathan, M. V. (1954). Some properties of beta and gamma distributions. *Ann. Math. Statist. 25,* 401-405.
[See Section 8.2.8(1)(e).]

Johnson, N. L. (1959). On an extension of the connexion between Poisson and χ^2 distributions. *Biometrika 46,* 352-363.
[See Sections 8.2.17(2)(d); 8.2.19(2)(c).]

Johnson, N. L., and Kotz, S. (1969). *Discrete Distributions.* Houghton Mifflin Co., Boston.
[See Sections 1.4.1(1)(c); 1.4.2(2)(e), (f); 1.4.3(2)(b), (c); 1.4.4(2), (3)(a); 1.4.5(2)(a)-(c), (3)(a); 1.4.6(2)(a), (3)(b), (c); 4.6.2(3), (4); 6.6.1(4); 6.6.2(4); 8.1.4(1)(a), (3); 8.1.5(1)(b); 10.9.1; 10.9.2(1).]

Johnson, N. L., and Kotz, S. (1970a). *Continuous Univariate Distributions--I.* Houghton Mifflin, Boston.
[See Sections 1.5.2(2); 1.5.3(2)(b); 1.5.4(3); 1.5.14(2)(a); 4.1.1; 4.13.3(1); 5.3.3(4); 5.3.4(15); 6.7.3(3); 8.2.4(1)(b); 8.2.14(3)(b), (c).]

Johnson, N. L., and Kotz, S. (1970b). *Continuous Univariate Distributions--II.* Houghton Mifflin, Boston.
[See Sections 1.5.7(1)(c), (2); 1.5.12(2)(c); 1.5.13(2)(a); 1.5.18(2), (3); 3.5.10(1); 4.13.7(6); 8.2.8(2)(e); 8.2.13(2); 8.2.14(2)(d); 8.2.15(2)(a), (3)(a); 8.2.17(1)(a), (2)(a).]

Jolley, L. B. W. (1961). *Summation of Series.* Dover Publications, Inc., New York.
[See Section 10.13.]

Jordan, C. (1965). *Calculus of Finite Differences.* Chelsea Publishing Co., New York.
[See Sections 10.1.2(6); 10.3.2(1)-(5); 10.4.2(1)-(4), (7), (8).]

Jowett, G. H. (1963). The relationship between the binomial and F distributions. *Statistician 13,* 55-57.
[See Section 8.1.1(2)(d).]

Kadane, J. B. (1971). A moment problem for order statistics. *Ann. Math. Statist. 42,* 745-751.
[See Section 3.2.4(3).]

Kagan, A., Linnik, Y. V., and Rao, C. R. (1973). *Characterization Problems in Mathematical Statistics*. John Wiley and Sons, Inc., New York.
[See Sections 4.9.1; 4.10.1; 4.10.2(1); 4.10.3(1); 5.1(3); 5.2.1(1); 5.2.2(2); 5.2.3(6); 5.2.4; 5.3.1(3), (14)-(17); 5.3.3(7); 5.3.5(5)-(8); 5.3.8(6); 5.3.11.]

Kamat, A. R. (1965a). Incomplete and absolute moments of some discrete distributions. *Classical and Contagious Discrete Distributions. Proc. Int. Symp. Classical and Contagious Discrete Distribution, Montreal*. Pergamon Press, New York, 45-64.
[See Sections 1.1.6(5); 1.4.1(1)(c); 1.4.2(1)(c); 1.4.3(1)(c); 1.4.4(1)(c); 1.4.5(1)(c); 1.5.16(1)(d).]

Kamat, A. R. (1965b). A property of the mean deviation for a class of continuous distributions. *Biometrika 52*, 288-289.
[See Section 4.3.2(5).]

Karlin, S. (1957). Pólya type distribution, II. *Ann. Math. Statist. 28*, 281-308.
[See Sections 4.4.1; 4.4.2(3).]

Karlin, S., Proschan, F., and Barlow, R. E. (1961). Moment inequalities of Pólya frequency functions. *Pacific J. Math. 11*, 1023-1033.
[See Section 4.5.2(4).]

Karlin, S., and Studden, W. J. (1966). *Tchebychef's Systems, with Applications in Analysis and Statistics*. Interscience Publishers, New York.
[See Sections 2.2.1(7)-(11); 2.2.2(9)-(11); 3.2.9(4).]

Katti, S. K. (1967). Infinite divisibility of integer-valued random variables. *Ann. Math. Statist. 38*, 1306-1308.
[See Section 4.12.5(5).]

Keilson, J. (1972). A threshold for log-concavity for probability generating functions and associated moment inequalities. *Ann. Math. Statist. 43*, 1702-1708.
[See Section 2.1.1(7).]

Keilson, J., and Gerber, H. (1971). Some results for discrete unimodality. *J. Amer. Statist. Assoc. 66*, 386-389.
[See Sections 4.11.1; 4.11.2(4), (6), (7); 4.11.3(4), (5); 4.12.1(6); 4.12.2(6).]

Kelker, D., and Matthes, T. K. (1970). A sufficient statistics characterization of the normal distribution. *Ann. Math. Statist. 41*, 1086-1090.
[See Sections 5.3.1(11); 5.3.5(10).]

Kendall, M. G., and Stuart, A. (1958). *The Advanced Theory of Statistics*, 1. Hafner Pub. Co., New York.
[See Sections 1.1.1(7); 1.1.2a(9), (10); 1.1.3(1), (2); 1.1.6(4); 1.3.1(4); 1.4.1(2)(a), (b), (d), (e); 1.4.2(2)(a), (b); 1.4.4(3)(d); 1.5.1(2)(a), (d), (3)(a); 2.1.1(3); 4.1.2(1)-(3), (6), (7); 4.2.2(4); 6.1.3(5); 8.1.1(1)(a); 8.2.9(1)(b); 10.8.]

Kendall, M. G., and Stuart, A. (1967). *The Advanced Theory of Statistics*, 2. Hafner Pub. Co., New York.
[See Sections 3.5.11(1); 4.2.2(4); 6.1.3(4), (5); 6.1.5(4); 6.2.2(4); 6.3.2(1); 6.3.4(2), (3); 6.4.2(2), (6), (7); 6.4.3(2); 6.5.3(2)(a), (6); 6.7.10(5)(a), (6)(b); 7.1.3(1)(b); 7.1.5(3); 7.3.10(1)(a), (b).]

Khamis, S. H. (1965). Some basic properties of the incomplete gamma function ratio. *Ann. Math. Statist. 36*, 926-937.
[See Section 10.2.2(3).]

Kharshikar, A. V. (1969). Remarks on Teicher's inequality. *Sankhyā A 31*, 493-496.
[See Sections 8.1.1(3)(d); 8.1.3(3)(a).]

Khatri, C. G. (1959). On certain properties of power series distributions. *Biometrika 46*, 486-490.
[See Sections 4.6.2(3); 4.6.3(6).]

Khatri, C. G. (1962a). A characterization of inverse Gaussian distribution. *Ann. Math. Statist. 33*, 800-802.
[See Section 5.3.2.]

Khatri, C. G. (1962b). Distributions of order statistics for discrete case. *Ann. Inst. Statist. Math., Tokyo 14*, 167-171.
[See Sections 3.2.6(1)-(3).]

Kimeldorff, G., and Sampson, A. (1973). A class of covariance inequalities. *J. Amer. Statist. Assoc. 68*, 228-230.
[See Section 2.1.2(4).]

Koopmans, L. H., Owen, D. B., and Rosenblatt, J. I. (1964). Confidence interval for the coefficient of variation for normal and lognormal distributions. *Biometrika 51*, 25-32.
[See Sections 7.3.1(4)(c); 7.3.2(2).]

Kotlarski, I. (1966). On characterizing the normal distribution by Student's law. *Biometrika 53*, 603-606.
[See Section 5.3.1(12).]

Kotlarski, I. (1972). On a characterization of some probability distributions by conditional expectations. *Sankhyā A 34*, 461-466.
[See Sections 5.1(8); 5.3.3(6); 5.3.6(2); 5.3.8(5).]

Kotz, Samuel (1974). Characterization of statistical distributions: a supplement to recent survey. *Int. Statist. Rev. 42* (1), 39-65.
[See Chapter 5.]

Kounias, E. G., and Weng, T. S. (1969). An equality and almost sure convergence. *Ann. Math. Statist. 40,* 1091-1093.
[See Section 2.2.2(4).]

Krishnaiah, P. R., and Rizvi, M. H. (1966). A note on recurrence relations between expected values of functions of order statistics. *Ann. Math. Statist. 37,* 733-734.
[See Section 3.2.4(9).]

Lachenbruch, P. A., and Brogan, D. R. (1971). Some distributions on the positive real line which have no moments. *Amer. Statist. 25* (1), 46-47.
[See Section 1.1.2b(1)(c).]

Laha, R. G. (1961). On a class of unimodal distributions. *Proc. Amer. Math. Soc. 12,* 181-184.
[See Sections 4.11.2(5); 4.11.3(1).]

Laubscher, N. F. (1960). Normalizing the noncentral t and F distributions. *Ann. Math. Statist. 31,* 1105-1112.
[See Section 10.6.4.]

Laurent, A. G. (1965). Probability distributions, factorial moments, empty cell test. *Classical and Contagious Discrete Distributions. Proc. Int. Symp. Classical and Contagious Discrete Distributions, Montreal.* Pergamon Press, New York, 437-442.
[See Section 1.1.6(1).]

Lehmann, E. L. (1959). *Testing Statistical Hypotheses.* John Wiley and Sons, Inc., New York.
[See Sections 3.2.3(4); 4.2.2(2), (5); 4.5.3(1), (4)-(6); 6.3.2(3); 6.4.2(4); 7.1.5(1)(b).]

Lehmann, E. L., and Scheffé, H. (1950). Completeness, similar regions, and unbiased estimation--Part 1. *Sankhyā 10,* 305-340.
[See Sections 6.6.4(1); 6.7.4(1), (2).]

Leone, F. C., Rutenberg, Y. H., and Topp, C. W. (1961). The use of sample quasi-ranges in setting confidence intervals for the population standard deviation. *J. Amer. Statist. Assoc. 56,* 260-272.
[See Sections 7.3.1(4)(e); 7.3.5(2).]

Lessing, R. (1973). An alternative expression for the hypergeometric moment generating function. *Amer. Statist. 27* (3), 115.
[See Section 1.4.4(3)(b).]

Lieberman, G. J., and Owen, D. B. (1961). *Tables of the Hypergeometric Probability Distribution.* Stanford University Press, Stanford, Ca.
[See Sections 1.4.4(1)(b); 8.1.1(2)(g); 8.1.4(1)(b), (2)(b), (d), (e); 10.12(12)-(15).]

Lieblein, J. (1953). On the exact evaluation of the variance and covariances of order statistics in samples from the extreme value distribution. *Ann. Math. Statist. 24,* 282-287.
[See Section 3.5.9(1).]

Lieblein, J., and Salzer, H. E. (1957). Tables of the first moment of ranked extremes. *J. Res. Nat. Bur. Stand. 59,* 203-206.
[See Section 3.5.9(2).]

Lindgren, B. W. (1968). *Statistical Theory.* The MacMillan Co., New York.
[See Sections 8.1.1(2)(e), (g).]

Linhart, H. (1965). Approximate confidence limits for the coefficient of variation in gamma distributions. *Biometrics 21,* 733-738.
[See Section 7.3.7(2).]

Loève, M. (1960). *Probability Theory.* D. Van Nostrand Co., Inc., Princeton, New Jersey.
[See Sections 2.1.1(4); 2.2.1(5).]

Lukacs, E. (1956). Characterization of populations by properties of suitable statistics. *Proc. 3rd Berkeley Symp. Math. Statist. Prob. II.* University of California Press, Los Angeles and Berkeley, 195-214.
[See Sections 5.3.1(1), (2), (5)-(7); 5.3.3(1), (5); 5.3.5(1)-(4).]

Lukacs, E. (1965). Characterization problems for discrete distributions. *Classical and Contagious Discrete Distributions. Proc. Int. Symp. Classical and Contagious Discrete Distributions. Montreal.* Pergamon Press, New York, 65-74.
[See Sections 5.1(2), (5); 5.2.1(2); 5.2.2(1), (5); 5.2.3(7), (8).]

Lukacs, E. (1970). *Characteristic Functions* (2nd Ed.). Hafner Pub. Co., New York.
[See Sections 1.1.5(8)(b); 1.3.1(1)(b), (2)(b), (3); 1.3.2(3), (4), (7); 1.3.3(1)-(6); 1.5.1(2)(c); 1.5.9(2)(b), (c); 1.5.12 (2)(b); 1.5.16(2)(b); 4.11.1; 4.11.2(1), (3); 10.10.]

Lukacs, E., and Laha, R. G. (1964). *Applications of Characteristic Functions.* Hafner Pub. Co., New York.
[See Sections 4.9.3(2); 5.1(6); 5.2.2(6); 5.3.1(13).]

Malik, H. J. (1966). Exact moments of order statistics from the Pareto distribution. *Skand. Aktuarietidskr. 49,* 144-157. [See Sections 3.5.8(1), (2).]

Malik, H. J. (1967). Exact moments of order statistics from a power function distribution. *Skand. Aktuarietidskr. 50,* 64-69. [See Section 3.5.6.]

Malik, H. J. (1970). A characterization of Pareto distribution. *Skand. Aktuarietidskr. 53,* 115-117. [See Section 5.3.9(2).]

Malik, H. J. (1970). Distribution of product statistics from a Pareto distribution. *Metrika 15,* 19-22. [See Section 8.2.10(2)(b).]

Mallows, C. L., and Richter, D. (1969). Inequalities of Chebyshev type involving conditional expectation. *Ann. Math. Statist. 40,* 1922-1932. [See Section 2.1.2(12).]

Mann, N. R., and Fertig, K. W. (1973). Tables for obtaining Weibull confidence bounds and tolerance bounds based on best linear invariant estimates of parameters of the extreme value distribution. *Technometrics 15,* 87-101. [See Sections 7.3.8(1)(c), (e).]

Mardia, K. V., and Thompson, J. W. (1972). Unified treatment of moment-formulae. *Sankhyā A 34,* 121-132. [See Section 1.1.4(4).]

Margolin, B. H., and Winokur, H. S., Jr. (1967). Exact moments of the order statistics of the geometric distribution and their relation to inverse sampling and reliability of redundant systems. *J. Amer. Statist. Assoc. 62,* 915-925. [See Sections 3.4.1(1), (2).]

Marshall, A. W., and Proschan, F. (1965). Maximum likelihood estimation for distribution with monotone failure rate. *Ann. Math. Statist. 36,* 69-77. [See Section 4.7.3(6).]

Menon, M. V. (1966). Another characteristic property of the Cauchy distribution. *Ann. Math. Statist. 37,* 289-294. [See Section 5.3.3(2).]

Mitrinovic, D. S. (1970). *Analytic Inequalities.* Springer-Verlag, Heidelberg and New York. [See Sections 10.14.1-10.14.6; 10.14.8; 10.14.10.]

Molenaar, W. (1970). *Approximations to the Poisson, Binomial, and Hypergeometric Distributional Functions.* Mathematical Centre Tracts 31. Mathematisch Centrem, Amsterdam. [See Sections 8.1.1(2)(f), (g); 8.1.2(2)(f); 8.1.4(2)(d).]

Mood, A. M., Graybill, F. A., and Boes, D. C. (1974). *Introduction to the Theory of Statistics*. McGraw-Hill Book Co., New York. [See Sections 1.4.4(2); 1.4.16(3)(a); 1.5.6(3); 1.5.10(2), (3); 1.5.11(2); 1.5.12(3); 1.5.16(3)(a); 1.5.17(3)(a); 4.5.1; 6.1.3(2)(b); 6.1.4; 6.2.2(5); 6.2.3; 6.2.4(1); 6.3.1(1)-(3); 6.3.2(2); 6.3.3(1), (2); 6.3.4(1); 6.4.1; 6.4.2(1); 6.4.3(1); 6.5.1; 6.5.2(1)(b); 6.5.3(1), (2)(a), (b), (3), (5); 7.1.4(1)(a), (2), (3); 8.1.3(1)(d); 8.2.1(1)(d), (2)(a), (d); 8.2.5(1)(b), (d); 8.2.8(2)(d); 8.2.9(1)(c), (2)(b); 8.2.16(1)(c); 9.4.1(1).]

Moors, J. J. A., and Muilwijk, J. (1971). An inequality for the variance of a discrete random variable. *Sankhyā B 33,* 385-388. [See Section 2.1.2(7).]

Moran, P. A. P. (1968). *An Introduction to Probability Theory*. Clarendon Press, Oxford. [See Sections 1.1.6(3); 1.3.2(5), (8), (9); 2.2.2(1); 4.9.2(1); 4.12.2(5); 4.12.3(5); 4.13.5(6); 4.13.7; 9.1.3(2)-(5); 9.3.2.]

Morimoto, H., and Sibuya, M. (1967). Sufficient statistics and unbiased estimation of restricted selection parameters. *Sankhyā A 29,* 15-40. [See Section 6.7.10(1)(c).]

Mullen, K. (1967). A note on the ratio of two independent random variables. *Amer. Statist. 21* (3), 30-31. [See Section 2.1.2(5).]

Neuts, M. F. (1973). *Probability*. Allyn and Bacon, Boston. [See Section 1.3.2(10).]

Nicholson, W. L. (1956). On the normal approximation to the hypergeometric distribution. *Ann. Math. Statist. 27,* 471-483. [See Section 8.1.4(2)(d).]

Noack, A. (1950). A class of random variables with discrete distributions. *Ann. Math. Statist. 21,* 127-132. [See Section 4.6.2(2).]

Norden, R. H. (1972). A survey of maximum likelihood estimation. *Int. Statist. Rev. 40,* 329-354. [See Section 6.2.2(6).]

Okomoto, M. (1959). Some inequalities relating to the partial sum of binomial probabilities. *Ann. Inst. Statist. Math., Tokyo 10,* 29-35. [See Section 8.1.1(3)(c).]

Ord, J. K. (1972). *Families of Frequency Distributions*. Hafner Pub. Co., New York. [See Sections 4.1.1; 4.1.2(4), (5); 4.6.2(5); 4.13.1(1); 4.13.5(1); 4.13.7(1).]

Owen, D. B. (1962). *Handbook of Statistical Tables.* Addison-Wesley Pub. Co., Reading, Mass.
[See Section 3.5.1(2).]

Owen, D. B. (1968). A survey of properties and application of the non-central t-distribution. *Technometrics 10,* 445-478.
[See Sections 8.2.15; 8.2.18; 8.2.18(1)(c).]

Owen, D. B., and Gilbert, E. J. (1959). The relationship of the binomial probability distribution to other probability distributions with a selected bibliography on the subject. Technical Report SCIM 1-59(51), Sandia Corporation, Albuquerque, N.M.
[See Sections 8.1.1(2)(c), (3)(f), (g); 8.2.8(3)(b).]

Pachares, J. (1960). Tables of confidence limits for the binomial distribution. *J. Amer. Statist. Assoc. 55,* 521-533.
[See Section 7.2.1(1).]

Park, C. J. (1973). The power series distribution with unknown truncation parameter. *Ann. Statist. 1,* 395-399.
[See Sections 6.6.7(1), (2).]

Parzen, E. (1960). *Modern Probability Theory and Its Applications.* John Wiley and Sons, Inc., New York.
[See Sections 1.1.4(1); 2.1.1(5); 8.1.1(1)(f); 8.1.2(2)(f).]

Parzen, E. (1962). *Stochastic Processes.* Holden-Day, Inc., San Francisco.
[See Sections 1.2.4(4); 8.1.2(2)(b).]

Patel, J. K. (1973). A catalog of failure distributions. *Commun. Statist. 1* (3), 281-284.
[See Sections 4.12.5(4); 4.12.6(3); 4.13.3(4).]

Patel, J. K. (1973). Complete sufficient statistics and MVU estimators. *Commun. Statist. 2* (4), 327-336.
[See Sections 6.6; 6.7.]

Patil, G. P. (1962a). Maximum likelihood estimation for generalized power series distribution and its application to a truncated binomial distribution. *Biometrika 49,* 222-232.
[See Sections 4.6.1; 4.6.3(7)(a).]

Patil, G. P. (1962b). Certain properties of the generalized power series distributions. *Ann. Inst. Statist. Math., Tokyo 14,* 179-182.
[See Sections 4.6.1; 4.6.2(1); 4.6.3(1)-(5); 4.12.3(3); 4.12.5(3).]

Patil, G. P. (1963a). Minimum variance unbiased estimation and certain problems of additive number theory. *Ann. Math. Statist. 34,* 1050-1056.
[See Sections 4.12.1(3); 4.12.2(3); 6.6.3(4); 6.6.5(4).]

Patil, G. P. (1963b). A characterization of the exponential-type distribution. *Biometrika 50,* 205-207.
[See Section 4.3.2(3).]

Patil, G. P., and Seshadri, V. (1964). Characterization theorems for some univariate probability distributions. *J. R. Statist. Soc. B 26,* 286-292.
[See Sections 5.1(4); 5.3.4(12).]

Patil, G. P., and Shorrock, R. (1965). On certain properties of the exponential-type families. *J. R. Statist. Soc. B 27,* 94-99.
[See Section 4.3.2(2).]

Patil, G. P., and Wani, J. K. (1965). On certain structural properties of the logarithmic series distribution and first type Sterling distribution. *Sankhyā A 27,* 271-280.
[See Section 5.2.5(1).]

Patil, G. P., and Wani, J. K. (1966). Minimum variance unbiased estimation of the distribution function admitting a sufficient statistic. *Ann. Inst. Statist. Math., Tokyo 18,* 39-47.
[See Sections 6.5.3(7); 6.7.1(4)(b), (4)(c); 6.7.6(4); 6.7.10(2)(d).]

Paulson, A. S., and Uppuluri, V. R. R. (1972). A characterization of the geometric distribution and a bivariate geometric distribution. *Sankhyā A 34,* 297-300.
[See Section 5.2.3(4).]

Peizer, D. B., and Pratt, J. W. (1968). A normal approximation for binomial, F, beta and other common, related tail probabilities, I-II. *J. Amer. Statist. Assoc. 63,* 1416-1483.
[See Sections 8.1.1(2)(f); 8.1.2(2)(f); 8.1.3(1)(a), (b), (3)(c); 8.2.14(1)(b); 8.2.15(3)(b).]

Philipson, Carl (1963). A note on moments of a Poisson probability distribution. *Skand. Aktuarietidskr. 46,* 243-244.
[See Section 1.4.2(2)(d).]

Pitman, E. J. G. (1956). On the derivatives of a characteristic function at the origin. *Ann. Math. Statist. 27,* 1156-1160.
[See Section 1.3.3(7).]

Prochaska, B. J. (1973). A note on the relationship between the geometric and exponential distributions. *Amer. Statist. 27* (1), 27.
[See Section 8.1.3(2)(b).]

Puri, P. S., and Rubin, H. (1970). A characterization based on the absolute difference of two i.i.d. random variables. *Ann. Math. Statist. 41,* 2113-2122.
[See Sections 5.1(7); 5.3.4(3).]

Puri, P. S. (1973). On a property of exponential and geometric distributions and its relevance to multivariate failure rate. *Sankhyā A 35,* 61-78.
[See Sections 5.2.3(5); 5.3.4(11); 8.2.14(1)(b), (3)(a).]

Quesenberry, C. P., and Hurst, D. C. (1964). Large sample simultaneous confidence interval for multinomial proportions. *Technometrics 6,* 191-195.
[See Section 7.3.4.]

Rahman, N. A. (1968). *A Course in Theoretical Statistics.* Hafner Pub. Co., New York.
[See Sections 1.1.2a(4), (5); 1.4.6(2)(b), (3)(a); 1.5.5(2)(b); 1.5.9(2)(d).]

Raj, Des (1968). *Sampling Theory.* McGraw-Hill Book Co., New York.
[See Section 1.1.4(5)(g).]

Rao, C. R. (1952). *Advanced Statistical Methods in Biometric Research.* John Wiley and Sons, Inc., New York.
[See Sections 8.1.1(1)(a), (c), (2)(a), (b); 8.1.2(1)(a), (c), (2)(a); 8.2.6(1)(b), (c); 8.2.14(1)(c); 10.6.4.]

Rao, C. R. (1973). *Linear Statistical Inference and Its Applications.* John Wiley and Sons, Inc., New York.
[See Sections 1.1.5(1), (4); 2.1.1(1), (2); 2.2.1(3)(b), (13); 2.2.2(2); 6.1.5(1); 6.2.4(2); 6.4.2(3)(b); 6.5.2(1)(a); 6.5.3(4); 8.2.18; 10.6; 10.6.1; 10.6.2; 10.6.3.]

Revankar, N. S., Hartley, M. J., and Pagano, M. (1974). A characterization of the Pareto distribution. *Ann. Statist. 2,* 599-601.
[See Section 5.3.9(4).]

Riordan, J. (1968). *Combinatorial Identities.* John Wiley and Sons, Inc., New York.
[See Sections 10.2(8)-(10).]

Roberts, C., and Geisser, S. (1966). A necessary and sufficient condition for the square of a random variable to be gamma. *Biometrika 53,* 275-277.
[See Section 5.3.5(9).]

Rogers, G. S. (1963). An alternative proof of the characterization of the density Ax^B. *Amer. Math. Monthly 70,* 857-858.
[See Section 5.3.8(4).]

Rosenblatt, J. (1966). Confidence interval for standard deviation from a single observation. *Technometrics 8,* 367.
[See Section 7.3.1(4)(b).]

Rossberg, H. J. (1972). Characterization of distribution functions by the independence of certain functions of order statistics. *Sankhyā A 34,* 111-120.
[See Section 5.3.5(14).]

Roussas, G. G. (1973). *A First Course in Mathematical Statistics.* Addison-Wesley Pub. Co., Reading, Mass.
[See Sections 7.3.1(2)(b), (c), (4); 9.1.1(1), (2), (4); 9.1.2(1), (5), (7)-(9); 9.2.2(2).]

Roy, J., and Mitra, S. K. (1957). Unbiased minimum variance estimation in a class of discrete distributions. *Sankhyā A 18,* 371-378.
[See Sections 4.6.3(7)(b), (c).]

Samanta, M. (1972). Characterization of the Pareto distribution. *Skand. Aktuarietidskr. 55,* 191-192.
[See Sections 5.3.9(3).]

Sarhan, A. E. (1954). Estimation of the mean and standard deviation by order statistics. *Ann. Math. Statist. 25,* 317-328.
[See Section 3.5.13.]

Sarhan, A. E., and Greenberg, B. G. (Eds.) (1962). *Contributions to Order Statistics.* John Wiley and Sons, Inc., New York.
[See Sections 3.5.3(1), (2); 3.5.7.]

Sathe, Y. S., and Varde, S. D. (1969). On minimum variance unbiased estimation of reliability. *Ann. Math. Statist. 40,* 710-714.
[See Sections 6.7.5(4); 6.7.7(4).]

Satterthwaite, F. E. (1957). Binomial and Poisson confidence limits. *Industrial Quality Control 13* (11), 56-59.
[See Sections 7.2.1(2); 7.2.2(2).]

Savage, I. R. (1961). Probability inequalities of the Tchebycheff type. *J. Res. Nat. Bur. Stand. 65* (B), 211-222.
[See Sections 2.2.1(1)-(3)(a), (4), (6); 2.2.2(5)-(9).]

Scheffé, H. (1959). *The Analysis of Variance.* John Wiley and Sons, Inc., New York.
[See Section 8.2.14(3)(d).]

Sclove, S. L., Simons, G., and van Ryzin, J. (1967). Further remarks on the expectation of the reciprocal of a positive random variable. *Amer. Statist. 21* (4), 33-34.
[See Section 2.1.2(1).]

Seber, G. A. F. (1963). The non-central chi-squared and beta distributions. *Biometrika 50,* 542-544.
[See Section 8.2.17(2)(b).]

Serfling, R. J. (1967). A note on the covariance of a random variable and its reciprocal. *Amer. Statist. 21* (4), 33.
[See Section 1.1.6(6).]

Serfling, R. J. (1968). Contribution to central limit theory for dependent variables. *Ann. Math. Statist. 39,* 1158-1175.
[See Section 9.3.2.]

Shah, B. K. (1966). On the bivariate moments of order statistics from a logistic distribution. *Ann. Math. Statist. 37,* 1002-1010.
[See Section 3.5.11(1).]

Shah, B. K. (1970). Note on moments of a logistic order statistic. *Ann. Math. Statist. 41,* 2150-2152.
[See Section 3.5.11(1).]

Shanbhag, D. N. (1967). On some inequalities satisfied by the gamma function. *Skand. Aktuarietidskr. 50,* 45-49.
[See Sections 10.2.2(5).]

Shanbhag, D. N. (1970). Characterizations for exponential and geometric distributions. *J. Amer. Statist. Assoc. 65,* 1256-1259.
[See Sections 5.2.3(1), (2); 5.3.4(1), (2).]

Shanbhag, D. N. (1974). An elementary proof for the Rao-Rubin characterization of the Poisson distribution. *J. Appl. Prob. 11,* 211-215.
[See Section 5.2.2(7).]

Shuster, J. (1968). On the inverse Gaussian distribution function. *J. Amer. Statist. Assoc. 63,* 1514-1516.
[See Sections 8.2.3(1), (2).]

Srikantan, K. S. (1962). Recurrence relations between the PDF's of order statistics and some applications. *Ann. Math. Statist. 33,* 169-177.
[See Sections 3.2.2(1)(a); 3.2.4(8).]

Srivastava, M.S. (1967). A characterization of the exponential distribution. *Amer. Math. Monthly 74,* 414-416.
[See Section 5.3.4(6).]

Srivastava, R. C. (1971). On a characterization of the Poisson process. *J. Appl. Prob. 8,* 615-616.
[See Section 5.2.2(4).]

Tate, R. F. (1953). On a double inequality for the normal distribution. *Ann. Math. Statist. 24,* 132-134.
[See Section 8.2.1(3)(b).]

Tate, R. F. (1959). Unbiased estimation: functions of location and scale parameters. *Ann. Math. Statist. 30,* 341-366. [See Section 6.7.5(3).]

Tate, R. F., and Klett, G. W. (1959). Optimal confidence intervals for the variance of a normal distribution. *J. Amer. Statist. Assoc. 54,* 674-682. [See Sections 7.3.1(1)(d), 7.6.1.]

Teicher, H. (1955). An equality on Poisson probabilities. *Ann. Math. Statist. 26,* 147-149. [See Section 8.1.2(3)(d).]

Teicher, H. (1961). Maximum likelihood characterization of distributions. *Ann. Math. Statist. 32,* 1214-1222. [See Sections 5.3.1(9), (10); 5.3.4(13).]

Teichroew, D. (1956). Tables of expected values of order statistics and products of order statistics for samples of size twenty and less from the normal distribution. *Ann. Math. Statist. 27,* 410-426. [See Section 3.5.1(2).]

Thoman, D. R., Bain, L. J., and Antle, C. E. (1969). Inferences on the parameters of the Weibull distribution. *Technometrics 11,* 445-460. [See Section 7.3.8(1)(b).]

Thomas, G. B. (1968). *Calculus and Analytic Geometry* (4th ed). Addison-Wesley Pub. Co., Reading, Mass. [See Sections 10.13.1(1), (2); 10.13.2.]

Thompson, W. A., Jr., and Endriss, J. (1961). The required sample size when estimating variances. *Amer. Statist. 15* (3), 22-23. [See Section 7.3.1(1)(d).]

Tomkins, R. J. (1971). On an equality of Heyde. *J. Appl. Prob. 8,* 428-429. [See Section 2.2.2(3).]

Tong, Y. L. (1970). Some probability inequalities of multivariate normal and multivariate t. *J. Amer. Statist. Assoc. 65,* 1243-1247. [See Section 2.1.2(2).]

Tukey, J. W. (1946). An equality for deviations from medians. *Ann. Math. Statist. 17,* 75-78. [See Section 2.1.2(9).]

Tweedie, M. C. K. (1957). Statistical properties of inverse Gaussian distributions, 1. *Ann. Math. Statist. 28,* 362-377. [See Section 1.5.3(2)(a).]

Von Bahr, B., and Esseen, C. G. (1965). Inequalities for the rth absolute moment of a sum of random variables, $1 \le r \le 2$. *Ann. Math. Statist. 36,* 299-303.
[See Section 2.1.2(10).]

Wallenius, K. T. (1971). A conditional covariance formula with applications. *Amer. Statist. 25* (3), 32-33.
[See Section 1.1.4(5)(g).]

Wani, J. K. (1967). Moment relations for some discrete distributions. *Skand. Aktuarietidskr. 50,* 50-55.
[See Sections 4.6.2(3); 5.2.2(3); 5.2.5(2).]

Wani, J. K. (1968). On the linear exponential family. *Proc. Camb. Phil. Soc. 64,* 481-483.
[See Section 4.3.2(4).]

Wasan, M. T. (1968). On an inverse Gaussian. *Skand. Aktuarietidskr. 51,* 69-96.
[See Sections 4.13.3(6); 8.2.3(3).]

Wasan, M. T. (1970). *Parametric Estimation.* McGraw-Hill Book Co., New York.
[See Sections 6.1.3(2), (3); 6.2.2(3); 6.4.3(3); 6.6.6(2), (3).]

Weibull, W. (1967). Estimation of distribution parameters by a combination of the best linear order statistics method and maximum likelihood. Technical Report AFML-TR-67-105, Aerospace Research Laboratories, Wright Patterson Air Force Base, Ohio.
[See Section 3.5.5(2).]

White, J. S. (1969). The moments of log-Weibull order statistics. *Technometrics 11,* 373-386.
[See Section 3.2.4(11).]

Wilks, S. S. (1962). *Mathematical Statistics.* John Wiley and Sons, Inc., New York.
[See Sections 3.2.8(1)-(3); 9.3.3(3); 9.4.1(2)-(5).]

Williams, E. J. (1969). Cauchy-distributed functions and a characterization of the Cauchy distribution. *Ann. Math. Statist. 40,* 1083-1085.
[See Section 5.3.3(3).]

Wise, M. E. (1950). The incomplete beta function as a contour integral and a quickly converging series for its inverse. *Biometrika 37,* 208-218.
[See Section 8.1.1(2)(f).]

Woodroofe, M. (1975). *Probability with Applications.* McGraw-Hill Book Co., New York.
[See Sections 9.2.1(1), (2), (4), (5); 9.2.2(1); 9.3.1(1)-(3).]

Young, D. H. (1967). Recurrence relations between the P.D.F.'s of order statistics of dependent variables, and some applications. *Biometrika 54,* 283-292.
[See Sections 3.2.2(2); 3.2.4(10).]

Young, D. H. (1970). The order statistics of the negative binomial distribution. *Biometrika 57,* 180-181.
[See Sections 3.4.2(1), (2).]

Zacks, S. (1971). *The Theory of Statistical Inference.* John Wiley and Sons, Inc., New York.
[See Sections 6.2.2(2), (7), (8); 6.5.3(2)(c), (8), (9); 6.6.2(3); 6.7.1(4)(d), (e); 6.7.10(1)(d); 7.1.3(3); 7.1.5(2).]

Zygmund, A. (1947). A remark on characteristic functions. *Ann. Math. Statist. 18,* 272-276.
[See Section 1.3.2(2).]

GLOSSARY OF SOME FREQUENTLY USED ABBREVIATIONS AND SYMBOLS

ABBREVIATIONS

a.s.	almost surely
cdf	cumulative distribution function
CI	confidence interval
cont.	continuous
df	degrees of freedom
DFR	decreasing failure rate
DFRA	decreasing failure rate average
GPSD	generalized power series distribution
IDD	infinitely divisible distribution
iff	if and only if
IFR	increasing failure rate
IFRA	increasing failure rate average
iid	independent and identically distributed
lim sup	limit superior
max	maximum

MLE	maximum-likelihood estimator
MLR	monotone likelihood ratio
NBU	new better than used
NBUE	new better than used in expectation
NWU	new worse than used
NWUE	new worse than used in expectation
pf	probability function
pdf	probability density function
pgf	probability generating function
UMVUE	uniformly minimum-variance unbiased estimator
wrt	with respect to

SYMBOLS

$f(x)$	pdf or pf of a random variable x according as x is continuous or discrete, respectively
E	expected value operator
$E_{Y\|X}$	expected value of Y given X
$f_{Y\|X}$	conditional pdf of Y given X = x
$\mu_r'(b)$	$E[(X - b)^r] \equiv$ rth moment of a random variable X about a constant b
μ_r	rth moment of a random variable X about $\mu = E(X)$, $E[(x - \mu)^r]$
μ_r'	rth moment of a random variable X about 0; i.e. $E(X^r)$
$\nu_r'(b)$	rth absolute moment of a random variable X about a constant b, $E[\|X - b\|^r]$

$\nu_r(\mu)$	$E[\|X - \mu\|^r]$
$\mu'_{(r)}$	$E[X^{(r)}]$
$\mu'_{(r)}(b)$	$E[(X - b)^{(r)}]$ rth factorial moment of a random variable X about a constant b where $Y^{(r)} = Y(Y - 1) \cdots (Y - r + 1)$
κ_r	rth order cumulant
$\mu_2=\sigma^2=\text{var}(X)$	variance of random variable X
cov(X,Y)	covariance between random variables X and Y
$\rho(X,Y)$	correlation between random variables X and Y
m(t)	moment generating function
$\phi(t)$	characteristic function
$\psi(t)$	factorial (probability) generating function
$\eta(t)$	cumulant generating function
$\frac{\partial^r}{\partial t^r}$	rth order partial derivative
[m]	greatest integer less than or equal to m
$\in$	belongs to
$X_{(r,n)}$	rth order statistic from a random sample of size n
PT_n	Pólya type n
$\chi^2_{(\gamma,m)}$	100γ lower percentage point of a chi square distribution with m df
$Z_{(\gamma)}$	100γ lower percentage points of a standard normal distribution
$t_{(\gamma,n)}$	100γ lower percentage points of a t distribution with n df

$F_{(\gamma,n,m)}$	100γ lower percentage points of an F distribution with df n and m
$I_p(a,b)$	incomplete beta function ratio
$\rightarrow$	tends to or converges to
$\overset{p}{\rightarrow}$	converges in probability
$\overset{a.s.}{\rightarrow}$	converges almost surely
$\overset{r}{\rightarrow}$	converges in rth mean
$\overset{d}{\rightarrow}$	converges in distribution
=>	implies
$\approx$	approximately equal to or asymptotically equal to

INDEX